BIOGEOCHEMICAL METHODS OF PROSPECTING

BIOGEOKHIMICHESKII METOD POISKOV RUDNYKH MESTOROZHDENII

БИОГЕОХИМИЧЕСКИЙ МЕТОД ПОИСКОВ РУДНЫХ МЕСТОРОЖДЕНИЙ

BIOGEOCHEMICAL
METHODS
OF PROSPECTING

by

Dmitrii Petrovich Malyuga

Authorized translation from the Russian

CONSULTANTS BUREAU
NEW YORK
1964

The original Russian text was published for the V. I. Vernadskii
Institute of Geochemistry and Analytical Chemistry by the Academy
of Sciences Press in Moscow, in 1963.

Дмитрий Петрович Малюга
Биогеохимический метод поисков рудных месторождений
(принцип и практика поисков)

Library of Congress Catalog Card Number 64-17203

PREFACE

The seven-year plan for development of the national economy of the USSR calls for a considerable increase in production of the ore-forming and also rare and disseminated chemical elements, and to accomplish this modern techniques are critical requirements. Furthermore, with each passing year prospecting operations are faced with an ever decreasing number of deposits easily discovered by the old visual methods.

Previously tried and widely used geophysical methods — magnetic prospecting, electrical prospecting — have proved to be insufficiently effective under existing conditions in the search for beryllium, vanadium, germanium, niobium, molybdenum, tantalum, tungsten, gold, and other rare and disseminated chemical elements.

At the First All-Union Conference on Geochemical Methods of Prospecting for Ore Deposits, and also in a number of printed works by Soviet and foreign scientists, the great effectiveness of geochemical prospecting methods were pointed out, particularly that of the biogeochemical method.

The use of geochemical methods is a reliable means for planning drilling operations, which permit us to realize, with less expenditure of time and material capital, "stores of hard-to-find deposits" and, even more, to expand the reserves of raw material in our country.

The application of fundamentally new biogeochemical techniques in prospecting requires the study of weathering conditions, of the environments in which aureoles of disseminated elements are formed, and of the effect of bioclimatic and soil conditions, setting up specific procedures for geochemical methods of prospecting.

The proposed biogeochemical method of prospecting for ore deposits was put into practice at the Biogeochemical Laboratory of the Academy of Sciences of the USSR as early as the thirties of the present century, when the ideas of biogeochemistry reached their highest development in the works of the leading geochemists of our country, V. I. Vernadskii and A. P. Vinogradov.

The present book makes use of many years of experience of the author in studying the effectiveness of the biogeochemical prospecting method, and makes some practical recommendations to be followed in prospecting for V, Cr, Mn, Fe, Ni, Co, Cu, Zn, Sn, Hg, U, Se, Mo, W, Nd, B, As, Ag, Au, and the rare earths, under various bioclimatic and soil-rock conditions.

The author expresses his thanks to Academician A. P. Vinogradov for scientific consultation and for his support in every way during this study of the biogeochemical method. He also thanks A. A. Saukov, corresponding member of the Academy of Sciences of the USSR, Professor V. V. Shcherbina, Professor A. I. Perel'man, and other scientists for their critical remarks about the method.

The author considers it his duty to express thanks to the director of the Biogeochemical Laboratory, V. V. Koval'-skii, and to his coworkers in the prospecting party, A. I. Makarova, N. S. Petrunina, and R. G. Nikitina, for their daily aid in the work.

CONTENTS

INTRODUCTION

The essence of the biogeochemical method of prospecting lies in the discovery of aureoles of disseminated ore deposits by analyzing soils and plants. As a guiding feature the method employs the increased content of individual ore elements above such deposits and the changes in relations of these elements in the humus layer of the soil and in the ash of plants. The biogeochemical method also makes use of restrictions on and changes of vegetation in ore districts.

The basis of the method is found in biogeochemistry, a science developed here in the USSR by Academician V. I. Vernadskii.

Among the various problems studied in biogeochemistry important places are occupied by both the study of the migration of the chemical elements through the activity of organisms and the consideration of concentrations of these elements in animals and plants. We know of many examples of accumulation of calcium, potassium, phosphorus, iron, manganese, nickel, molybdenum, and radium by organisms. V. I. Vernadskii said that "concentrations of radium and other radioactive elements by living organisms, from the energy point of view, represent a process that upsets the inhomogeneous equilibrium established by nature in the absence of life. From the energy point of view the stable state in the earth's crust is dissemination of the radioactive elements, not concentration."

Organisms possess the function of "collecting" the individual atoms of ions disseminated through an environment. This function exists on a scale fully comparable with geological processes, giving rise to accumulations of thick sequences of limestone of organic origin and deposits of coal, oil, and other natural materials called bioliths (Samoilov [1929]). A particular case of the concentrating role of organisms is the accumulation of ore-forming elements by terrestrial plants. Boron, manganese, iron, cobalt, nickel, zinc, copper, molybdenum, uranium are such elements among many others.

The biogeochemical process of the circulation of chemical elements in soils and terrestrial plants occurs in the following order: rock → soil → plants → soil (rock). An important link in this system, guaranteeing the further course of biogeochemical processes, is the soil and, especially, its layer of humus.

Under natural (forbidden) conditions, according to the general law of energy development on the earth's surface, soil has a completely determined, historically developed composition, which persists by introduction of chemical elements from the parent bedrock, such elements as Si, Ca, Mg, K, Na, P, S, Fe, Mn, and others, and by the return of these elements by dying plants.

In the upper parts of the soil layer organic materials (chiefly plant remains) commonly accumulate. These serve as food for various animals (worms, insects, rodents) and innumerable simpler organisms (fungi, molds, algae, and bacteria). As a result of this life activity, very persistent organic material is formed — soil humus, complex in composition and structure. The biogenic accumulation of elements in soils is associated specifically with this humus in the upper productive soil layer.

The mechanism of elemental accumulation in soils through the participation of terrestrial plants is shown in Fig. 1.

Plants, by means of their root systems, extend into the soil and subsoil layers. They absorb water and the ions of mineral salts dissolved in the water. The elements absorbed are sodium, magnesium, silicon, potassium, calcium, manganese, iron, and copper, which are carried to the surface in leaves and ground tissues. The presence of these elements is easily detected by analyzing ash consisting of SiO_2, carbonate, phosphate, and other salts.

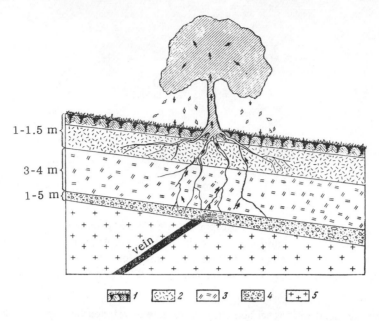

Fig. 1. Schematic view of accumulation of elements in soils and plants. 1) Concentrations of B, Cr, Mn, Fe, Co, Ni, Cu, Zn, Ge, As, and Mo in plant litter and humus; 2) soil; 3) loam; 4) deluvium; 5) bedrock.

After the death of a plant — of the roots and leaves (fallen) — the chemical elements remain in the soil in compounds with humus and organic remains, later changing to soluble salts, which are carried away by rain water or enter a new biological cycle.

The degree of its removal or concentration depends on the mobility of the element under the given biological and soil conditions: the solubility of its salts; its capacity to form stable compounds with organic and inorganic colloids.

The phenomena of natural accumulation in the humus layer of soil is characteristic of many chemical elements. An explanation of this process may lie in the capacity of plants to make selective concentrations of individual ash elements. We know from the work of A. P. Vinogradov [1945] that certain species of plants accumulate Li, B, Na, Mg, P, S, Cl, K, Ca, Mn, Cu, Zn, Se, Br, I, and Ra in ash in quantities exceeding the content of these elements in the soil or water.

Table 1 represents an example of the data relative to accumulation of nickel, cobalt, and copper in the humus layer of chernozem soil (near the Sea of Azov). We see from this table a marked accumulation of nickel, cobalt, and copper in the upper humus horizon of the soil (A) as compared with the underlying material (horizon C).

The effect of biogenic concentration of the chemical elements is especially marked in plants growing above ore deposits and possessing deep root systems (Astragalus, Haloxylon, scrub saltwort). In the ash of such plants one commonly observes chemical elements that are absent in the soil-forming rock, elements usually found in mantling loams above rocks containing ore. At the same time, ore elements appear in the upper humus horizon of the soil. Concentrations of these elements in the ash of plants and in the humus layer of the soil at times reaches tenths and hundredths of a percent (e.g., such elements as B, Cu, Zn, Mo, and some others).

There is consequently a fundamental similarity in technique in prospecting by soils and by plants, since in each we must consider the phenomenon of biogenic concentration of the elements. Depending on the bioclimatic and the soil-rock conditions, one or the other method is used.

The sources of mobile ions are the solutions that enter from deeper horizons of the soil-rock profile. The organic remains of land plants (roots, leaves, stalks) also are a source of these ions. The presence of ore elements in the humus of soils therefore corresponds in the best possible way to the most mobile metals characterizing a dissemination aureole; their presence consequently reflects most accurately the presence of mineralization zones. It was here,

TABLE 1. Relative Accumulation of Metals in the Humus Layer of Chernozem Soil (after Vinogradov [1957])

Horizon	Concentration, %				
	V	Cr	Ni	Co	Zn
Upper, A, 0-5 cm (humus layer)	$1.7 \cdot 10^{-2}$	$3 \cdot 10^{-2}$	$7.7 \cdot 10^{-3}$	$1.3 \cdot 10^{-3}$	$6.3 \cdot 10^{-3}$
Lower, C, 130-140 cm (rock)	$8.9 \cdot 10^{-3}$	$1.6 \cdot 10^{-2}$	$4.5 \cdot 10^{-3}$	$1 \cdot 10^{-3}$	$5.5 \cdot 10^{-3}$
Degree of enrichment in A horizon	1.9	1.9	1.7	1.3	1.1

TABLE 2. List of Ore Occurrences Found by the Biogeochemical Method

Indicator element	Deposit	Method of detection	Country	Author, year
Cr	Chromite	Holly	Maryland and Pennsylvania	Singewald (1928)
Zn	Zinc and lead-zinc	Calamine violet	Western Europe	Linstow (1929).
Zn	Lead-zinc in the Mississippi Valley	Humus soil layer	USA	Fowler (1950)
Cu	Copper	Mosses	Sweden	Pirrson (1948)
Cu	Copper	Ash from balsam branches	Quebec	Riddel (1952)
W	Tungsten	Ash from heather	Cornwall, Sweden	Palmqvist, N. Brudin (1939)
Sn	Cassiterite	Ash from heather	Far East of USSR	Tkalich [1938]
Fe	Sulfide-arsenide	Ash from grassy plants	Far East of USSR	Vogt et al. (1943a)
Cu	Copper	Ash from birch and willow leaves	Norway	Narten, Cannon (1960)
U	Uranium	Ash of juniper and pine	New Mexico	Cannon (1955)
Zn	Zinc	Ash of willow	New York region	Cannon (1960)
U	Uranium anomaly	Ash of juniper	USA, Utah	Cannon (1960)
U	Uranium anomaly	Ash of pine	USA, Utah	Kleinhampl, Cannon (1960)
Mo	Copper-molybdenum	Humus layer of soil and ash of plants	Kadzharan, Arm.SSR	Malyuga [1958]
Fe	Copper	Ash of birch and fir	Siberia, USSR	Tkalich [1952]
Cu, Ni	Copper sulfide vein	Humus layer of soil and ash of plants	Tuva ASSR	Vinogradov and Malyuga [1957]
Pb	Lead-zinc	Humus layer of soil	Akhtala, Arm.SSR	Makarova [1960]
Sn, Be	Rare metals in pegmatite veins	Humus layer of soil and ash of plants	Astrakhan, USSR	Grabovskaya et al. [1960]

during study of covered dissemination aureoles, that geologists and geophysicists began to turn more and more frequently to other methods of geochemical prospecting, such as "phase analysis," i.e., the use of extracts from soil and ore samples. According to N. I. Dolukhanova [1958] and S. D. Miller [1957], dissemination aureoles of Mo, Cu, Mn, Ni, Li, and Rb are better distinguished by saline extracts from soils than by bulk sampling of deluvium and eluvium.

By using aqueous solutions, plants produce "saline extracts" from a much greater volume of soils and friable rocks covering the ore than is accessible to the geologist. It is just this factor that explains the occasional high sensitivity and penetration of the biogeochemical method of prospecting.

In geochemical prospecting one normally uses geological maps of various scales. The disadvantage of such maps is that they do not depict completely the natural conditions under which the ore elements in the given region actually migrated. Furthermore, it is well known that these conditions are far from uniform on the Kola Peninsula, in the Altai, in Central Asia, and elsewhere. The character of the secondary dissemination aureoles at deposits of a single type, since found under various bioclimatic and soil conditions, is not uniform, and one must make specific investigation in selecting the particular geochemical method of prospecting: biogeochemical, lithochemical, or hydrochemical.

A proper solution of the problems of geochemical prospecting requires landscape-geochemical maps, which reflect the nature of weathering and soil-forming processes and consequently the conditions under which the ore elements migrate. Such maps have been prepared by A. I. Perel'man and Yu. V. Sharkov [1957], and on the basis of these A. P. Vinogradov [1957] and B. B. Polynov [1946] have proposed the idea of zoning the geochemical migration of elements in soils, water, and weathering crusts in different bioclimatic provinces.

According to A. I. Perel'man the concept of a geochemical landscape may be extended to broad zones and small segments of the earth's surface not exceeding in size the secondary dissemination aureole of a normal ore deposit.

The formation of secondary dissemination aureoles is part of the single process of weathering, denudation, sedimentation, and migration of the chemical elements that occurs in the landscape. It is necessary therefore to agree with M. A. Glazovskaya [1957], who pointed out the necessity of studying dissemination aureoles in respect to geologic time, not limiting oneself to current processes.

The use of the biogeochemical method of prospecting in various parts of the USSR requires thorough study of both the "internal" and "external" factors in the migration of chemical elements above ore deposits; the chief of these are: the individual peculiarities of the element, climate, geology, soil-forming process, vegetation. Of considerable significance during formation of secondary dissemination aureoles is the course of the soil-forming process, which is determined by all the indicated factors of migration. The weathering processes of rocks and minerals are thus continuously connected with the zonal process of soil formation: tundra, swamp, podzol-forest, steppe (chestnut, chernozem), desert and semidesert (gray soils), and laterite. Each of these is distinguished by a different pH value of the soil solutions, by different amounts of humus in the soil, by the nature of the distribution of the organic and mineral colloids, and, consequently, by the distribution of ore elements in horizons of the soil-rock profile; each thus has specific features involved in the technique of collecting biogeochemical samples.

On the basis of many years of experience of biogeochemical surveying crews in the USSR and foreign countries, regions have been defined for which one may recommend the biogeochemical method in preference to other methods. For example, the method may be used successfully in northern forested regions with podzol and gray forest soils, and also in regions covered by glacial deposits that are not too thick. In both cases the surveys are made by analysis of ash from plants, peat, and plant litter. The method is applicable in prospecting for rare and other elements in swamps, deserts and semideserts, arid plains and mountainous regions, in rocky talus, i.e., where other geochemical methods give no positive results.

The most important quality of the biogeochemical method is its penetration, 15-20 m on the average and commonly as much as 30-40 m. The penetration of the method is determined by the thickness of barren rock, in which there is preserved the capacity to detect signs of mineralization through the anomalously high content of ore elements in soils and plants and also through changes in the relationships between contents of elements and their geochemical background.

The penetration of the biogeochemical method of prospecting depends on geological, geomorphological, climatic, and geobotanical factors. Experience has shown that in most cases the sensitivity of the method depends on the depth of the root system of plants growing above deposits, although commonly it even exceeds this depth. Starting from this, the greatest penetration of the biogeochemical method will be found in arid and hot regions, where plants with deep root systems predominate (deserts and semideserts, arid plains, and high mountainous regions). The least penetration of the method will obviously be found in regions of tundra and taiga, where permafrost is present.

Prospecting investigations by the author on chromium, nickel, cobalt, copper, molybdenum, and other elements conducted in various bioclimatic zones of the USSR have shown great penetration, especially on copper-molybdenum and nickel deposits in Transcaucasia and in northern Kazakhstan, reaching depths of 20-30 m. The least penetration was observed above permafrost in Tuva, where it did not exceed 2-3 m.

After a comparatively short period of time the biogeochemical method has recommended itself as an effective means of searching for hard-to-find ore deposits. At present we know of tens of examples of the discovery of deposits by biogeochemical methods in the USSR and in foreign countries, as may be seen in Table 2. Elements for which we obtain positive effects in prospecting by soils and plants include B, V, Cr, Mn, Fe, Ni, Co, Cu, Zn, As, Se, Mo, (W), Pb, Sn, Hg, Nb, U, (Th), Ag, Au, and the rare earths. The number of such elements increases daily.

It seems to us that only joint use of lithochemical, hydrochemical, and biogeochemical methods will increase the effectiveness of geochemical methods to any considerable degree, especially in the search for rare and disseminated elements.

Still, even now there is confusion among a number of geologists and geophysicists in defining the biogeochemical method. S. M. Tkalich [1959] has written, for example: "Prospecting for ore deposits by studying the chemical composition of soils differs in no essential way from ordinary metallometry and should not be confused with the biogeochemical method." However, in the works of the Russian school of biogeochemists and soil scientists — A. P. Vinogradov, V. A. Kovda, and others — and in a number of works by foreign geologists, prospecting by analysis of soils and plants is called the biogeochemical method.

In contrast to other geochemical methods (metallometric surveys, the hydrochemical method) the biogeochemical prospecting method uses a group of natural phenomena that are not taken into account by these other methods. 1) increased content of metals in the ash of land plants above ore deposits, 2) biogenic accumulation of metals in the humus layer of soil and changes in the ratios of these metals, and 3) the restriction of biocoenoses to zones of mineralization and the variability of vegetation (endemic forms) under the influence of elevated contents of ore elements in the environment.

Thus, the biogeochemical method differs fundamentally from other methods of geochemical indication in that it considers specific biogenic migration of the chemical elements in disseminated aureoles above ore deposits.

CHAPTER I

HISTORY OF DEVELOPMENT OF THE METHOD

1. Information on the Use of the Method in the Past

Plants have been used for a long time in the search for water, valuable rocks, and ores. In the East the presence of water in the desert has been detected since ancient times from the presence of characteristic vegetation. For example, the inhabitants of Central Africa have been guided in their search for water by the Acacia Grandulifera. The knowledge of how to find ground water in deserts and dry steppes from the presence of individual plants apparently has been handed down from generation to generation to the present day. For example, in the Kara-Kum and Kyzyl-Kum in Central Asia the Syrian rue Peganum Harmala — a plant of the rue family — has been used since antiquity in the search for fresh water, which frequently is found in sands at a depth from 20 to 30 m.

The first European settlers in the North American prairies were guided by the vegetation in their quest for suitable lands for agricultural crops. This method can be used even now in the virgin lands when laying out fields for appropriate crops.

In medieval times miners were guided by certain vegetation known to indicate the presence of copper and other pyrite ores. For example, the Scandinavians were familiar with "pyrite plants" (Kisplant), which grow on copper ores, zinc flora was known in Belgium and in the Rhine region, and "copper grass" (Gypsophila Patrinii) has been used in the Altai for exploration for copper. It has been noted that European holly has an affinity to rocks rich in aluminum.

The presence of minerals also can be judged from the external appearance and condition of plants over ores.

As early as 1763, M. V. Lomonosov wrote: "In mountains, in which ores or other minerals are present, growing trees usually are not healthy, that is, their leaves are pale and the trees themselves are low, bent, distorted, gnarled, and rotten, before reaching old age." Later, discussing the special criteria indicating the presence of ore veins, he noted: "The grass growing over veins usually is shorter and paler."

Among the early cases of the discovery of a deposit through the presence of vegetation of a particular type was Tyson's discovery (1810) of chromite deposits in Maryland and Pennsylvania, guided by the presence of depressed flora on ore-bearing serpentinites (Singewald [1928]).

More systematic data on the geochemical affinity of plants appeared beginning with the second half of the 19th century, and especially during the present century. In the first major review of this problem, O. V. Linstow [1929] cites many examples of the affinity of plant species to geological soil conditions. He refers to these plants as "bodenanzeigende Pflanzen," which means "plants that indicate the soil." The facts that Linstow cites were gathered by scientists over the course of almost a century. In a study devoted to biological indicators in geology, S. V. Viktorov [1947] supplemented the Linstow summary with a large number of observations of Russian and foreign scientists. The early works of Unger [1836], A. Karpinskii [1841], and later G. I. Tanfil'ev [1886] devoted much attention to the problem of the relationship of plants to calcium — calcium soils and calcareous rocks. Certain plants concentrate calcium in quantities measured in whole percents (calcium flora). Very frequently the accumulation of calcium in plants indicates their affinity to limestone soils. Among woody species such plants include Pinus austriaca, Abies cephalonica, box, juniper, and many others. On limestone soils it is common to find the larch Larix sibirica, the beech Fagus orientalis, and others. In many cases calcium-loving plants are indicators of limestone soils on corresponding rocks. For example, N. I. Sprygin [1934] noted an affinity of Thymus Dubjanskyi Klok et Des.-Shost. to Senonian chalk, Th. Zhegulensis to limestones and dolomites, and Th. baschkiriensis to red marls (Middle Volga region).

On this same basis well-known halophytic vegetation has been found growing in abundance on the solonchaks of deserts and semideserts (the saltworts Suaeda maritima Dum., Salsola crassa M. B., Atriplex tatarica L., Salsola soda L., and many others). These plants extract many salts from the soil and these salts constitute the greater part of their ash content. Nevol [1926] noted the affinity of Dianthus capillifrons, Sempervivum Hillebrandii, and Sempervivum pittonii to serpentinites (rich in Cr, Mg, Ni, Co). Minguzzi and Vergano [1948] noted the affinity of Alyssum bertolonii to ophiolites and T. Vogt (1942) considers Alyssum adulterium and Viscaria alpina (L) to be plants characteristic of serpentinites and primary sulfides. In 1948 a member of our expedition, M. M. Storozheva, discovered modified forms of Pulsatilla patens (L.) Mill. on the Taiketkenskii nickel deposit in the steppe region of the Southern Urals, and in 1949 the author, also working on the Chugaev deposit, discovered the extremely widespread occurrence of deformed specimens of Linosyris villosa (L.) Benth et Hook.

One of the most interesting examples of the geochemical affinity of plants is the existence of galmei flora, characteristic of soils containing high concentrations of zinc. We will mention zinc-indicating plants which long have been known in the scientific literature: the galmei violet Viola lutea Huds var. Calaminaria Lej and penny cress, Thlaspi calaminare Lej et Curt, discovered for the first time on the zinc deposits of Western Europe. The content of zinc (ZnO) in these plants, especially in the leaves, is very high — more than 10%. Dorn [1937] mentions finding Ruta graveolens L., Ruta latifolia Mart., and other zinc concentrators on zinc deposits; these plants can be used as indicators of zinc ores. According to Vogt [1942] and Bailey [1889], Melandrium dioicum L., Viscaria alpina L., and Polycarpaea spirostylis F., discovered in great quantity on deposits in Norway, Northern Australia, Queensland, and elsewhere, are typical for sulfide ores (pyrrhotite, chalcopyrite, and sphalerite). The author and his colleagues have encountered in the Tuvinskaya Autonomous Region depressed forms of Gypsophila Patrinii Ser (v. thesifolia Schischk) of the pink family, which in a series of cases invariably indicated the presence of copper sulfide deposits.

An extremely important group of plants is the selenium flora which has been discovered in a number of regions in the United States (North and South Dakota, Wyoming), Canada (Alberta), and South America (Colombia), described in the writings of Beath [1935], Byers [1935], and Robinson et al. [1947]. The most typical among these plants are several species of Astragalus (pectinatus, pattersonii, and others), Stanleya pinnata Green, and many others. The occurrence of these plants on selenium-bearing soils associated with Jurassic carbonaceous sandstones, enriched with sulfur, vanadium, and uranium (Colorado, South Dakota), in certain cases makes it possible to use them as indirect indicators of secondary uranium ores (Cannon [1952]). Nemec et al. [1936] and Lundberg [1941] have published data on the affinity of individual species of Equisetum arvense and Lonicera confusa Ds. to quartzitic gold-bearing veins in Queensland. Increased quantities of gold were discovered in the ash of these plants by Nemec [1936] and Babichka [1954].

According to Bailey [1889] and others, Eriogonum ovalifolia and Lonicera confusa Ds. (in the United States and Queensland) can serve as indicators of silver.

It should be mentioned that, due to dissimilarities of soil and climatic conditions, these indicators do not always recur on new but similar deposits in other regions. An exception to the rule is edaphic flora, which is adapted to a certain level of chemical elements and which suffers when they are present in inadequate quantity: examples are halophytes, calcium flora, and others. Plants which obviously should be included in this group are those which accumulate heavy metals under ordinary conditions (Fe, Mn, Cu, Zn, Ni, and Co among others). This applies in particular to zinc indicators — Viola lutea Huds var. Calaminaria Lej and others; ferromanganese plants (according to Forchhammer [1865] and Tanfil'ev [1886]) — Zostera marina L. and Trapa natans L.; and according to our data [1946], to copper indicators — Cicuta virosa L. and the fungi Polycarpus. There also are lithium indicators — Thalictrum sp., Ranunculus sp.; aluminum indicators — Lycopodiaceae sp., Symplocus sp.; and others (according to Vinogradov [1949]).

The first attempt to provide a scientific basis for this phenomenon was made by the Russian botanist A. M. Karpinskii [1841]. In tracing the occurrence of plants on sandstones, clays, and limestones, the author concluded that certain species of vegetation have an affinity to limestones, others have an affinity to sandstones, etc. Karpinskii viewed skeptically the possibility of using individual species of plants for the purpose of identifying rocks and felt it was more correct to be guided by all the vegetation of a particular "limited sector of the earth's surface." His important contribution was that he was the first to note the natural factors which influence the formation of the soil and vegetation cover: underlying rocks, climate, the geographic position of the country, etc. Among these factors the soil-forming rocks are most important. Therefore, according to Karpinskii, soils and plants can be indirect indicators of the underlying rocks and the ores they contain.

As another example of the application of biological communities of indicating plants in scientific and practical work, we will mention the work of I. K. Vysotskii [1904]. While making geological investigations in the Northern Urals (Verkhotur region), he observed the close affinity of pine groves to olivine rocks (dunites), the affinity of a mixed pine-deciduous forest to diallogoid peridotites, and the affinity of cedar to gabbro-diorites. The boundary of pine forest was abrupt, with a transition from dunites to schists. L. K. Tyulina [1928], in the Il'menskii forest preserve, noted the affinity of pine forests to acidic rocks (granite-gneisses) where there was a complete absence of a grass cover, and the affinity of fir-larch forests with a rich grassy vegetation to alkaline rocks (maskarites). It is characteristic for forests to be absent on grass-covered serpentinites. This observation by Tyulina agrees with data in the literature on the poisoning effect of serpentinites, especially for woody vegetation. For further examples of the affinity of plants to certain geological conditions, we also should mention the work of N. V. Pavlov and S. Yu. Livshits [1934], who studied the flora of the Kara-Tau.

Both Soviet and foreign literature contain repeated references to the indication of rock types through the presence of plant communities. Without discussing this problem in greater detail, we will mention the studies of B. A. Keller (1938), M. E. Tkachenko et al. [1939], A. S. Salazkin [1936], A. K. Magak'yan [1941], M. G. Popov [1922], I. A. Raikov [1924], and N. I. Rubtsov [1941].

Both individual species of plants and plant communities are employed as indicators. However, for the time being we do not have sufficient justification for saying whether indication by plant species is superior to indication by plant communities, or vice versa. Historically they were developed at the same time and can only supplement one another.

2. Biogeochemical Provinces

The phenomenon of the mutability of plants and animals under the influence of chemical ecological factors is quite widespread on the earth's surface. It is expressed in the most varied forms: morphological and physiological changes, diseases of the organisms, abnormalities, and disruptions of life processes and viability. It has been found that many of these effects are associated with an excess or shortage of chemical elements in the environment: in the soils from which the plants obtain their nutrients and in the water which enters the animal organism in the process of its development.

A. P. Vinogradov [1949, 1960] has given the name "biogeochemical provinces" to both large and small regions where similar anomalous phenomena in plants and animals prevail. He wrote:

"We apply the name biogeochemical provinces to regions on the earth which differ from adjacent regions with respect to the content of chemical elements, and which as a result experience a different biological reaction on the part of local flora and fauna. In extreme cases, as a result of a sharp deficiency or excess in the content of any chemical element (or elements) the plants and animals will experience biogeochemical endemias within particular biogeochemical provinces...

"By regions of the earth we mean rocks, soils, and water basins, defined and limited in time and in space, especially defined parts of the sea, atmosphere, or sea and atmosphere together, populated by organisms. With respect to the content of one or more chemical elements in a particular region, that is, in rocks, soils, water, and the organisms of this region, we have in mind either the usual normal level or an inadequate or excess content of a particular chemical element or several elements (or their compounds). It should be noted that it is of importance to know not only the absolute content of elements in a particular region, in its rocks and soils, but also the content of any particular form of this element, for example, Fe^{2+} or Fe^{3+}; Mn^{2+} or Mn^{4+}; Se^{2+} or Se^{4+}. Thus, we often encounter not only an absolute shortage or excess, but also a relative deficiency or excess, depending on the degree of accessibility of any particular chemical element to particular types of flora and fauna. For instance, Co and many other chemical elements in areas where there is an alkaline soil reaction, for example as a result of calcification, are quite inaccessible to plants. On the other hand, under these conditions Mo is very accessible to plants as a result of the formation of easily soluble molybdates, while in an acidic medium Mo is scarcely accessible to plants due to its leaching into compounds which are not easily soluble.

"The biological reaction of flora and fauna of a particular region, arising under the influence of an excess or deficiency of any particular chemical element (or elements), is the most important and basic criterion for the delimitation of a biogeochemical province."

TABLE 3. Indicator Plants

Indicator	Plant	Element	Area	Author, year
L	Saltwort Salsola nitraria	B	Caspian Lowland	Buyalov, Shvyryaeva [1955]
L	Sea lavender Limonium suffruticosum	B	The same	Buyalov, Shvyryaeva [1955]
L	Star of night Clusia rosea	Fe	Venezuela	Buck [1951]
L	Alyssum Alyssum Bertolonii	Ni	Italy	Minguzzi et al. [1948]
L	Alyssum Alyssum murale	Ni	USSR, Georgia	Doksopulo [1961]
L	Asplenium adulterium	Ni	Norway	Vogt [1942]
L	Gypsophila Gypsophila Patrini	Cu	USSR, Rudnyi Altai	Nesvetailova [1955]
L	Polycarpea spirostilis	Cu	Australia	Bailey (1889)
L	Elscholtzia Elscholtzia haichowensis	Cu	China	Tsung-Shan [1957]
U	German catchfly Viscaria alpina	Cu	Norway	Vogt [1942]
L	Moss Merceya latifolia	Cu	Montana	Pirrson (1948)
U	Violet Viola Calaminaria (lutea)	Zn	Belgium and Germany	Linstow [1929]
L	Rue Ruta graveolens	Zn	USA	Dorn [1937]
U	Rattlebox Crotalaria cobalticola	Co	Katanga	Duvigneaund [1959]
U	Catchfly Silene cobalticola	Co	Katanga	Duvigneaund [1959]
U	Aster Aster venustus	Se	Western USA	Trelease et al.[1949]
U	Milk vetch Astragalus thompsonae	Se, U	Utah	Cannon [1960]
U	Milk vetch Astragalus pattersoni	Se, U	Colorado	Cannon [1952]
U	Milk vetch Astragalus bisulcatus	Se, U, V	Colorado	Trelease et al. [1949]
L	Milk vetch Astragalus declinatus	Mo, Cu	Kadzharan, Armenia	Malyuga et al. [1959]
L	Plume grass Erianthus giganteus	Pb	Tennessee	Cannon [1960]
L	False indigo Amorpha canescens	Pb	USA	Dorn [1937]
L	Eriogonum Eriogonum ovalifolium		Montana	Henwood [1857]
L	Honeysuckle Lonicera confusa	Ag, Au	Queensland, Australia	Bailey (1889)
L	Horsetail Equisetum arvense	Au	Czechoslovakia	Nemec, Babicka [1936]

At the same time, Vinogradov allows for the possibility of a natural selection and composition of local flora on a geochemical basis, as well as the mutability of local species, accompanied by the formation of abnormal specimens, morphological changes, and variations. These phenomena often are accompanied by a variability in the chemical composition of surface plants, which will be discussed below.

According to Vinogradov, biogeochemical provinces may have a zonal character, that is, may be related to specific soil and climatic zones. For example, there are biogeochemical provinces where the soil and water show a deficiency of iodine, calcium, phosphorus, cobalt, copper, and other elements (the zone of podzol and soddy podzol soils). These provinces are characterized by the occurrence of goiter in man and animals; a shortage of calcium and phosphorus leads to brittleness of the bones; and a shortage of cobalt results in a cobalt-deficiency disease, etc.

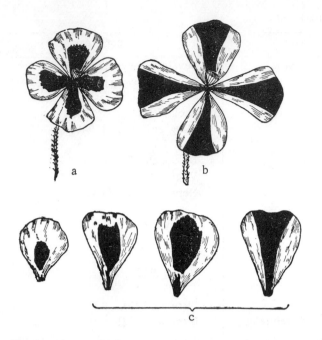

Fig. 2. Change in the color of the petals of the flower of the poppy Papaver commutatum F. et M. a) Normal flower; b) modified flower; c) degree of mutability of petals of the corolla.

Biogeochemical provinces which are related to zones of natural enrichment with chemical elements, including ore elements, have a more local "interzonal" character. Such provinces are boron, fluorine, molybdenum, lead, or other provinces (Vinogradov [1960], Koval'skii [1960]). The study of these provinces is made jointly with the biogeochemical exploration for ore deposits, in a unified plan of study of the geochemical phenomena associated with life.

3. Indicator Plants

As we know, the use of the criterion of mutability of plants has a long history in exploration work. The method has been used most extensively in the USSR in geological and soil mapping, for the detection of tectonic dislocations, and especially in exploration for ground water, petroleum, sulfur, and borates (Viktorov [1955]). Similar work has been done abroad in Canada, Australia (Cannon [1960]), and in the United States.

At the present time this exploration method is known as the biogeochemical or geobotanical method and is used rather widely in exploration for ore deposits, such as in the preliminary sampling of new areas, in the study of the character and depth of ground water, and in the determination of the presence of geological structures often associated with ore deposits.

The method is based on the existence of relationships between both plant associations and individual species and specific geological conditions: structural elements, rock outcrops, and ore deposits. It is based on a study of the changes in the color and morphology of plants caused by an excess of individual chemical elements in the environment (teratological changes).

TABLE 4. Mutability of Plants Under the Influence of Excesses of Metals

Element	Effect	Author, year
Al	Shortening of roots, curling of leaves, mottling	Wallace [1951]
B	Dark leaves, singing of edges of leaves, lag in growth, creeping forms, lag in maturing of seeds, galls	Buyalov, Shvyryayeva [1955]
Cr	Yellow leaves with green veins	Cannon[1960]
Mn	Chlorosis of leaves, reddening of stem and slips, curling and dying of edges of leaves	Wallace, Cannon (1960)
Fe	Low growth, thin roots, elongated cells	Wallace, Cannon (1960)
Co	White spots on leaves	Vinogradov [1954]
Ni	Chlorosis and white spots on leaves, reduction in petals of corolla, abnormal forms	Malyuga, Petrunina [1961]
Zn	Chlorosis of leaves, white dwarf forms, dying of tip of leaf, underdevelopment of root	Millikan [1949]
Mo,Cu	Unusual development of black bands on petals of poppy (black cross)	Malyuga et al. [1959]
Pb,Zn	Appearance of different forms of double-flowering in poppy	Malyuga et al. [1959] Viktorov [1955]
U	Increase in number of chromosomes in nucleus, curvature of form of plants	Cannon [1960]

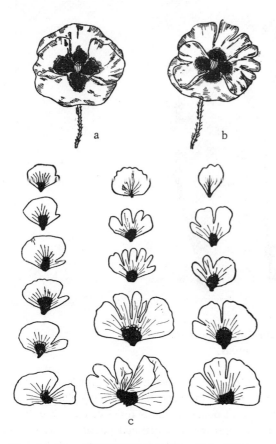

Fig. 3. Mutability of the petals of the large-headed poppy Papaver macrostomum B. et H. a) Normal flower; b) modified flower; c) degree of mutability of the petals of the corolla.

The ash residue of surface plants includes a great number of chemical elements, including rare and dispersed elements. However, the proportion in the ash of such elements as Mn, Fe, Ca, Na, K, Mg, P, Se, and others differs sharply in different plants. This diversity in the mineral content can be attributed to the complexity of the natural conditions under which surface plants developed historically. Some plants reflect the environmental geochemical conditions — the chemical composition of soils and rocks, and sometimes ground water — more clearly than others. Such plants have been called indicators. On the basis of modern concepts it is possible to distinguish universal from local indicators (Nesvetailova [1955]).

Universal indicators are plants which are associated rigorously with specific conditions of the chemical medium, such as a high metal content in soils, rocks, and ores; they are thus indicators of this medium, that is, of the presence of ore deposits. Local indicators differ from other plants only in that they have adapted better to ore zones and therefore often predominate over ores. Examples of universal indicators are selenium flora and zinc flora. Typical local indicators are individual species of Alyssum, which concentrate nickel, and Gypsophila, a characteristic indicator of copper deposits. Table 3 gives a list of indicator plants. Almost all, with few exceptions, are local indicators, denoted by the letter L. Universal indicators are denoted by the letter U.

The literature describes many cases of affinity of plants for rocks which are rich in zinc, copper, nickel, and chromium. Often the same plants are described in different regions as indicators of either zinc or lead or zinc or copper. For example, Silene latifola grows on zinc-bearing limestones in New Jersey and also on cuprous shales in Vermont (Cannon [1960]). Obviously, the affinity of plants is determined not only by the presence of a particular metal, but also by other factors inherent in a sulfide deposit: the acidity of the soils and subsoils, the presence of sulfur, etc. Often plants which are indicators of zinc and lead are discovered on spoil banks and are absent on the deposit.

Plants which are indicators of copper are more reliable. For the most part they are members of three families: pinks, mints, and mosses. "Cuprous" mosses in Sweden were used to detect three deposits (Persson [1948]). Equally important indicators are Gypsophila, of the pink family, and Elsholtzia, of the mint family. It was possible to discover several copper deposits in Rhodesia by means of the plant Ocimum homblei.

Plants which are selenium indicators have been used successfully in uranium exploration on the Colorado Plateau and in the Peruvian Andes (Cannon [1960]).

Of equally great importance in geobotanical investigations are the "teratological" changes in plants occurring under the influence of an excess soil content of specific chemical elements. These changes are noticeable in the external appearance of the flowers and leaves, various indications of disease, the rhythm of development, etc. There is an abundance of factual data on the mutability of the color of flowers under the influence of manganese, zinc, copper, and other chemical elements (Bazilevskaya and Sibirtseva [1950]). According to Ensche's data (1894) a zinc excess in the soil causes a change in the blue color of corolla to yellow and red.

In our investigations on the copper-molybdenum deposit at Kadzharan (Armenian SSR) we noted a well-expressed nonuniformity in the development of the black spots on the petals of the poppy Papaver commutatum F. et M. (Malyuga et al. [1959]). In normal forms, the lilac-red petals have one small black spot at the base. In the modified forms the spots are elongated, reaching the edge of the petal and forming the image of a black cross (Fig. 2). The modified forms were found in a ravine where the soil was moistened by ground water enriched with copper and molybdenum.

Fig. 4. Mutability of the flower of the anemone Pulsatilla patens Mill.
a) Normal form; b) modified specimens.

There also is another type of change in the appearance of plants which can be used in exploration work. In the polymetal deposit "Atkyz" at Kadzharan we discovered double-petaled forms of the large-headed poppy Papaver macrostomum, not characteristic for this species of poppy. The double-petal phenomenon is manifested in the different degree of incising of the petals, often to the base, which creates the impression of additional petals in addition to the normal four (Fig. 3). The "double-petaled" forms of Papaver macrostomum were observed in sectors of the deposit with a high content of zinc and lead in a chestnut soil. The predominant influence of zinc on the mutability of the flower of the poppy was demonstrated on the basis of a considerable increase in the zinc content in modified flowers of the poppy.

The second case of the modification of a flower under the influence of metals was observed in the anemone Pulsatilla patens (L.) Mill. on a nickel silicate deposit in the Kimpersaiskii ore region (Aktyubinskaya Oblast). The modification was manifested in the reduction of the leaflets of the floral envelope and the total disappearance of petals (Fig. 4).

The teratological changes in plants over ore deposits are manifested in different ways. They are dependent on the degree of moistness or dryness of the soil, that is, on the presence of mobile and assimilable forms of ore and companion elements — Ca, Mg, and others. We noted that the number of abnormal forms of the shaggy goldilocks Linosyris villosa over nickel ores decreases sharply when a dry and hot summer is followed by one which is colder and moister.

Table 4 gives the most important forms of the physiological and morphological modification of plants under the influence of toxic and other ore elements.

In addition to the direct indication of ore zones on the basis of the affinity of plant species and associations, indicator plants, and teratological changes, in practice it is possible to be guided by the presence of bare spots of soil amid the ordinary vegetation cover. For example, according to the observations made by N. I. Buyalov and A. M. Shvyryaeva [1955], plants are completely absent on boron-bearing sectors (areas with a high boron content in the soil). Such areas devoid of vegetation have been studied in exploration work for borates. This method was employed during exploration work for copper in the Congo and Rhodesia and for sulfide ores in Italy (Cannon [1960]). It was this criterion which was used in the discovery of the Tyson chromium deposits in Pennsylvania and Maryland, in areas associated with serpentinites and devoid of any vegetation.

Thus experience in the application of the geobotanical method in the USSR and abroad indicates that it can be used as an exploration technique. However, these investigations have not been developed properly. It is obvious that

12

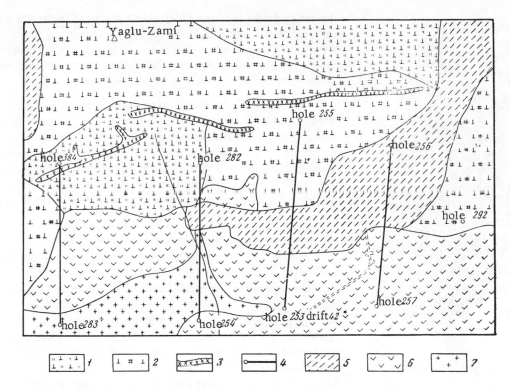

Fig. 5. Schematic geological map of the Karmir-Karskii sector. 1) Weakly modified porphyrites; 2) strongly modified porphyrites; 3) granodiorite-porphyry dikes; 4) geological profiles between holes; 5) hornfels; 6) unmodified monzonites; 7) syenites.

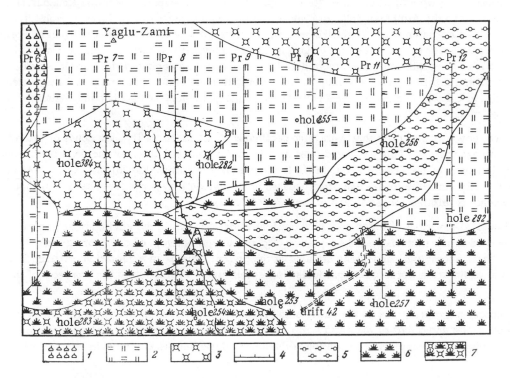

Fig. 6. Schematic geobotanical map of the Karmir-Karskii sector. 1) Campion association (Silene compacta F.); 2) grass association; 3) legume-grass association; 4) biogeochemical survey profiles; 5) nipplewort association (Lapsana communis L.); 6) thyme-tragacanth association; 7) thyme-tragacanth association with legumes and various grasses.

13

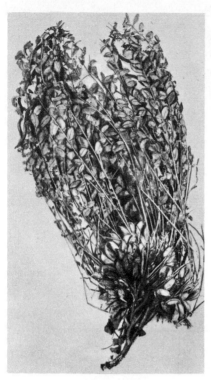

Fig. 7. *Astragalus declinatus* W.

this method does not have independent practical importance in exploration for ores. The experience of our work in Armenia and in the Tuvinskaya Autonomous Region shows that it is desirable to use the geobotanical method in conjunction with a biogeochemical survey in a preliminary study of the prospects of the areas to be investigated.

The affinity of individual species of plants and their associations to ore-bearing rocks is used for this purpose. The geobotanical sampling method provides for the schematic geobotanical mapping of the area where exploration work is to be carried out. For this purpose the vegetation of the delimited sector is studied along determined routes and profiles. The affinity of plant associations to topographic features is noted on the topographic base, and geobotanical data are compared with the geological map.

The data accumulated by geobotanical mapping are used to determine more precisely the details on the geological map. Simple mining work is done for this purpose at the necessary points where the data on the geological map do not coincide with the data obtained in geobotanical observations. When geobotanical anomalies are discovered the surveyed territory is checked by the study of reference sectors in those places where the geological structure of the sector is unambiguous. A comparison of the geobotanical data for the reference sectors with the composition of the vegetation of "anomalous" sectors can be of help in interpreting the results of a geobotanical survey. In the event of suspicion of the presence of a particular kind of mineralization a study is made to find indicator plants. Thus, geobotanical investigations can be of substantial assistance in the determination of the ore-bearing properties of a new sector.

As an illustration, we will discuss a single example, based on our experience in the Kadzharanskii copper-molybdenum deposit in the Armenian SSR. In 1956, while making biogeochemical investigations on the left bank of the Okhchi River at Kadzharan (Karmir-Karskii sector), we noted an affinity of a thyme-tragacanth vegetation association to anomalies detected by the soil-plant biogeochemical survey. It was found that these anomalies corresponded to outcrops of ore-bearing monzonites. A more detailed geobotanical mapping of the Karmir-Karskii sector made it possible to establish a rather close relationship between the individual plant associations and the outcrops of the corresponding rocks, as can be seen clearly by a comparison of the geological and geobotanical maps of the sector represented in Figs. 5 and 6.

It also was noted at that time that *Astragalus declinatus* W. grows primarily over zones of hydrothermal copper-molybdenum mineralization. This was noted most clearly in the principal sector of the deposit on Mount Pirdoudan and along the left bank of the Okhchi River, in the Davachinskii and Karmir-Karskii ore regions. *Astragalus declinatus* can be spotted easily amid the local vegetation because of its pinnate leaves and large seed pods that occur at ground level and therefore is suitable for use in exploration work (Fig. 7).

The biological reactions of plants to a high concentration of metal in the environment — in soil and soil water — often are expressed in the mutability and adaptation of plants due to outcrops of ore-bearing rocks and the nearness of ore deposits. These anomalous phenomena are used at the present time as an exploration criterion in the complex of biogeochemical exploration work, and in particular for a preliminary evaluation of the prospects of the area being investigated.

Geochemical principles, that is, the patterns and regularities observed in the processes of migration of the chemical elements in the upper part of the earth's crust, form the basis of the method of biogeochemical exploration of ore deposits. The principal exploration criterion is the accumulation of ore elements in soils and plants over zones of mineralization.

4. Geochemical Prospecting Using Soils and Plants

The first information on the finding of heavy metals in plant ash date back to the middle of the 16th century. Two hundred years later the Swedish chemist Urban Jerne (1753) noted the presence of about 10 heavy metals in plants: iron, copper, tin, mercury, lead, gold, arsenic, and others.

TABLE 5. Mean Content of Chemical Elements in Rocks, Soils, and Surface Plants (in %)

Element	Lithosphere	Soil	Plant (in ash)	Element	Lithosphere	Soil	Plant (in ash)
Li	$6.5 \cdot 10^{-3}$	$3 \cdot 10^{-3}$	$1.1 \cdot 10^{-3}$	Zn	$5 \cdot 10^{-3}$	$5 \cdot 10^{-3}$	$9 \cdot 10^{-2}$
Be	$6 \cdot 10^{-4}$	$6 \cdot 10^{-4}$	$2 \cdot 10^{-4}$	As	$5 \cdot 10^{-4}$	$5 \cdot 10^{-4}$	$3 \cdot 10^{-5}$
B	$6 \cdot 10^{-4}$	$1 \cdot 10^{-3}$	$4 \cdot 10^{-2}$	Se	$6 \cdot 10^{-5}$	$1 \cdot 10^{-6}$	—
F	$2.7 \cdot 10^{-2}$	$2 \cdot 10^{-2}$	$1 \cdot 10^{-3}$	Br	$1.6 \cdot 10^{-4}$	$5 \cdot 10^{-4}$	$1.5 \cdot 10^{-2}$
Na	2.64	0.63	2	Rb	$3.1 \cdot 10^{-2}$	$6 \cdot 10^{-3}$	$1 \cdot 10^{-7}$
Mg	2.10	0.63	7	Sr	$4 \cdot 10^{-2}$	$3 \cdot 10^{-2}$	$3 \cdot 10^{-2}$
Al	8.80	7.13	1.40	Zr	$2 \cdot 10^{-2}$	$3 \cdot 10^{-2}$	—
Si	27.60	33	15	Mo	$3 \cdot 10^{-4}$	$2 \cdot 10^{-4}$	$2 \cdot 10^{-2}$
P	$8 \cdot 10^{-2}$	$8 \cdot 10^{-2}$	7	Ag	$1 \cdot 10^{-5}$	$n(10^{-5})$	$1 \cdot 10^{-4}$
S	$9 \cdot 10^{-2}$	$8.5 \cdot 10^{-2}$	5	Cd	$5 \cdot 10^{-5}$	$5 \cdot 10^{-5}$	$1 \cdot 10^{-6}$
Cl	$4.5 \cdot 10^{-2}$	$1 \cdot 10^{-2}$	$n \cdot 10^{-2}$	Sn	$4 \cdot 10^{-3}$	$1 \cdot 10^{-3}$	$5 \cdot 10^{-4}$
K	2.60	1.36	3	I	$3 \cdot 10^{-5}$	$5 \cdot 10^{-4}$	$5 \cdot 10^{-3}$
Ca	3.60	1.37	3	Cs	$7 \cdot 10^{-4}$	$5 \cdot 10^{-4}$	$n \cdot 10^{-4}$
Ti	$6 \cdot 10^{-1}$	$4.60 \cdot 10^{-1}$	$1 \cdot 10^{-1}$	Ba	$5 \cdot 10^{-2}$	$5 \cdot 10^{-2}$	$n \cdot 10^{-2}$
				Au	$5 \cdot 10^{-7}$	—	$1 \cdot 10^{-4}$
V	$1.5 \cdot 10^{-2}$	$1 \cdot 10^{-2}$	$6.1 \cdot 10^{-3}$	Hg	$7 \cdot 10^{-6}$	$1 \cdot 10^{-6}$	$1 \cdot 10^{-7}$
Cr	$2 \cdot 10^{-2}$	$2 \cdot 10^{-2}$	$2.5 \cdot 10^{-2}$	Pb	$1.6 \cdot 10^{-3}$	$1 \cdot 10^{-3}$	$1 \cdot 10^{-3}$
Mn	$9 \cdot 10^{-2}$	$8.5 \cdot 10^{-2}$	$7.5 \cdot 10^{-1}$	Ra	$1 \cdot 10^{-10}$	$8 \cdot 10^{-11}$	$2 \cdot 10^{-11}$
Fe	5	3.80	1	Th	$8 \cdot 10^{-4}$	$6 \cdot 10^{-4}$	—
Co	$1 \cdot 10^{-3}$	$1 \cdot 10^{-3}$	$1.5 \cdot 10^{-3}$	U	$3 \cdot 10^{-4}$	$1 \cdot 10^{-4}$	$5 \cdot 10^{-5}$
Ni	$6 \cdot 10^{-3}$	$4 \cdot 10^{-3}$	$5 \cdot 10^{-3}$				
Cu	$1 \cdot 10^{-2}$	$2 \cdot 10^{-3}$	$2 \cdot 10^{-2}$				

The use of chemical fertilizers in agriculture encouraged the study of the composition of soils and plants. According to data published by J. Liebig [1936], by the middle of the 19th century there had been thousands of general analyses of plants for potassium, sodium, calcium, magnesium, sulfur, phosphorous, chlorine, iron, and in some cases manganese, aluminum, iodine, and other chemical elements.

Later nickel, cobalt, and copper were detected in plants (Malyuga [1946]). In making analyses of soil, sea water, and sea and land plants, J. Forchhammer always found them to contain iron, manganese, nickel, cobalt, and copper. On the basis of these observations he concluded that there was a dependence of the metal content in plants on the metal content in soils and water.

The comparative study of the chemical composition of soils and plant ash has indicated the existence of a close chemical relationship between them. Nevertheless, for a long time there was no basis for the development of a method of biogeochemical prospecting. Its development became possible only after the development of the science of biogeochemistry, when the random facts of the finding of large and small concentrations of metals in organisms were applied by V. I. Vernadskii in his theory of the biogenic migration of chemical elements in the earth's crust ([1921, 1922, 1926, 1931, 1934] and others).

Importance of the Work in the Biogeochemical Laboratory, Academy of Sciences of the USSR

Vernadskii, the founder of modern geochemistry, could not but appreciate the role of living organisms in geochemical processes and in the formation of rocks and minerals. The most important products of the life activity of organisms are limestones, dolomites, mineral fuels (coal, petroleum, sapropels), and ore deposits (iron, manganese, copper, and vanadium), which have been called bioliths (Samoilov [1929]). As Vernadskii wrote, "during their lives, living organisms determine the composition of the atmosphere, the chemistry of the sea, especially the composition of sea water, and the character of natural waters (in rivers and lakes)." The geochemical significance of life is reflected very clearly in the following words of Vernadskii: "Undoubtedly, these manifestations of life powerfully affect all chemical processes in the earth's crust. Primarily because of them the history of the chemical elements is completely different than it would have been if the chemistry of the earth's surface were the result solely of the composition and thermodynamic field of this surface. We know that because of these phenomena an enormous part of the chemical elements of the biosphere is caught up by living matter and directed into other channels of chemical reaction than would be the case if life were absent on the earth."

TABLE 6. Nickel and Cobalt Content in Soils and in Plant Ash

Soil and plant	Content, %		Co : Ni ratio	Abundance ratio*	
	Co	Ni		Co	Ni
Abundance of cobalt and nickel in soils	$1 \cdot 10^{-3}$	$4 \cdot 10^{-3}$	4	1	1
Chernozem soils. Kamennostepnaya Agricultural Station. A_1 horizon 0-5 cm	$7 \cdot 10^{-4}$	$3.9 \cdot 10^{-3}$	5.5	0.7	1
Soddy-podzol soil. Ufaleiskii nickel deposit. A_1 horizon 0-5 cm	$1.2 \cdot 10^{-3}$	$1.3 \cdot 10^{-2}$	11	1	3
Chestnut soil. Nickel deposit, Southern Urals. A_1 horizon 0-5 cm	$3.6 \cdot 10^{-2}$	$3.1 \cdot 10^{-1}$	9	36	78
Ash of Stipa capillata L.	$2.2 \cdot 10^{-4}$	$8.7 \cdot 10^{-4}$	4	1	1
Kamennostepnaya Agricultural Station. Nickel deposit, Orskii Rayon	$2.8 \cdot 10^{-2}$	$6.4 \cdot 10^{-1}$	23	127	735
Ash of Pinus silvestris L. Pushkino, near Moscow	$6.5 \cdot 10^{-4}$	$3.6 \cdot 10^{-3}$	5	1	1
Ufaleiskii nickel deposit	$4.5 \cdot 10^{-3}$	$6.2 \cdot 10^{-2}$	14	7	20

*The degree of enrichment of a particular element in comparison with the mean content (according to Vernadskii, [1937]).

Almost all the chemical elements of the earth's surface are indirectly associated in their occurrence with living matter. The content of many (Si, Al, Fe, Mg, Mn, S, Sr, P, K, Na, Cl, and Zn, in addition to the most common) is of the order of percents, whereas the content of others, the so-called microelements, constitutes insignificant fractions of one percent.

The occurrence of these chemical elements in various organisms is by no means a random phenomenon. In completing their cycle of biogenic migration in surface plants, the chemical elements perform highly important biological functions and then are accumulated in the soil, thereby maintaining the natural reproductivity of soil.

As early as 1910 Vernadskii pointed out the need for determining rare and disperse chemical elements in soils. Later Vinogradov [1935] formulated the problems involved in the investigation of individual rare elements in soils, and, as a result, the Biogeochemical Laboratory undertook the systematic study of the zonal soils of the East European Plain (Vinogradov [1940], [1948], [1949]; Selivanov [1946]; Malyuga [1944], (1946); and others). Since that time the Laboratory has accumulated significant factual data on the geochemistry of soils and plants. These data on soil studies were generalized by Vinogradov [1950] in his study The Geochemistry of Rare and Dispersed Chemical Elements in Soils, in which he noted the extremely important role of dispersed chemical elements in the life of the vegetation cover and of animals and man. The abundance ratios for soils derived by Vinogradov [1950] made it possible to represent precisely the "level" of rare and dispersed chemical elements in the normal soil cover (Table 5).

Examples of Biogeochemical Exploration in the USSR and Abroad

As early as 1934, on the initiative of Vernadskii and Vinogradov, the author undertook work on the study of the dispersion haloes of iron and nickel ore deposits for the purpose of clarifying the influence of high metal contents in rocks and ores on their distribution in soils and plants. The first studied samples of soddy-podzolic soils from the ore deposits of the Central Urals (Alapayevskii deposit, and others) revealed an appreciable accumulation of nickel and iron in the upper humus horizon of the soil A_1. This was the first instance in which it was noted that there is a non-uniform distribution of nickel in a horizontal soil profile with an obviously expressed tendency to concentration in the humus layer. In the period 1935-1936 the author noted an accumulation of nickel in trees and grasses growing over the nickel deposits of the Central and Southern Urals. Table 6 shows part of the accumulated data.

The data in Table 6 show a sharp increase in the content of nickel and cobalt in soils and plant ash for samples taken from nickel deposits. The presence of nickel ores was accompanied also by an appreciable change in the Ni : Co ratio known for these elements in soils and plants (Malyuga [1947a, 1950, 1951, 1954]).

The results of these studies were approved by the Scientific Council of the Institute of Geochemistry and Mineralogy of the Academy of Sciences of the USSR in 1939. The planned program of biogeochemical exploration work was not carried out because the Second World War broke out soon thereafter. In 1948, after the war, the work was resumed in the Southern Urals and in other regions of our country.

As early as 1923-1925, S. P. Aleksandrov investigated the ash of plants collected on one of the deposits and discovered a high content of uranium and vanadium in comparison with plants collected at some distance. In this connection, A. E. Fersman [1955] wrote about the possibility of using plants in geochemical exploration.

S. M. Tkalich undertook a study of problems related to biogeochemical prospecting in 1935. He outlined the dispersion halo of the Unashinskii arsenopyrite deposit (Dalnevostochnii Krai). For this purpose he collected 15 specimens of reed grass along three profiles at right angles to the strike of the profile. The plants were burned and the iron in the ash was examined. Despite the limited number of samples studied, it was possible to outline the dispersion halo of the main vein of the Unashinskii arsenopyrite deposit rather precisely.

At approximately the same time we made the first test of the prospecting value of the humus layer of the soil. The origin of the method can be dated back to this time. In the above-mentioned study, Tkalich wrote: "The problem which we have discussed, that of using plants in geological exploration work, is still backed by insufficient experimental data, so that for the time being it does not appear possible to suggest an unconditional possibility of widespread practical use of plants by geologists."

During the past 20 years the situation has changed greatly. Many new studies have appeared in the USSR and abroad which make it possible to give a more optimistic evaluation of the possibilities of the biogeochemical − soil − plant − method. This has been facilitated greatly by the work of the Soviet geophysicists E. A. Sergeev [1936, 1937, 1941, 1946], B. L. Flerov [1935, 1938], N. I. Safronov [1936], M. I. Roklin [1938], E. A. Ratsbaum [1939], N. I. Tikhomirov and S. I. Miller [1946], M. V. Yuneev [1948], and A. P. Solovov [1957], and many others, in the study of dispersion haloes and the development of the methods used in metallometric surveys (for tin, molybdenum, etc.).

Biogeochemical investigations for molybdenum were made by M. N. Senilova (1950) on the Shalginskii and other deposits of Central Kazakhstan. She established that under the conditions prevailing in the semidesert, molybdenum is very mobile (causing the formation of molybdite and powellite) and is easily assimilated by plants. Because of this the content of molybdenum in plant ash (Artemisia terrae-albae H.Krasch., and others) sampled over the zone of mineralization attains 0.01%, exceeding by several times the background values. The molybdenum content in plant ash, when plotted on the map, correlated quite well with the outline of the zone of mineralization established by other methods.

A systematic study of the biogeochemistry of molybdenum was made by Kh. G. Vinogradov (1943), [1954].

Major investigations for the study and checking of the biogeochemical method have been made by N. N. Sochevanov and others (working with the All-Union Scientific Research Institute of Geophysical Prospecting). In a report of that institute in 1952 they gave a comparative evaluation of the biogeochemical method and other methods of indication, including physical and chemical methods. The authors noted the positive aspects of the biogeochemical method, its high sensitivity, effective depth, etc.

In 1952 Tkalich renewed his work on the biogeochemical delimitation of sulfide deposits. He made a more precise determination of the limits of occurrence of impregnated copper ores on the basis of an investigation of the iron content in the leaves of the birch.

Over a period of years N. S. Parfent'eva (1955) did much work in checking the effectiveness of the plant and soil-plant exploration methods on the lead deposits of the central Kara-Tau. It was established that the soils and plants of this region accumulate lead to a considerable degree. The highest contents correspond to zones of mineralization detected during geological exploration. The resulting maps based on the floristic survey (plant analysis) more precisely define the mineralized sectors than a metallometric survey. The lead content in the soils and the ash of plants growing over the ore varies from $3 \cdot 10^{-3}$ to $1 \cdot 10^{-1}$%. For example, the lead content in the ash of certain plants in the central Kara-Tau (warty cherry, giant fennel, and others) corresponds to its content in the soil. A particularly great amount of lead was discovered in thickened underground organs (giant fennel, prangos, etc.). In the opinion of the authors, the soil-plant method possesses a greater effective depth than a metallometric survey (up to 10 m).

As already mentioned, the ideas of Vernadskii on the role of organisms in the concentration of rare and dispersed elements in the biosphere have been received with great interest both in the USSR and abroad. Many scientists abroad have begun the study of rare and other elements in soils, plants, and animals: Bertrand [1925, 1933, 1939], McHargue [1925], Fox and Ramage [1931], Kidson [1937], Noddack [1939], and many others. In his geochemical studies devoted to supergene processes, Goldschmidt (1933), [1937], has turned repeatedly to Vernadskii's ideas on biogeochemistry, for example, in explaining the accumulation of dispersed chemical elements (Ge, Pb, Au, and others) in the ash of coal and coaly shales. At the same time, in certain later articles by foreign scientists (Rankama [1954], Lundberg [1941], Warren and Delavault [1949], and others) there seems to be a tendency to belittle the work of Vernadskii; the idea of the biogenic concentration of chemical elements which he suggested as early as 1922-1925 has been ascribed to Goldschmidt under the name "the principle of biogenic concentration of elements."

The biogeochemical method has been tried out abroad under field conditions by the Swedish scientists Palmqvist and Brundin [1939]. Using the spectral method, they analyzed the ash of grassy plants, the fallen leaves of forest species, and sometimes of soils sampled in regions of possible occurrence of ores. The high content of Pb, Sn, and W noted in a number of cases led to the discovery of insignificant zones of mineralization, which in a general way confirmed the applicability of the method. The relatively modest results obtained by the Swedish exploration company in its major explorations in a number of regions (Cornwall, Devonshire, Wales, among other places) must be attributed to the incorrect mechanical application of the method without proper allowance for factors determining the geochemistry of the individual elements in the zone of supergenesis. A prolonged study of the method was required, such as that made, for example, by the Norwegian scientist Vogt [1939, 1942-1948].

Copper, Zinc

In his study of the biogeochemical method, Vogt attempted to take into account the content of copper and zinc in mine water, soils, and plants associated with a deposit. For this purpose he selected the Røros ore region, which has been well studied in geological respects. The Røros sulfide veins, with pyrrhotite, chalcopyrite, and sphalerite, are associated with basic and ultrabasic rocks (dunites, gabbro, serpentinites, syenites), almost everywhere covered with a glacial moraine. The shallowness of these deposits (2-3 m) does not hinder the migration of the chemical elements to the surface, which is reflected in the high content of ore elements in the soils and plants — up to $1.0 \cdot 10^{-2}$ and $7.0 \cdot 10^{-2}\%$ zinc in the dry leaves of Betula nana (copper in soils up to 0.7%).

Plants associated with the sulfide veins of the Røros region are Viscaria alpina (L.) and Melandrium dioicum (L) Schinz et Thell ("Kisplant"). The author has demonstrated that it is possible to define sulfide deposits on the basis of the ion SO_4^{2-} and ions of heavy metals in waters emanating from the zones of mineralization. In general, the maps which they have compiled by various methods correctly define the ore regions. Unfortunately, this work, after publication of a series of brief reports, was interrupted before a proper theoretical evaluation of the results was made. Due to the high content of copper, zinc, and other elements in the ash of plants growing beyond the limits of the sulfide deposits (background), the data for plants were poorer than the data for soils. The latter rather precisely define the location of the sulfide ores, which can be seen quite clearly by a comparison of the isoconcentrations of the elements in soils against geological maps.

Nickel, Copper

Almost simultaneously, and under approximately the same geological conditions (regions of basic and ultrabasic rocks), similar work was done by Rankama [1954] in Finland in the Petsamo region. The author's objective was to determine the influence of the thickness of morainal sediments covering rocks and, consequently, copper-nickel sulfate ores, on the accumulation of nickel and copper in plants. He made spectral determinations of the nickel in the ash of the leaves of the birch and other vegetation (Betula tortuosa, Betula nana, and others). At Kaulantunturi, where the morainal thickness was insignificant, the nickel content in the ash was from 0.02 to 0.5%, whereas in places where the moraine was several meters thick (Kolosioki) the quantities of nickel were negligible — from $1 \cdot 10^{-3}$ to $6 \cdot 10^{-3}\%$. Thus, the thickness of sediments making it possible to judge the presence of ores in the Petsamo region (northern Finland) is not in excess of 5-10 m.

Copper, Molybdenum

In the post-war period, work on the development of the biogeochemical methods of exploration has been done abroad primarily in the United States and Canada. Judging from published articles, these investigations were suspended in Sweden before the war, and in Norway in 1947 (the work of Vogt). Recently a single article, by Marmo, has appeared [1953]. His objective was to check the existence of a correlation in the content of Cu, Zn, and Mo in rocks (ores), ground water, and plants in the vicinity of Nokia, Khiirola, and Rautio in Finland.

The rocks at Nokia consist of phyllites, within which there is a stratum of shales with a high content of sulfides (pyrrhotite, chalcopyrite, sphalerite). At Khiirola the predominant rocks are mica gneisses and shales containing pyrrhotite, while at Rautio there are granites and granodiorites, enriched with molybdenite, and in part with chalcopyrite. This is the geological substrate on which soils and plants have developed.

18

The high content of copper and zinc in rocks (phyllites, mica shales) associated with mineralization (from 0.01 to 0.5%) was the cause of a corresponding increase of these elements in natural waters from $5 \cdot 10^{-4}$ to $2 \cdot 10^{-3}\%$. The study of the leaves of Vaccinium vitis-idaea (foxberry) in the Nokia region revealed a copper content in the ash from $2 \cdot 10^{-3}$ to $3 \cdot 10^{-3}$ and of zinc from $5 \cdot 10^{-3}$ to $6 \cdot 10^{-3}\%$. Due to the low nickel content in phyllites the nickel was believed associated with sulfides (pyrrhotite and pentlandite). The copper content in the ash of Ledum palustre (at Khiirola) was considerably greater — from $1.8 \cdot 10^{-2}$ to $5 \cdot 10^{-2}$. The molybdenum content in the ash of Ledum palustre (in the Rautio granites) varies from $5 \cdot 10^{-4}$ to $3.5 \cdot 10^{-3}\%$.

Marmo concludes that the plant analysis, despite the very low content of Cu, Ni, Zn, and Mo in the ash, reveals the presence of high quantities of metals in rocks and ores, but does not reflect this phenomenon linearly. His error was that he did not investigate the soils, assuming that natural ground water was the principal source from which heavy metals enter into plants.

The application of the biogeochemical exploration method on the American continent began only a few years ago, if we exclude random plant samplings made by Dingwall et al. (Dingwall, McKibbin, and Beans [1934]) for molybdenum in Quebec Province and by Lundberg [1941] in Newfoundland. The work has been concentrated primarily in various regions of the Colorado Plateau in the United States and British Columbia in Canada. Chronologically, the work was undertaken earlier in Canada, and we will use the same sequence in our discussion.

Manganese, Iron

The chemical research method was adopted for determination of metals. Various parts of plants were analyzed and the most stable results were obtained when using stems and twigs (second-year growth), rather than using fruits, leaves, etc.

The study of the plants Pinus contorta, Salix sp., Tsuga heterophylla, and others revealed the distribution of zinc and copper as a function of the place where the samples were taken: over a vein, downslope from the vein, or outside the deposit. The variations in zinc in dry material ranged from $1 \cdot 10^{-3}$ to $1 \cdot 10^{-1}\%$ and those in copper from $1 \cdot 10^{-3}$ to $7 \cdot 10^{-2}\%$. In this case there was a change in the Cu:Zn ratio from the normal 10-15 to higher values over copper ores. A check by Warren (Warren and Delavault [1954]) of the manganese and iron content of plants on sulfide ores gave positive results of their exploration significance. It was noted that there is a high content of these elements in plants sampled near ore concentrations, and in this case manganese almost always predominates over iron (Fe:Mn = 0.3). Because of this, it was considered possible that these species could be used in the exploration of epithermal deposits of gold, silver, and other elements.*

An investigation of plants directly for gold and silver—Equisetum sp., Pseudostuga taxifolia (Douglas fir), Salix sp.—sampled in promising areas, revealed gold contents up to $7.5 \cdot 10^{-6}\%$ (using dry material), which is significantly higher than normal. This observation confirms the data obtained by Nemec and others [1935-1936] on the value of plants as indicators of gold.

A valuable aspect of Warren's work was a study of the influence of various factors (age and species of plants, natural conditions, etc.) on the content and ratio of iron, manganese, zinc, and copper in plants. A serious shortcoming of this work is that the author was not concerned at all with soils — the principal link in the biogenic migration of heavy metals.

Copper, Zinc, Lead

The biogeochemical investigations in British Columbia were made by Warren and other scientists from the University of Vancouver (in 1947-1952). For the most part the work was concentrated on the large Sullivan and Britannia copper-lead-zinc deposits 20 miles to the north of Vancouver.

The sulfide veins, represented by pyrite, chalcopyrite, and in part by sphalerite, lie in argillites, quartzites (Precambian), and chloritic and sericitic rocks (Britannia deposit). Certain veins approach the surface and create rather clearly expressed anomalies in metal dispersion. In a number of cases they are covered by glacial deposits of differing thickness.

In similar work, also done in British Columbia, White [1950] had the objective of investigating the behavior of copper and zinc in plants over four sulfide deposits in relationship to the country rock (granodiorites, quartz-monzonites,

---

*Similar work has been done by Tkalich [1938, 1952].

limestones). The copper and zinc contents in coniferous plants (fir, pine) in all of the studied deposits were equal. In one of them (the Copperado mine) the copper content varied from $1 \cdot 10^{-4}$ to $7 \cdot 10^{-4}\%$ (using dry material), and the zinc content from $7 \cdot 10^{-3}$ to $3 \cdot 10^{-3}\%$. The Cu:Zn ratio averaged 0.3. In another deposit the zinc content was as high as $1 \cdot 10^{-2}\%$ or more, with insignificant quantities of copper. The sensitivity of the method was lowered by the high background concentrations of the metals, so that indication required the presence of considerable concentrations of metals in plants over the zone of mineralization. In this case the author attempted to use the Cu:Zn ratio. The effective depth of the method is set at 10 m. The work suffers from the same shortcomings as the preceding work done by Warren and others.

The work in the United States has been done primarily on the Colorado Plateau, in the Mississippi Valley (near the Great Lakes), in the tri-state region of Missouri, Kansas, and Oklahoma, in southeastern Kansas, and elsewhere. This work was carried out at the initiative of the United State Geological Survey, sometimes with the participation of local universities. It was subsidized by various mining companies. The principal objective of the programmed investigations was to check the biogeochemical exploration method to determine its possible applicability in practical work.

Robinson et al. [1945, 1947] devote particular attention to the processes of chemical interrelationships between plants, soils, and rocks (ores). In a study published in 1945 he provides a bibliography, detailed for that time, on the problem of the presence of a number of microelements in plants, including the rare earths, selenium, copper, nickel, cobalt, and molybdenum. In a second study, published in 1947, he gave the results of his own investigations, including analyses of plants sampled on old soil banks of a zinc deposit at Friedensville. In this study he employed the chemical, dithizone method for the determination of zinc. The studied plants were characterized by a considerable zinc content (in dry stems), from $6 \cdot 10^{-2}\%$ in Solidago sp. to $4.5 \cdot 10^{-1}\%$ in Equisetum arvense. The species sampled at a considerable distance from the zinc deposits contained considerably smaller quantities of zinc, not exceeding $1 \cdot 10^{-2}\%$. The selected plants (such as poplar and ragweed) possess the ability to accumulate zinc (up to $3 \cdot 10^{-2}\%$) when its content in the soil is insignificant ($3 \cdot 10^{-3}\%$). These plants can be used in the exploration of sulfide deposits as specific concentrators of zinc.

Harbaugh [1950] made similar biogeochemical investigations in the tri-state region of Missouri, Kansas, and Oklahoma on sulfide deposits of zinc, lead, and copper (sphalerite, galenite, and chalcopyrite). The strata-like and lens-like ore bodies in this region lie in limestones, covered by shales of varying thickness — from 1 to 20 m. The method was checked by determining zinc, lead, and copper in plants by the dithizone method (see below) on known ore areas at Sullivan.

The sectors were defined on the basis of the content of ore elements (Zn, Cu, Pb) in plants. Their degree of concentration was determined in comparison with ore-free zones. In this case it was established that trees (leaves, shoots) and grassy plants are enriched appreciably with zinc. Its content in leaves and young shoots (in the ash) sometimes attains $1 \cdot 10^{-1}\%$ and always is 1.5 times greater than that in the same plants sampled outside the deposit. This dependence was expressed less strongly for other elements. The mean content of elements (on the basis of 300 samples) in the ash of Quercus marilandica was (in %): Cu, $2.1 \cdot 10^{-2}$; Pb, $3.3 \cdot 10^{-2}$; Sn, $1.7 \cdot 10^{-3}$; Ni, $4.2 \cdot 10^{-3}$; Co, $8 \cdot 10^{-4}$, and Ag, $2 \cdot 10^{-4}$. The distribution of zinc in plants correlated with the development of mineralization, although it did not always precisely correspond to zones of mineralization. A high Zn:Pb ratio was one of the criteria for the presence of mineralization. Close to normal content of nickel and cobalt revealed an absence of corresponding mineralization. Harbaugh does not touch upon the study of soils.

Following the experience of Russian geophysicists and geochemists (Sergeev [1941]; Malyuga [1939], among others), certain American authors have undertaken the study of the dispersion haloes of ore deposits on the basis of analyses of soils and residual material.

Hawkes and Lakin [1949] investigated the soils and eluvium-talus on a sulfide zinc deposit at Friend Station (18 miles northeast of Knoxville, Tennessee). The sulfide deposit in this area lies in dolomites, from which a crust of residual clays 5 to 17 m in thickness has developed. The chemical analysis of these clays revealed a mean zinc content of $5 \cdot 10^{-2}\%$. The contoured maps drawn on the basis of the zinc content in clay at a depth of 120 cm defined the position of the vein quite clearly. The upper humus horizon of the soil, usually enriched with zinc, was greatly deformed as a result of plowing and erosion by surface water, so that its zinc content was extremely unstable, which made it impossible to use it in soil sampling.

TABLE 7. Content of Ore Elements in Ground Water

No. of hole	Depth of ground water, m	pH	Total content of salts, %	Water content, %	
				Cu	Zn
86	50	7.7	—	$2 \cdot 10^{-6}$	$1 \cdot 10^{-6}$
73	100	7.4	0.025	$2 \cdot 10^{-6}$	$2 \cdot 10^{-6}$
M	212	7.5	0.025	$6 \cdot 10^{-6}$	$6 \cdot 10^{-6}$
64	178	7.5	0.024	$8 \cdot 10^{-6}$	$6 \cdot 10^{-6}$
63	189	7.5	0.026	$4 \cdot 10^{-6}$	$2 \cdot 10^{-6}$
Q	204	7.6	0.025	$2 \cdot 10^{-6}$	$2 \cdot 10^{-6}$
L	206	7.5	0.028	$2 \cdot 10^{-6}$	$1 \cdot 10^{-6}$

A second study by Hawkes [1949] gives bibliographical references on the subject. He checked the results [1951] on another copper sulfide deposit (the Malachite mine) in Colorado. The soils in that area were eroded severely from the surface layers and therefore it was impossible to use them for the purpose of checking the method. The samples were obtained from residual material at a depth of 60 cm or more. The high copper content in the sample corresponded to a zone where a vein was intersected by a profile, and was in a position displaced somewhat downslope.

The soil sampling method was used by Fowler [1950] in the tri-state region, by Fulton [1950] in a lead-zinc deposit at Austinville, Virginia, by Gilbert [1951] and Cooper and Huff [1954] on sulfide vein deposits of copper, lead, and zinc in the vicinity of Park City, Utah, in Arizona, Wisconsin, and elsewhere.

The general opinion of the authors who have made use of the soil method is that it offers promise for exploring veins of copper, zinc, lead, and other metals. A study of the dispersion haloes of known deposits by sampling in a grid has revealed that the detected areas are associated with mineralized zones. The method of intersecting ore-bearing veins by individual profiles likewise has revealed a good coincidence of results for a whole series of deposits. The determination of zinc, copper, and lead was done using the dithizone method in all cases, as described by Sendel [1949], Holms [1945], and Lakin et al. [1949]. The study of the metal content in samples of soils taken from a vertical profile has made it possible to determine the most enriched layers. As a result of the insufficient stability of the upper humus horizon, its content of zinc and other elements varies to a greater extent than in residual material. The content of copper and lead residual material is more constant and was, on the average, tenths of a percent. According to Gilbert's data, the metal content in the upper humus horizon is higher than in residual material, which indicates it possibly can be used in carrying out exploration work in individual regions.

Numerous investigations of samples made by Huff and others confirm the earlier observations made by Soviet geophysicists, that there is a constant downslope displacement of the centers of the anomalies. The value of the displacement is directly proportional to the angle of slope.

The absence of a description of the soil profiles in the above-mentioned studies makes it impossible to judge how the samples were obtained. From the depths at which the samples were taken it can be deduced that a study was made of the subsoil horizon, close to the eluvium (residuum). Thus the "soil" sampling made by these authors constitutes an ordinary metallometric survey with all its positive and negative aspects. A general shortcoming of these studies is the absence of biogeochemical observations (the soil formation process, the role of plants), so that there is no explanation of the forms of compounds of Zn, Pb, and Cu to determine their mobility or stability in the biogeochemical profile.

Problems involved in biogeochemical exploration for copper under semidesert conditions have been discussed in Lovering et al. [1954]. The work was done in the San Manuel deposit (near Tucson, Arizona) where the copper deposit is associated with quartz-monzonites and aplites of the Precambrian, and with Middle Tertiary volcanic rocks and Gila conglomerates (Early Quaternary). The greater part of the ore zone lies under these conglomerates. The ore is represented by primary sulfides (pyrite, chalcopyrite) and minerals of the oxidized zone (chrysocolla, cuprite, and others). A study was made of rock, alluvium, soil, ground water, and plant life. The results of the field and laboratory analyses revealed that the greater part of the copper was associated with soil and alluvium. The copper content in the soil over the ore reaches 1% (from 0.1 to 1%), whereas in ore-free sectors the copper content does not exceed hundredths and thousandths of a percent. In exactly the same way, the fine fractions of alluvium obtained below the outcrop

TABLE 8. Uranium and Vanadium Content in Soils and Plants (in %)

Rock, soil, and plant	U		V_2O_5	
	in rock, soil	in plant ash	in rock, soil	in plant ash
Thompson, Utah Ore Zone				
Rock, depth 120 cm	$5.4 \cdot 10^{-2}$	–	$2 \cdot 10^{-1}$	–
Juniperus monosperma (shoots)	–	$8 \cdot 10^{-4}$	–	$2 \cdot 10^{-3}$
Juniperus monosperma (roots near surface	–	$1.6 \cdot 10^{-1}$	–	$3.6 \cdot 10^{-1}$
Top soil	$1.7 \cdot 10^{-2}$	–	–	–
Oryzopsis hymenoides (shoots)	–	$8.2 \cdot 10^{-3}$	–	$2 \cdot 10^{-2}$
Astragalus preusii (roots)	–	$7 \cdot 10^{-3}$	–	$2.6 \cdot 10^{-1}$
Quercus Gambelii (leaves, in May)	–	$1 \cdot 10^{-3}$	–	$9 \cdot 10^{-3}$
Quercus Gambelli (leaves, in August)	–	$4 \cdot 10^{-3}$	–	$2 \cdot 10^{-2}$
Quercus Gambelli (roots)	–	$1.9 \cdot 10^{-2}$	–	$1.7 \cdot 10^{-1}$
Ore-free Zone				
Top soil	$2 \cdot 10^{-4}$	–	$2 \cdot 10^{-2}$	–
Juniperus monosperma (shoots)	–	$1.1 \cdot 10^{-4}$	–	$6 \cdot 10^{-3}$
Astragalus confertiflorus (shoots)	–	$8 \cdot 10^{-5}$	–	$9 \cdot 10^{-3}$
Querus Gambelii (shoots)	–	$5 \cdot 10^{-5}$	–	$5 \cdot 10^{-4}$
Quercus Gambelii (roots)	–	$2 \cdot 10^{-4}$	–	$5 \cdot 10^{-3}$
Atriplex canescens (leaves)	–	$6.8 \cdot 10^{-5}$	–	$1 \cdot 10^{-3}$

of the oxidized ore contained from 0.1 to 0.5% copper (less than in the soil). The lower concentrations of copper in the ash of plants sampled over an ore soil were attributed by the authors to the poor mobility of copper at the present stage of development of the zone of oxidation, which is confirmed by its insignificant content in ground water (Table 7).

The samples from holes 86 and 73 were taken above the ground water table from a nonmineralized zone; their copper and zinc contents therefore are lower than those in waters flowing directly from the ore (samples from holes 64, M, and others). The relatively low copper and zinc contents in the ground water of the San Manuel deposit nevertheless do not exclude the possibility of the chemical migration of heavy metals in the dispersion halo of the copper deposit. This is in fact indicated by the accumulation of copper and zinc in plant ash and in the humus layer of the soil.

The authors note the ecological affinity of Quercus turbinella and other species to oxidized copper ores, which makes it possible to use them as geoindicators.

In a study made under these same conditions in the Ray copper deposit in Arizona, Clark, [1953] confirms the observations made by Lovering. His data show an appreciable increase in the copper content in soils and plants sampled over the deposit in comparison with the surrounding background. The copper content in soils and plants changes appreciably, depending on the type of rock, local drainage conditions, and the degree of erosion, factors which must be taken into account when applying the biogeochemical exploration method.

Radioactive Elements

We now will discuss the work of Cannon [1952], devoted to the influence of uranium deposits on the vegetation of the Colorado Plateau.

The uranium deposits of the Colorado Plateau are associated with Jurassic sandstones and consist of uranium-vanadium lens-like bodies. The lenses vary from 0.3 to 20 m in thickness and are over 30 m in length. The uranium-vanadium ores contain 0.25% U_3O_8 and about 2% V_2O_5. The principal ore mineral is carnotite – $K_2(UO_2)_2V_2O_8 \cdot 3H_2O$. In addition to uranium and vanadium, the ores contain Se, Mo, Pb, Co, Ni, Cr, and Cu.

These investigations were made primarily in Thompson, Utah. The purpose of the investigation was to study the distribution of uranium and vanadium in plants over ores and the physiological effects of high uranium concentrations in plants. The author collected extensive data, which implied that the plants sampled over the mineralized zone have an ash content of from $2 \cdot 10^{-4}$ to $1 \cdot 10^{-2}$% of uranium and from $4 \cdot 10^{-3}$ to $2 \cdot 10^{-2}$% of V_2O_5. The normal uranium content in plant ash does not exceed $1 \cdot 10^{-4}$%. Consequently, the uranium concentration in plants over the deposits exceeds the background content by the order of tens. The uranium and vanadium distribution in plants sampled in the area of the uranium deposits of the Colorado Plateau is shown in Table 8.

The data in Table 8 show a clear accumulation of uranium and vanadium in plants sampled over the deposits in comparison with ore-free sectors. The data cited in the study show a nonuniform distribution of uranium in different organs — shoots, leaves, and roots. The greatest quantity of uranium was found in the roots of plants growing over carbonate and asphaltite ores.

The plants in which a high uranium content was discovered, such as plants growing on spoil banks of oxidized ores, obviously suffered from the toxic effect of uranium. However, this effect is masked by the simultaneous excess content of vanadium and — especially — selenium.

The author selected several species of plants — selenium concentrators such as Stanleya pinnata, and others — which can be used as indirect indicators of uranium, since uranium and selenium are correlated quite well in the ores of the Colorado Plateau.

In discussing the mechanism of entry of uranium into plants, Cannon and Kleinhampl (1956) note that the uranium absorptivity of plants depends on the pH of the cell sap of the root hairs. Uranium is absorbed easily by plants in which the pH of the cell sap is less than 5.2, such as conifers and certain members of the rose family. Such plants absorb much calcium, sodium, sulfur, and selenium, but little potassium.

The maximum thickness of covering rocks through which the uranium ore (carnotite) can be detected is 20-25 m; the great depth apparently can be attributed to the deep penetration of the roots of the pine and juniper along fissures in the rock to water-bearing ore horizons.

About ten ore bodies in the states of Utah and New Mexico have been discovered by the use of the biogeochemical exploration method.

Investigations on the use of the radiometric biogeochemical exploration method were made almost at the same time. For example, Anderson and Kurtz [1955] used the method on a known uranium deposit, Annie Laurie, in Arizona. This deposit lies several meters below the surface. The measurement of the radioactivity of the ash of plants — oak (Quercus emoryi), mesquite (Prosopis juliflora var. velutina), and others — revealed an appreciable increase of radioactivity in plants growing above the zone of mineralization. Individual zones with the richest uranium mineralization were defined. The authors demonstrated that there was a nonuniform accumulation of uranium in different plant species growing together. Pine and juniper are very poor concentrators of uranium, while mesquite, oak, and others are better. The sensitivity of the radiometric scintillation method that was employed (based on α-radiation) did not exceed 10 mg/kg of ash for uranium.

Cannon, Anderson, and Kurtz did their work in the dry climate of the Colorado Plateau and Arizona. In the USSR the biogeochemical method for exploration of uranium has been used in the forested and swampy regions of the taiga.

U. I. Moiseenko (1959) checked the effectiveness of the method by defining a known ore deposit partially covered by a peat bog. The region was covered by a spruce-birch forest with an admixture of aspen, willow, and alder. The vegetation of the peat bog consists for the most part of mosses and sedges. The method was used in sectors with a high activity in soils and in areas where radiation was absent, since ore bodies there were covered with moraines. The uranium content in plant ash in the region of the deposit attained $1 \cdot 10^{-4}$ to $5 \cdot 10^{-4}\%$, which corresponds to values somewhat higher than the geochemical background of uranium. At points with an anomalous content there is an increase of uranium from $5 \cdot 10^{-4}$ to $4 \cdot 10^{-2}\%$. The soils and peat are richer in uranium, but the reverse relationship also is observed. For example, in the ash of the moss Scorpidium scorpioides the uranium content is $1.6 \cdot 10^{-2}\%$, while in the soil it is $6.5 \cdot 10^{-3}\%$; in the leaves of the spruce Picea excelsa the uranium content is $4 \cdot 10^{-2}\%$, while in soils it is only $8 \cdot 10^{-4}\%$, etc.

This study showed the possibility of using the biogeochemical exploration method in the search for uranium in the swampy taiga regions of the Soviet Union. The luminescence method was used to determine the presence of uranium.

The work of A. L. Kovalevskii [1960] in checking the possibility of using the biogeochemical method of exploration for uranium using radium was done under similar conditions. The determination of the uranium content in plant ash was done on the basis of α-radiation, using highly sensitive apparatus. A good correlation was obtained between the uranium content in plant ash and the dispersion haloes of ore bodies. Similar work is being done at our institute by graduate student M. M. Botova under desert and semidesert conditions.

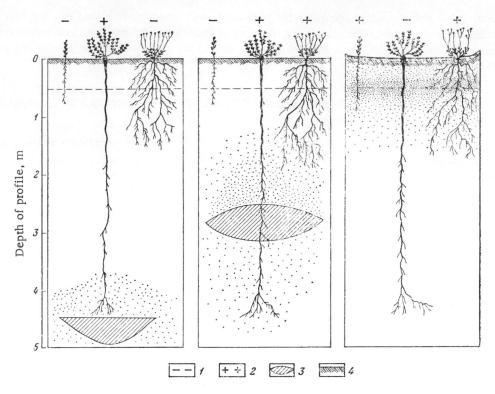

Fig. 8. Diagram of plant indication of boron, dependent on the structure of root systems (according to Shvyryaeva and Petrunina, 1957). 1) Background content of boron; 2) high boron content; 3) horizons enriched with boron; 4) soil.

Rare and Disperse Elements: Li, B, Be, Zr, Nb, Sn, Th, Hg, Ag, and Au

A study of the problem of the use of the biogeochemical method for exploration for boron using soils and plants was made by A. M. Shvyryaeva [1957] on aerogeological expedition VAGT No. 10 in the ascharite and ulexite deposits. Appropriate profiles were used for the sampling and study of the ash of the saltwort Salsola nitraria Pall., thrift Limonium suffruticosum, Anabasis salsa, wormwood, and others in the search for boron. On the basis of data from an analysis of soils and the ash of plants collected over a known zone of boron, it was possible to compile maps of the isoconcentrations of boron. The anomalies detected from analyses of plant ash correlated more clearly with the outlines of the ore zones than did the analyses made using soils.

When a comparison was made of data from an analysis of plants of different species with a given kind of root system, it was found that the boron content was not uniform. Plants with a shallow root system clearly showed the presence of boron in the soil (saltwort), while plants with long roots (Anabasis aphylla) reveal it only to a depth of 3 to 4 m (Fig. 8).

By knowing the depth of the root system of individual plants and the degree of concentration of boron it is possible not only to determine the outlines of the anomaly, but also the depth and morphology of the ore body.

Soviet investigators have become experienced in the exploration for rare and rare earth elements. N. A. Tyutina, V. B. Aleskovskii, and P. N. Vasil'ev [1959] checked the possibility of using the biogeochemical method in exploration for niobium. For this purpose the plant samples — leaves and branches of trees and stems of grass — were collected over a known rare metal deposit and studied for their niobium content.

The plant ash was analyzed for niobium using a specially developed chemical colorimetric method (using potassium thiocyanate) of determination after separation of niobium from molybdenum and other elements by means of $MnO(OH)_2$. Analytical data revealed an appreciable enrichment with niobium of the ash of the Arctic raspberry Rubus arcticus L., the willow herb Chamaenerion angustifolium L., and the leaves of the birch Betula pubescens Ehrh., using from 8 to 60 mg of Nb_2O_5 per kilogram of dry matter. In this case there was a good correlation between the content of niobium in plants and the specific location of the zones of mineralization.

A study of great interest is the systematic work of E. A. Astrakhan, L. I. Grabovskii, and others (1960), regarding the possibility of using the biogeochemical method in an exploration of rare metal deposits (Li, Be, Zr, Nb, Sn, and RE) under various geological and bioclimatic conditions: the wooded steppe, the podzol swamp zone, the chernozem and dark chestnut mountain steppe zone, etc.

Although the first data on the finding of rare earths were obtained many years ago (Starynkevich-Borneman et al. [1941], Robinson [1949]), only recently has it been shown to be fully possible to use soils (the humus layer, the forest soil litter) and plants in exploration for rare earth elements. A high content of Li, Be, Zr, Sn, and RE has been found in Stellaria chameaysme, Adonis amurensis, and others, of thousandths to tenths of a percent, depending on the nearness of the zones of mineralization. A dependence of the distribution of plants on the composition of the bedrock also has been established. The possibility of the effective use of the biogeochemical exploration method was confirmed by the finding of pegmatite veins enriched with rare elements.

Successful systematic work on the use of the biogeochemical method in exploration for tin and other rare and disperse elements has been done by E. S. Burkser and B. F. Mitskevich [1960] in the Ukraine (Ukrainian Poles'e).

The possibility of the application of the biogeochemical method in the search for mercury became quite realistic after the appearance of the extremely thorough monograph on this element by A. A. Saukov [1946]. The slow adoption of the method is due to difficulties in determining the presence of mercury in soils (the humus layer) and plants. At the present time plans call for systematic work on exploration for mercury in the Rudnii Altai and in the Abkhaz ASSR. The processing of biogeochemical samples collected in Eastern Trans-Baikalia (Grobovo) for determination of their mercury content has begun.

Experience in systematic investigations of the possibility of extensive application of the biogeochemical method in exploration for ore deposits is being gathered steadily. The list of elements for which the method is used is constantly being expanded, and the number of bioclimatic zones in which such investigations have been made is ever increasing.

In recent years work involving nickel, gold, uranium, and other elements has been carried out. Among such studies of interest are those of V. B. Aleksovskii, A. A. Mokhov, and V. N. Spirov [1959] on nickel in the tundra zone, Razin on gold in the permafrost zone (Yakutiya), I. I. Ginzburg, K. M. Mukanov, and N. P. Poluzerov [1960] on copper and lead under the conditions prevailing in Central Kazakhstan, among others.

To date biogeochemical studies of 30 elements have been made. However, it should be noted that the majority of the published studies in the USSR and abroad are devoted to a relatively small number of elements. For example, of the almost one hundred studies which we will cite, more than half are devoted to the four elements nickel, copper, zinc, and lead. Experience in study of the remaining elements is relatively limited. Our main problem, therefore, is the application of available experience to other elements, particularly to rare and dispersed elements.

It has been established in the studies by Vinogradov, Tkalich, Malyuga, Vogt, Warren, Rankama, Lovering, Cannon, and others that many ore elements form biogeochemical haloes reflecting high metal contents in soils and plants over zones of mineralization.

The content of nickel, copper, zinc, lead, molybdenum, and other elements in residual soils (orthoeluvium) and in plants depends on the underlying rocks (granites, diorites, ultrabasites), that is, on the content of these elements in the rock. There are of course exceptions. For example, limestones facilitate the accumulation of humus and at the same time a number of heavy metals, although they contain the latter in extremely small quantities (Huff [1954]). The initial content of metals in rock is reflected in the value of the geochemical background and, consequently, influences the sensitivity of the method.

The thickness of the covering rocks influences the effective depth of the exploration method. The degree of this influence depends on geological and climatic conditions. In northern regions morainal deposits of as little as 2 or 3 m prevent the detection of anomalies, whereas in desert and semidesert zones even thick strata of clay-like loams and sands do not hinder the appearance of anomalies at the surface.

The ability of nickel, copper, zinc, molybdenum, uranium, and other elements to migrate in the soil-geological profile is often identical. The mobility of iron, manganese, cobalt, and lead may be limited by external zonal factors — a high pH, arid climate, high temperatures, etc.

The chemical and physicochemical properties of the elements have an important role in the comparative study of the biogeochemical migration of ore elements in soils: the ability to yield compounds not easily soluble, high activity in the formation of complexes with organic and other compounds, ion exchange, etc.

It can be concluded from a review of the literature that until recently there has been no clear interpretation of the biogeochemical method of prospecting for ore deposits. In many studies a geochemical approach to the solution of obviously geochemical problems is lacking. The method often is used without taking into account the geochemistry of individual elements and processes transpiring in the rock (ore) → soil → plant system.

The interpretation of facts related to the accumulated data has been oversimplified. Each author attempts to approach the solution of the problem from the position of his own specialty: geophysics, botany, etc. Many problems involved in the theoretical basis of the method therefore have only been formulated, by no means solved: e.g., the problem of the participation of the organic matter of the soil in the accumulation and preservation of microelements, the problem of mobile and assimilable forms of elements, and the problem of the significance of internal and external migration factors in the dispersion halo.

The large amount of factual data obtained as a result of experimental and systematic work carried on in the USSR and abroad in checking the possibility of the application of the biogeochemical method indicates the great effectiveness of the method in exploration for a whole series of useful chemical elements: Li, Be, B, Cr, Mn, Co, Ni, Cu, Zn, Se, Mo, Ag, Sn, RE, Au, Pb, Ra, U, and others.

The data available in the literature show that the biogeochemical exploration method is applicable under the most varied geological and bioclimatic conditions and possesses a number of advantages over other geochemical methods when working in the swampy tundra, in the coniferous taiga podzol zone, and in desert and semidesert zones.

The sensitivity of the biogeochemical method is dependent on the concentration of chemical elements in soils and plants, which in turn is determined by the conditions of depth of the ore bodies, the ability of surface plants to assimilate a particular ore element, and the favorable influence of internal and external migration factors.

Recently many new chemical elements have been included among those elements for which and by means of which biogeochemical exploration work has been carried out. Among these is a significant number of rare and dispersed elements: Li, Be, Zr, Nb, Au, RE, Ra, and others.

Methods for speedy quantitative determinations of the presence of metals in soils and plants are being improved, including spectral, radiometric, luminescence, polarographic, and colorimetric methods.

A number of studies have made an attempt to provide a theoretical basis for the biogeochemical method. However, this is hindered by the lack of a proper understanding of the essence of the method, especially among geophysicists concerned with the application of lithochemical exploration methods — metallometric surveys, the bottom sediment method, etc.

Plans call for the gradual but extensive adoption of the biogeochemical exploration method in the practice of the geological services of the USSR and foreign countries. At the same time, the area of primary application of the biogeochemical method in conjunction with other geochemical methods is being determined.

CHAPTER II

INTERNAL FACTORS GOVERNING THE MIGRATION
OF CHEMICAL ELEMENTS OVER ORE DEPOSITS

Migration is a process leading to the concentration or dispersion of chemical elements in the earth's crust under the influence of internal and external factors. The theoretical problems of migration and its various manifestations have been treated in numerous studies published by the Russian geochemists V. I. Vernadskii, A. E. Fersman, A. P. Vinogradov, B. B. Polynov, and their students. They were the first to point out the exceptional importance of the processes of the geochemical and biogeochemical migration of chemical elements: weathering, denudation, and soil formation. These processes are related to the development over ore deposits of secondary "chemical" dispersion haloes, that is, an increase in the content of metals in the unconsolidated products of weathering of ore-forming rocks, in soils, waters, and surface plants.

E. Fersman (1934) divides migration factors into internal ones, dependent on the properties of the atoms and ions of the metals, and external ones, associated with the external conditions of migration. The combination of internal and external factors also determines the behavior of the chemical elements in natural processes, including supergene processes which are of direct interest to us.

Among the internal migration factors are the following: valence, ionic radius, polarization of ions, and other properties following from the position of the element in the Mendeleev periodic system (the solubility of minerals and compounds, sorption properties of ions).

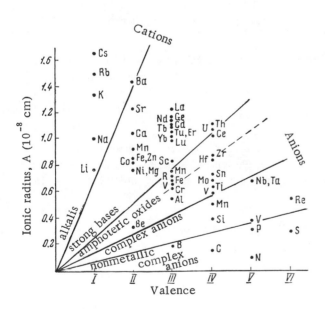

Fig. 9. Diagram of acidic and basic properties of the chemical elements as a function of the ratio between valence and ionic radius (according to Goldschmidt, with additions by Shcherbina).

Important constants of the chemical elements in geochemistry are the ionic radii and valences, since the behavior of ions in aqueous solutions depends on them. As an example we will examine a diagram reflecting the dependence of the acidic and basic properties of chemical elements on the ratio of valence to ionic radius, called the ionic potential (Fig. 9).

Figure 9 shows that the value of the ionic potential is used to define groups of elements possessing similar properties in aqueous solutions: elements with basic properties — Li, Na, K; weak and strong bases — Co, Ni, Cu, Zn, Ca, Sr, Ba; amphoteric oxides — V^{3+}, Fe^{3+}, Mn^{3+}, Cr^{3+}, Al^{3+}, Ti^{4+}; metals forming complex anions — V^{5+}, Cu^{6+}, U^{6+}, Mo^{6+}, Mn^{4+} (Nb, Ta, Re); complex anions of the type PO_4^{3-}, SO_4^{2-}, BO_3^{3-}, and others.

The arrangement of the chemical elements according to values of the ionic potential shows that there is no absolute uniformity in the properties of the elements in a given group. For example, in the group of bivalent elements basic properties are manifested in elements with a small ionic potential (Ca, Sr, Ba) and weak basic properties are manifested in the heavy metals (Mn^{2+}, Fe^{2+}, Co^{2+}, Ni^{2+}, Cu^{2+}, and Zn^{2+}) possessing a higher ionic potential (from 2 to 3).

TABLE 9. Migration Series of Chemical Elements (According to Polynov [1947])

Series	Element	Order of migration, %
Vigorously migrating	Cl (Br, I), S	$n \cdot 10^1$
Easily migrating	Ca, Na (Mg, K)	$n \cdot 10^0$
Mobile	SiO_2 (from silicates) P, Mn	$n \cdot 10^{-1}$
Inert (poor mobility)	Fe^{3+}, Al^{3+}, Ti^{4+}	$n \cdot 10^{-2}$
Virtually immobile	SiO_2 (quartz) and others	$n \cdot 10^{-\infty}$

The values of the ionic potentials to a certain degree determine the stability of minerals and the relative solubility of the phosphates, sulfates, and halides that determine the mobility of chemical elements in the biosphere. "The degree and means of migration," notes Fersman [1934], "depend on the stability of the basic compounds of a particular element under corresponding conditions," i.e., on the ability to form compounds which are not easily soluble.

The most soluble and most easily mobile are halides, carbonates, and sulfates of alkalis, followed by halides and bicarbonates of calcium and magnesium, and then halides, bicarbonates, and sulfates of Mn^{2+}, Fe^{2+}, Co^{2+}, Ni^{2+}, Cu^{2+}, Zn^{2+}, and others. Among the not easily soluble compounds are: strontium sulfate, barium and strontium carbonates, copper and zinc hydrocarbonates and, in particular, the oxides of Ti^{4+}, Zr^{4+}, Th^{4+}, and Sn^{4+}, the hydroxides of Fe^{3+}, Mn^{3+}, and Co^{3+}, and silver chloride. Such natural compounds as rutile, zircon, thorianite, cassiterite, limonite, and asbolane are found among these.

The solubility, and therefore the mobility, of natural compounds of useful metals under the conditions prevailing at the earth's surface depends on changing external migration factors such as redox conditions, pH, temperature, influence of atmospheric gases (CO_2, O_2), companion elements and compounds, and, finally, is dependent on the mineral composition of rocks and minerals, the initial source of many of the chemical elements in the biosphere.

Polynov [1947] divided the chemical elements into the migration series shown in Table 9, according to the degree of mobility of their soluble salts in river water.

In the series of mobile elements, in addition to P and Mn, he proposes the inclusion of Fe^{2+}, Co^{2+}, Ni^{2+}, Cu^{2+}, Zn^{2+}, V^{5+}, Cr^{6+}, Mo^{6+}, U^{6+}, and other heavy metals. The following should be included with the inert elements, in addition to iron, aluminum, and titanium: Th^{4+}, Sn^{4+}, the rare earths, and certain rare elements (Nb, Ta). The concept of a coefficient of water migration "Kx" was introduced by A. I. Perel'man [1956] for evaluating the place of the elements in the migration series.

Many ore-forming elements possess variable valence. During the oxidation of sulfide ores not easily soluble, the sulfur enters a hexavalent state, forming mobile sulfates of iron (Fe^{2+}), cobalt, nickel, copper, zinc, and other chemical elements possessing good migration properties, in accordance with the equation

$$FeS_2 + 7O + H_2O \rightarrow FeSO_4 + H_2SO_4.$$

A further oxidation of iron leads to the precipitation of hydroxides with the partial separation of iron from nickel, copper, and zinc. In contrast to manganese and iron, vanadium, chromium, uranium, and molybdenum are capable of forming extremely mobile oxidized forms of compounds under certain conditions, which are stable in natural surface waters: e.g., vanadates, chromates, etc.

TABLE 10. pH Value for Hydrolysis of Metal Salts (According to Lovering [1954])

Ion	pH	Ion	pH	Ion	pH
Mg^{2+}	10.5	Co^{2+}	6.8	UO_2^{2+}	4.2
Mn^{2+}	8.5—8.8	Ni^{2+}	6.7	Al^{3+}	4.1
Ag^{1+}	7.5—8.0	Cd^{2+}	6.7	Hg^{1+}	3.0
Hg^{2+}	7.3	Fe^{2+}	5.5	Th^{4+}	3.5
Zn^{2+}	5.3—6.8	Cu^{2+}	5.3	Sn^{2+}	2.0
Pl^{2+}	6.8	Cr^{3+}	5.3	Fe^{3+}	2.0

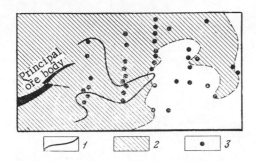

Fig. 10. Isolines showing the copper and lead content in the A horizon of soils in the Uspenskii deposit (according to Ginzburg et al. [1960]). 1) Isolines for Pb content of 0.005%; 2) areas with Cu content of 0.005%; 3) soil profiles.

The sequence of precipitation of the chemical elements from solutions of ground and fissure water therefore is dependent on the redox potential of the metal ion, the pH of hydrolysis, etc. Table 10 gives the hydrolysis pH of metal salts in water solutions.

It should be noted that the presence of organic and inorganic complexing agents in a solution can seriously influence the change of the above-cited constants, and with the presence of ions of precipitators the reaction of separation can set in considerably before the hydrolysis pH is reached (precipitation of $SrSO_4$, $PbSO_4$, and others).

Sorption processes in rocks and in newly forming colloidal clay-like sediments exert an extremely important influence on the course of geochemical reactions during the separation of metal ions from solutions. This process is facilitated by a relatively high pH of ground water, close to 7, since the hydrolysis of the salts of most heavy metals sets in below this pH value (Table 10).

Observations show that acidic waters are neutralized along their path from a sulfide deposit and successively lose lead, iron, molybdenum, and at a certain distance manganese, nickel, copper, and zinc. Because of this, the secondary dispersion haloes formed by individual ore elements sometimes differ sharply from one another, as is clear from Fig. 10.

It is known that the waters of sulfide deposits contain hundreds of times more metals than does ordinary ground water. They facilitate the formation of salt dispersion haloes enriched with nickel and cobalt, and especially with copper and zinc. In a number of cases hydrocarbonate and bicarbonate waters, supersaturated with carbonic acid, are enriched with metals. Upon emerging at the surface, these waters form concentrations of metals at places where pressure is lost, most frequently in unconsolidated fragmentary rocks of residual material and in the soil layer. Under favorable geomorphological and bioclimatic conditions rich dispersion haloes are created in this manner, easily detectable by the biogeochemical method.

An important property of certain ore-forming elements is the ability to sorb negatively charged particles of clay-like and humus substances, manganese, and vanadium hydroxides.

It follows from the preceding discussion that the internal and external migration factors operate in unison, in close relationship to one another, since under natural conditions there are no reactions not dependent on the surrounding medium.

CHAPTER III

EXTERNAL MIGRATION FACTORS

The principal objective in geochemical and biogeochemical exploration work is the finding of primary and secondary dispersion haloes of ore deposits and the explanation of their patterns of development. The formation of secondary haloes or dispersion fields is related to processes of the weathering of rocks and minerals, that is, to the migration of chemical elements in the zone of supergenesis.

An enormous amount of work is done on the earth's surface in the modification of parent rocks (physical destruction, solution) and the transporting of the weathered products into the seas and oceans (denudation). Ore deposits earlier hidden in crystalline rock strata gradually approach the surface and increasingly are subjected to the influence of external weathering factors: temperature, water, gases, and organisms. The effectiveness of these natural agents is in their continuity and duration.

In light of the work of the Russian geochemists and soil scientists V. V. Dokuchaev [1949], V. I. Vernadskii [1934], B. B. Polynov [1934], among others, the influence of life on geological processes consists essentially of the soil-forming process, which is a zonal weathering factor. Therefore, the degree of influence of organisms on weathering processes differs on different parts of the earth's surface. As a result of the physical, chemical, and biological changes of igneous and metamorphic rocks, there has developed a layer of friable secondary formations called the weathered crust. Paleogeographic investigations reveal that the thickest weathered crusts are found in the tropical and subtropical countries, in which a warm and moist climate and exceptionally luxurious surface vegetation are characteristic. Examples of such ancient weathered crusts are those of the Southern Urals, Kazakhstan (Eocene), Ukrainian SSR, and Western Siberia (Lower Paleogene).

Many mineral deposits are hidden in both new and old weathered crusts. In the weathering process and during denudation a part of the ore material is transported downward or beyond the limits of the deposit; another part, less significant, remains in place, forming haloes or dispersion fields. Dispersion haloes almost always indicate the presence of primary mineralization and are the object of geochemical exploration.

On the assumption that this manual will be used not only by geologists, but also by specialists in other fields — chemists, geobotanists, and others — we will give a brief exposition of the basic concepts of weathering, sedimentation, and soil formation. Persons who have a greater interest in these problems should consult the studies of F. W. Clarke [1924a, b], V. I. Vernadskii [1934], A. P. Vinogradov [1957], B. B. Polynov [1934], N. M. Strakhov [1960], L. V. Pustovalov [1940], and K. I. Lukashev (1956), [1958], among others.

In this chapter we also will discuss factors influencing the migration of ore elements in soils and their importance in the formation of chemical dispersion haloes.

1. Weathering

We can draw conclusions concerning the processes of weathering and denudation in the past on the basis of the earth's outermost layers — the lithosphere, which consists both of ancient and recent sedimentary formations.

Weathering is primarily destruction, the grinding and abrasion of deep crystalline rocks at the earth's surface. Accompanying the physical destruction of the primary matter there is a chemical modification under the influence of water, heat, and the gases of the atmosphere (CO_2, O_2). The products formed in weathering are extremely stable, since they correspond well to the new thermodynamic conditions of the zone of weathering.

The physical and physicochemical modifications observed in the process of weathering of crystalline rocks are accompanied by a considerable increase in the active surface of neogenesis (clays, loams), as well as by the release of energy as a result of exothermal chemical reactions (the oxidation of the sulfides of metals and replacement reactions). At the same time, the earth's surface, while undergoing weathering processes, is a region of biogenic accumulation of solar energy by surface plants (photosynthesis).

B. B. Polynov [1934] distinguishes four types of weathered crust: 1) coarsely fragmented orthoeluvium, for the most part formed as a result of physical weathering. It is characteristic of high-mountain and northern regions and high-mountain deserts (the Northern Urals, "high alpine" mountain regions, the Pamir). The weathering is accompanied by the very slight subtraction of chlorine, sulfur, and certain mobile cations (K, Na); 2) calcitized orthoeluvium, or saturated sialic weathered crust. In contrast to the first type, it is characterized by an appreciable subtraction of Cl, S, K, Na, and the relative stability of compounds of calcium (magnesium), primarily in the form of carbonates. It is found in mountainous and steppe regions with a dry, sharply expressed continental climate. Secondary alumosilicates, montmorillonite minerals, and nontronite (pH > 7) predominate in the crust. It is characteristic of areas in the Southern Transcaucasus, Tuva, and Southern Kazakhstan; 3) sialic orthoeluvium or residual unsaturated sialic weathered crust. This is accompanied by a subtraction of alkalis and calcium carbonate (pH < 7) and losses of SiO_2, with some increase in sesquioxides. The principal clayey minerals are halloysite and kaolinite. The sialic type is found in areas of the very moist mountainous taiga of Siberia, Northwestern Europe, and elsewhere; 4) lateritic or alitic residual weathered crust. This type is characterized by a high degree of hydration, a total subtraction of alkalis and alkaline earths, a subtraction of SiO_2, and of many heavy metals, and a considerable accumulation of Fe_2O_3 and Al_2O_3. It is found in areas with a hot and moist climate. In the USSR something similar to this type of crust is the red earth of the Black Sea coast of the Caucasus.

The above-mentioned types of weathered crust are a graphic example of the nonuniform development of the process of chemical change of rocks. The factor responsible is not the "stage" character of the weathering process, as postulated by B. B. Polynov, but rather its bioclimatic zonality "multiplied" by time.

The weathered crust is a zone of development of a wide range of geochemical processes: the decomposition of primary minerals, the migration of mobile chemical compounds, and the synthesis of new, hypergene minerals. These processes transpire most actively in the soil layer and at its boundary with the parent rock. According to B. B. Polynov [1934], the weathering process proceeds in "stages," that is, it is directed from primary alkaline to sialic to alitic (lateritic). In each climatic zone the weathering occurs at a definite stage in the process. Therefore, in the northern tundra, for example, it sets in with the fragmentary stage, in the temperate zone in the sialic stage, etc. These concepts are not in agreement with the classical theory of the zonality of the weathering and soil-formation processes. V. V. Dokuchaev [1949] therefore subjected these concepts to a critical review. For example, the "stage" theory does not agree with facts relating to the different direction of soil-formation processes in the temperate taiga zone. Depending on relief conditions, the character of the rocks, and the species of woody vegetation, the soils formed will be podzols, gray forest soils, or other types. In much the same way, in the sialic weathering process montmorillonite minerals and beidellite are formed on basalts and kaolinite and other minerals on granites.

The most favorable conditions for the formation of a thick weathered crust is gentle relief, as well as a warm and moist climate. Figure 11 shows a schematic profile of the weathered crust in a tectonically inactive area (according to N. M. Strakhov [1960]). This diagram clearly shows two sections of energetic weathering. The first corresponds to the taiga podzol zone of the temperate latitudes (thickness about 2 m), and the second to the moist tropics, where the thickness of the weathered crust can be hundreds of meters. The tundra, desert, and semidesert zones are characterized by a relatively poor development of the weathered crust.

Each biochemical zone differs in the mineralogical and chemical composition of the newly formed materials in the soil and in the weathered crust. For example, the hardpan horizon is a characteristic feature of certain podzols, a lateritic crust (Al_2O_3, Fe_2O_3) is characteristic of the alitic process in the tropics and subtropics, and sulfate-carbonate salinization of the profile is evidence of a desert weathering process.

As we will see below, processes of biogenesis have a very important effect on the course of chemical processes and mineral formation in soils.

In the mechanism of the chemical reactions occurring in the "humid" weathered crust, it is postulated that there is the action of the active ion of hydrogen H^+, which forms as a result of the dissociation of water and carbonic acid ($H_2CO_3 \rightarrow H^+ \rightleftharpoons HCO_3^-$).

In the first stage of weathering, which, as is well known, transpires under alkaline conditions, there is a hydrolysis of alumosilicates with a subtraction of chlorides and sulfates of alkaline and alkaline earth metals (Ca, Mg) and in part

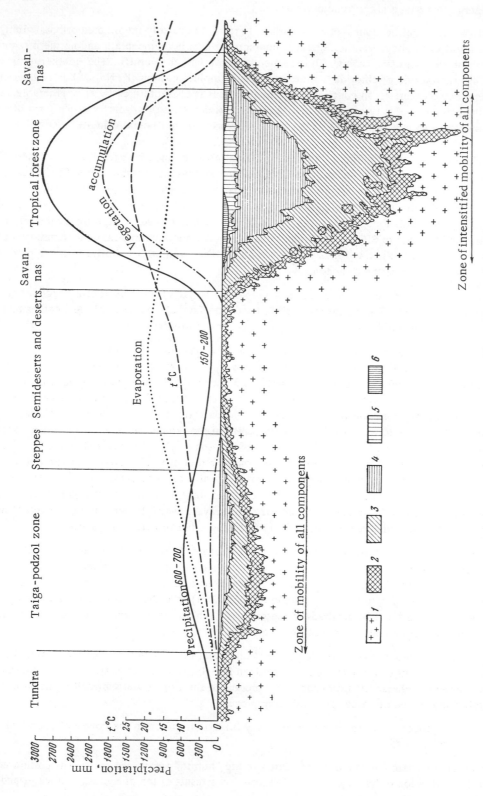

Fig. 11. Diagram of the formation of the weathered crust in tectonically inactive areas. 1) New crust; 2) grus zone, chemically little modified; 3) hydromica–montmorillonite–beidellite zone; 4) kaolinite zone; 5) ochers, Al_2O_3; 6) hard layer $Fe_2O_3 + Al_2O_3$ (according to Strakhov, [1960]).

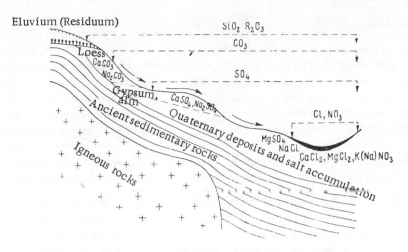

Fig. 12. Diagram of salt accumulation on a continent
(according to Kovda [1954]).

Mn^{2+}, Zn^{2+}, and silica. In an eluvial crust (orthoeluvium) there remain salts of alumosilicic acid $(KH)O \cdot Al_2O_3$ $\cdot nSiO_2 \cdot 2H_2O$ and hydroxides of iron, aluminum, and TiO_2.

In the acidic crust, corresponding to the taiga-podzol zone, there is a further decomposition of the alumosilicates with the formation of kaolinite $Al_2O_3 \cdot 2SiO_2 \cdot 2H_2O$ (on acidic rocks) and an almost complete loss of sesquioxides of iron, aluminum, and TiO_2.

In an alitic weathered crust there is a total destruction of alumosilicates, a subtraction of SiO_2, and the formation of laterite (Al_2O_3, Fe_2O_3).

When carrying out geochemical exploration work (lithochemical, biogeochemical) we deal primarily with recent unconsolidated formations (eluvium, residual material, and alluvium). On gently sloping drainage divides and on other relatively level parts of the relief the orthoeluvium is relatively stable and usually is covered by a "mature" soil layer.

Under the influence of physical, chemical, and biological weathering factors, and in the case of relatively slight denudation, the bedrock sometimes is covered by a thick layer of unconsolidated deposits. Depending on conditions of weathering, these deposits assume a different structure: coarse fragments, small grains, elutriated, or enriched with calcium carbonates, and others. The texture of the bedrock can be preserved below the eluvium, being streaked with fractures and leached to considerable depths, from 5 to 50 m.

In contrast to the eluvium of the drainage divides, the unconsolidated sediments on the slopes move under the influence of gravity and water and have been given the name residual material. "In metallometric surveys," wrote A. P. Solovov [1959], "it is very common to encounter eluvial-residual material, by which is meant slightly displaced products of weathering, in composition and site still retaining a clear relationship to the parent rocks."

In many cases unconsolidated deposits of eluvium lie under overburdened deposits of later origin. Such an ancient weathered crust is found on the serpentinites of the Southern Urals, and is frequently covered by Tertiary clays and loams which are unrelated genetically to the bedrock. Such morainal and aeolian deposits are widely developed on the territory of the European part of the USSR and adjacent countries.

Within the limits of a major area, simultaneously with the formation of orthoeluvium on the gently sloping drainage divides an accumulative weathered crust has been formed on distant slopes and along the path to the region of removed material. The distribution of individual accumulations is of a regular character, although it is not strictly delimited.

Figure 12 represents a certain idealized profile of the sialic weathered crust; it gives a schematic profile of the eluvial-residual and alluvial-accumulative weathered crust. In the first case (the upper part of the profile), the orthoeluvium is lacking in mobile components (Cl, S, K, Na, Ca, Mg), including ore elements, as compared with their content in the bedrock; in the second case the sediments are enriched by the mechanical and chemical products of weathering.

2. Soil Formation

According to present-day concepts, the character of soil-forming processes is inseparable from the characteristics of weathering in the various surface zones. According to the concepts of V. V. Dokuchaev, in the latitudinal and vertical zonality of weathering and soil formation it is possible to indicate the principal soil types which will be most likely encountered when carrying out biogeochemical surveys in search of ores: 1) gleyey tundry soils on products which have been modified very little by chemical and biological processes; 2) podzol and podzolized soils of the taiga forest zone on leached loams; 3) gray forest soils on the slopes of large and small mountain formations (often podzolized); 4) steppe chernozem and chestnut soils on a sialic-calcareous weathered crust, consisting of clayey and loesslike loams saturated with calcium carbonates; 5) gray soils of the desert and semidesert on clayey-sandy accumulations enriched with chloride-sulfate-carbonate salts of alkalis and alkaline earths; 6) red soils (and yellow soils) on a lateritic (alitic) weathered crust, widespread in the moist tropics and subtropics.

Thus, the principal soil types agree with the natural zones characterizing types of weathered crust. As is well known, depending on the relief, soils are classified as eluvial and accumulative. The principal difference between the eluvium of the weathered crust and an eluvial soil is that in the soil, in addition to the subtraction of the chemical products of weathering, there is also the reverse process — biological accumulation of vitally important components: phosphorous, nitrogen, potassium, and other ash elements. Therefore, under natural conditions, where life is vigorously developing, there is not and cannot be an impoverishment of the soil of nutrients. This function of organisms is manifested even in the very initial stage of rock weathering with the participation of lithophilous vegetation (microorganisms, mosses, and ferns) in the formation of fine-grained products enriched with organic substances and in the accumulation of biogenic and chemical elements — phosphorus, potassium, calcium, nitrogen, iron, etc. (Polynov [1934], Glazovskaya [1956], Yarilova [1956]).

The influence of organisms, and especially surface plants, on the soil-forming processes involves the activation of weathering processes and also the migration (dispersion) and accumulation of chemical elements. The latter function is expressed in the accumulation of organic substances in the soil (humus) and in the synthesis of organic and organomineral compounds.

The degree of influence of surface vegetation and soil flora (and fauna) on the soil-forming processes is usually evaluated on the basis of the humus accumulation. However, the large quantities of humus in peat and swamp soils are not an indicator of the degree of activity of the soil process. Likewise, the exceedingly small amount of humus in certain soils of the desert and semidesert (gray soils) does not exclude the influence of the biogenic process in desert soils as is indicated by the presence of new chemical products in the soils. These products include: elementary sulfur, nitrates, phosphates, and compounds of calcium, magnesium, silicon, iron, and manganese (desert varnish) whose biogenic origin has been demonstrated.

3. Factors in the Soil-Formation Process

Soil is a natural new formation in the upper part of the weathered crust, described by V. V. Dokuchaev in 1886 in the following way: "The word 'soil' should be applied to the exposed or outer horizons of rocks (it makes no difference what kind), naturally modified by the joint influence of water, air, and various kinds of organisms, living and dead" [1949]. Dokuchaev considered the principal soil-formation factors to be: 1) the parent rock; 2) climate; 3) vegetation; 4) relief; and 5) time.

Igneous, metamorphic, and sedimentary parent rocks determine to a considerable degree the chemical and mineralogical composition of the weathered crust and its upper layer, the soil. However, the soil, being subject to the most active influence of chemical and biogeochemical processes, sometimes loses many of the characteristics of the primary crystalline rock on which it was formed (limestones, metamorphic schists, etc.).

The most active soil-forming factors are climate and surface vegetation; these determine many of the chemical processes transpiring in the soil.

According to the observations of K. D. Glinka (1927), the most important weathering and soil-formation factors are dissolved carbon dioxide and organic acids — the products of the functions of surface plants, minerals, mosses, algae, and soil microflora.

Rain water contains small quantities of carbon dioxide, not exceeding 1 mg/liter HCO_3^- (see table on next page). When rain water and soil water come into contact, the content of HCO_3^- increases sharply, and as a result they become more virulent in relation to the substrate of parent rock.

Water	HCO$_3^-$
Rain water	0.9
Ground water	9
Soil water	76

Climate is the principal factor in soil formation. Its influence is a complex combination of many variables of which the most important are: precipitation, temperature, surface, and soil organisms. "An important property of soil formations," wrote V. R. Vil'yams [1949], "distinguishing them from the parent rock, is that in soil formations are concentrated those forms of ash and nitrogen which are necessary for plant nutriton. This property is a direct and obvious function of biological processes transpiring in the surface layers of the bedrock." This property is expressed most clearly in chernozems, enriched with humus.

The conditions for formation and subsequent existence of organic soil substances constitute the biogeochemical peculiarity of zonal soils. Soil zonality is characterized by definite temperature gradients and specific quantities of precipitation. The content of organic substances in the soil layer is related to the latter factor. Figure 13 clearly shows the regular decrease of the content of humus matter from the chernozems to the gray soils of the desert and semidesert.

Naturally, each bioclimatic and soil zone has its specific conditions and peculiarities with respect to the migration of chemical elements in the soil-geological profile. Nevertheless, we will discuss two examples: the forest podzolization process and the meadow-steppe (chernozem and chestnut soils) process. Without touching upon the climatic and other specific conditions characterizing and distinguishing the forest taiga zone from the meadow-steppe zone, we will note the differing functions of humus in the distribution of chemical elements in soils.

It is known that the accumulation of organic matter in podzols proceeds unusually slowly in the uppermost layer of the soil with a thickness of 1-2 cm. In this case the products of the decomposition of leaves, branches (forest litter), and soil flora (fungi) are a source forming humic acids: humic, ulmic, crenic, and others. According to data provided by V. R. Vil'yams [1949], the ash elements of the forest litter are transformed into easily soluble salts of crenic and other organic acids and carried into the lower-lying horizons of the podzol profile or are intercepted by plants. An acid reaction is set up in the soil profile and this is sustained by the addition of crenic acid from the decomposing forest litter.

In cases where there is an acidic reaction and excessive moisture, the primary silicates and alumosilicates are subject to strong weathering and hydrolysis with the liberation of free silica. The liberated alkaline, alkaline-earth, and other chemical elements Fe^{3+}, Mn^{3+} migrate with the soil water into the lower horizons of the profile or are carried off into rivers and seas. As a result of these processes the upper eluvial horizon of the soil, deprived of bases and sesquioxides (Al_2O_3, Fe_2O_3), is transformed into a structureless siliceous layer of white powdery soil called podzol. This horizon is very impoverished in metals and cannot be used in sampling work in geochemical surveys.

The conditions for the accumulation of humus in meadow-chernozem and chestnut steppe soils and its role in the migration of chemical elements differs sharply from the above-described conditions for podzols. A characteristic of meadow-steppe chernozems and chestnut soils is the deposition of the organic matter which is transformed into humus (the sod-formation process). The relative dryness of the climate, and the resulting low, inadequate moisture content of the soil, results in the accumulation of sesquioxides and bases, and these are evenly distributed in the profile of the steppe soil.

In cases where the relief is gentle and there is good permeability and aeration of the soil, there is a carbonate ($CaCO_3$) horizon, a characteristic of steppe and transitional soils. All these peculiarities of the profile of meadow-steppe soils are reflected in the migration of chemical elements in the soil-geological profile. For example, there is an appreciable enrichment of the humus horizon with iron, manganese, and other heavy metals and a relatively even distribution of these metals in the lower-lying horizons.

The saturation of the soil with bases, the neutral reaction (to alkali), and the high oxidation potential favor the migration of multivalent elements — metals which are mobile in oxidized form (V^{5+}, Cr^{6+}, Mo^{6+}, U^{6+}), and hinder the migration of others (Ti^{4+}, Fe^{3+}, Mn^{3+}, Ni^{2+}, Co^{2+}, Cu^{2+}, Zn^{2+}, Pb^{2+}). Both groups of chemical elements are intercepted

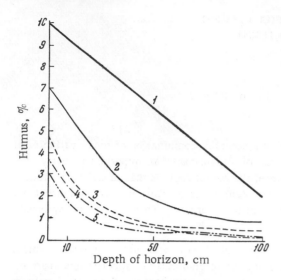

Fig. 13. Distribution of humus in zonal soils to depths of 100 cm (according to Bolotina [1947]). 1) Thick chernozems; 2) ordinary chernozems; 3) gray forest soils; 4) chestnut soils; 5) podzols.

by plants and accumulate in soil humus. The accumulation of ore elements in the upper horizon of steppe soils is a convenient indicator when the humus layer is used in a search for these elements. The appreciable concentration of molybdenum, chromium, uranium, and vanadium in plant ash makes it possible to use steppe vegetation in the biogeochemical exploration for these metals.

An extemely important factor in weathering and soil formation is time. Only with the passage of time is there a clear manifestation of processes which we do not even suspect when they are observed directly. The study of the rate of the processes of weathering and soil formation in definite rigorously dated periods of time (in ancient stone structures) shows their regular development in full agreement with the surrounding natural conditions (bioclimatic zonality). Under favorable conditions of relief and climate, the soil-forming process attains its equilibrium state (maturity). Maturity is expressed by a clear definition of the elements of the soil profile — podzol and hardpan horizons in the taiga forest zone, a lateritic profile in the moist tropics and subtropics, etc. However, the "maturity" of a profile is not observed in all cases, since it is dependent on limiting circumstances; deterrents to maturity are steepness of slope, wind and rain erosion, and the influence of overburden.

The maturity of the profile often characterizes the age of the secondary dispersion halo, as well as the chemical attributes and mineralogical composition of the newly formed products. Therefore, in carrying out geochemical exploration work, the problem of age is just as important as in many geological investigations. The most important indicators of the history and age of the soil profile are minerals and other organic and organomineral newly formed products which develop in the process of weathering and biogenesis. In this connection, we will discuss briefly the processes of mineral formation in soils.

4. Secondary Minerals in Soils

To a considerable degree soils inherit the primary and secondary minerals of the weathered crust. For example, the following minerals are found in the sialic weathered crust of granites: quartz, orthoclase, plagioclase, muscovite, and ilmenite. The following hypergene minerals occur widely in soils: dispersed oxides — silica SiO_2, anatase TiO_2, hydrargillite (gibbsite) $Al(OH)_3$, goethite and limonite $HFeO_2$ (aq), asbolan, and wad carbonates — calite $CaCO_3$, dolomite $(Ca, Mg) (CO_3)_2$, and others; clayey minerals — kaolinite $Al_2O_3 \cdot 2SiO_2 \cdot 2H_2O$, montmorillonite $Al_2O_3 \cdot 4SiO_2 \cdot H_2O + nH_2O$; organic and organomineral substances — organic acids, humates of metals, and phytolitharia.

Under certain conditions in the development of the weathered crust and soil formation the soils also inherit many other secondary minerals: in peaty soils, phosphates and carbonates of iron, siderite $FeCO_3$ and vivianite $Fe^{2+} + (PO_4)_2 \cdot 8H_2O$; in a desert climate, carbonates and sulfates of calcium and the halides; in a lateritic profile, goethite and gibbsite.

In the zone of oxidation of sulfide deposits there is formation of secondary minerals of iron, manganese, cobalt, nickel, copper, molybdenum, lead, and other elements, which sometimes constitute commercial enrichments.

The formation of secondary minerals in soils and the weathered crust transpires with the direct and indirect participation of organisms and the processes of their life activity and decay. For example, E. I. Parfenova [1956] states that the principal source of secondary quartz in the subsoil horizon is silica of biogenic origin. About 60 kg/hectare of biogenic silica enters the soil annually in the form of silicified tissues and phytolitharia (the skeletons of diatoms and the spicules of fungi). As pointed out by E. A. Yarilova [1952], in this process the phytolitharia are capable of being converted into chalcedonies and secondary quartz. However, the most interesting and important phenomenon is the biogenic formation in soils of secondary clayey minerals from organomineral gels containing sesquioxides and silica. According to data collected by E. I. Parfenova and E. A. Yarilova, the minerals obtained from podzol and chernozem soils belong to the montmorillonite group.

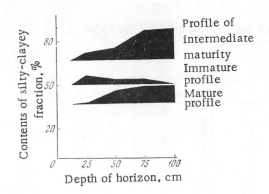

Fig. 14. Distribution of the silty-clayey fraction in podzolic soil profiles of different maturity.

In studying the formation of the soil layer as a function of time, it is possible to note the affinity of certain groups of clayey minerals to specific bioclimatic zones of the earth's surface. According to Sedletskii [1945], "the weathering of granites under tundra conditions results primarily in hydromicas; under the conditions prevailing in the podzol zone, in hydromica, kaolinite, and quartz; in the chernozem zone, in montmorillonite and ilmenite; in the subtropics, in metahalloysite, goethite, and hydrohematite; and in the tropics, in metahalloysite, gibbsite, and hematite." The author emphasizes the entire complex of conditions under which the formation of secondary minerals takes place: the stage of weathering and the composition of the soil forming rocks, climate, topography, and the life processes of plant and animal organisms. According to Gorbunov [1952], the composition of clayey minerals in zonal soils differs somewhat from that which was established by I. A. Sedletskii. This obviously is the result of the different composition of the primary soil-forming rocks.

Montmorillonite is the most common of the clayey minerals found in soils. Kaolinite also is characteristic of acidic soils. As a result of their well-expressed adsorption properties, these minerals are the principal carriers of ions of the alkaline, alkaline-earth, and other metals found in an exchange-absorption state: Ca, Mg, Na, K, Ni, Cu, Zn, Pb, and many other rare and dispersed chemical elements.

Important colloidal-dispersed minerals in the soil include humate substances, whose exchange and absorption capacity exceeds that of mineral colloids by a factor of ten. According to data collected by A. V. Peterburskii [1959], the humus of chernozem soils is bonded to 60% of the exchangeable bases of the total quantity, although in mass clayey colloids sharply predominate over humus colloids.

The negative charge of humus colloidal particles fully explains their well-expressed absorptive properties relative to cations, although these properties differ for different cations and change easily, depending on the conditions of the medium (pH, redox); the latter phenomenon explains the differences in mobility of individual chemical elements in zonal soils.

5. Colloidal-Dispersed Compounds in Soils

The influence of colloidal minerals and other dispersed systems on the geochemical distribution of chemical elements in soils is undisputed. It involves the entry of the individual ions of metals into the structure of organic and inorganic complexes and exchange and chemical sorption of these ions on colloids. It should be noted that these processes transpire under complex natural conditions and therefore always occur differently, due to the nonuniformity of the chemical medium and the composition of the most active particles — colloids.

We first will discuss the factors involved in the formation of dispersed systems in the soil. Such factors include: the soil-forming rock, climate, age (maturity) of the soil profile, and morphological characteristics of the region.

For example, the content of the sandy fraction from 1 to 0.01 mm, and the silty-clayey fraction from 0.01 mm and smaller in the podzol profile developed on arkose sandstones varies appreciably as a function of the maturity of the soil profile (McLanghlin [1955]). It has been established that the content of the silty-clayey fraction increases in the illuvial horizon B_2, with a decrease of this fraction in the horizon of leaching A_2.

Figure 14 shows diagrams representing the distribution of the silty-clayey fraction in podzol profiles of different maturity. It is possible to see clearly the leaching out of dispersed material from the upper horizons into the lowerlying horizons. This process is expressed most clearly in a mature profile and is most poorly expressed in an immature profile. In a profile of intermediate maturity the dispersed particles are accumulated closer to the mother rock, at depths of 75 to 100-120 cm, while in a mature profile they are distributed through the profile, beginning at depths of 50-70 cm, and even lower.

According to data collected by R. Kh. Aidinyan [1947], in the highly podzolized soil of Moskovskaya Oblast the content of the silty-clayey fraction from 0.01 to less than 0.001 mm in the A_1 horizon, with a thickness from 3 to 4 cm, is 33.65%; in the A_2 horizon, with a thickness of 10 to 20 cm, it is 30-84%; and in the B_2 horizon, with a thickness of 34 to 45 cm, it is 44.54%. Thus, in this case there is the same regularity as in the soils of New Zealand.

TABLE 11. Composition of Humus in Principal Soil Groups of the USSR in the 0-20 cm Layer
(According to Tyurin [1949])

Soil	Mean humus content,%	Humic acid, % of humus	Fulvic acids, % of humus	Insoluble humus, % of humus	Ratio of humic to fulvic acids
Podzol	3.5	15-25	47	28	0.4
Thick chernozem	10	40	39	19	1
Ordinary chernozem	7.5	35	37	25	1
Dark chestnut	3.5	34	35	26	1
Gray soils	1.5	21	41	32	0.5
Red soils	5	15	50	33	0.3

The content and distribution of the silty-clayey fraction in other zonal soils of the USSR, according to Aidinyan, is as follows: in typical chernozem of Kurskaya Oblast from 0 to 15 cm, 50.16%; from 20 to 30 cm, 49.74%; and from 50 to 70 cm, 51.64%; in the red soils of Georgia, from the surface to a depth of 18 cm, 65.34%; and in the layer 18-26 cm, 44%. At a depth of about 8 m the content of the silty-clayey fraction does not exceed 1%. Thus, in the chernozem soils the silty-clayey fraction is distributed uniformly through the soil horizons, but in red soils it enriches the upper humus horizon from 0 to 25 cm.

In the distribution of macro- and microelements in the soil-geological profile it is important to study not only the quantitative content of clayey minerals by soil horizons, but also their chemical and mineralogical composition. The most important component of the silty-clayey fraction of the soil is humus matter.

In the process of humus formation the plant residue is subjected to complex transformations which take place under the influence of the animals and microorganisms populating the soil. This results in the formation of high-molecular compounds (humic acids), which include "polycondensates" of polyphenyls, quinones, polypeptides, and aminoacids (Kononova, 1951). The humic acids of the soil are colloidal-dispersed organic substances possessing an acidic reaction and are in the closest relationship to mineral (clayey) colloidal particles.

Constant components of the soil, humus substances actively participate in the processes of the weathering of minerals in the soil (crenic acid) and in the mixing of the products of decomposition through the soil horizons — alkalis and alkaline earths, sesquioxides, etc. The importance of humus as a factor in geochemical processes is dependent on the humus content and its activity, which in turn are determined by zonality factors. Zonal soils differ sharply from one another in their humus content: from 0.96% in the gray soils of the semideserts to 10% in well-developed southern chernozems (see Fig. 13). As already noted, the humus consists of humic acids, fulvic acids (ulmic, crenic, apocrenic) and organomineral substances of coaly rock insoluble in alkalis. It is characteristic that the composition of humus differs in different zonal soils. For example, the content of humic acids and fulvic acids changes as a function of soil-formation conditions, as clearly shown by the data in Table 11.

Table 11 shows a low ratio of humic acids to fulvic acids in podzol soils and red soils of the subtropics in comparison with steppe soils, which is completely predictable, since acidic soils always are enriched with fulvic acids. But the reason for the high content of fulvic acids in gray soils still remains unclear.

The distribution of humus in the zonal soils of the USSR and its composition is represented graphically (according to Kononova [1955]) in the form of diagrams in Fig. 15. The figure shows that the soils differ from one another not only in the humus content, but also in its composition. For example, in podzolic soils the content of fulvic acids is twice as great as in humic acids. In red soils there are relatively more fulvic acids than in podzols.

Humus substances can be classified as those which are soluble in weak alkali solutions without preliminary processing of the soil by acid and those which are soluble after the removal of exchangeable calcium by acids. In either case, fulvic acids and humic acids enter into the alkali solution. The most stable part of the organic matter of the soil (carbon) passes into solution under the influence of alternate processing with 5% H_2SO_4 and alkali.

Fulvic acids of acidic soils, not bonded to calcium, can be induced into solution by treatment with a 0.1-0.4 normal solution of HCl. Free fulvic acids and their salts with aluminum, iron, manganese, and other heavy metals (salts of crenic and apocrenic acids) enter into solution.

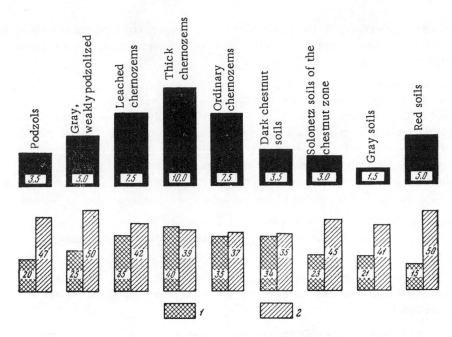

Fig. 15. Humus content in the principal soil groups of the USSR. Top — mean humus content, in %; bottom — relative content of humic acids (1) and fulvic acids (2) (according to Kononova [1955]).

In steppe soils, often saturated with bases (chernozem and chestnut soils), poorly soluble humates and fulvates are formed with calcium. In this case there are virtually no free humic acids (Kononova [1951]). In acidic soils, less saturated with bases, humic acids in considerable quantities are present "in the form of free polymer complexes," more easily soluble, and therefore more mobile in the natural soil profile.

Problems relating to the interaction and chemical relationship between clayey and organic colloids are very inadequately discussed in the literature. Our information is limited to extremely conventional concepts concerning the physical and physicochemical aggregation of colloidal soil particles. It is known, for example, that the humus substances in chernozem soils have a granular structure as a result of the poor dispersion of calcium humates. On the other hand, in podzol and red soils the humus substances (fulvic acids) form complexes with R_2O_3, easily mobile in an acidic medium. This factor is responsible for the high dispersion and activity of humus substances in acidic soils.

Problems relating to the interaction of ions and colloids have been studied thoroughly: phenomena of exchange and chemical absorption, sorption, and desorption of ions, etc.

6. Behavior of Metal Ions on Soil Colloids

In current literature, problems relating to ion exchange soil colloids are considered without subdivision into clayey, siliceous (SiO_2, nH_2O), organic, etc. The following fractions are defined in mechanical fraction analysis:

from 1 to 0.1 mm	medium sand
from 0.1 to 0.01 mm	fine sand
from 0.01 to 0.001 mm. . . .	silt
<0.001 mm	colloid

In each of the fractions there are particles of different origin: alumosilicates, siliceous and organic compounds. The fractions 0.01 mm and smaller, constituting up to 50% of the content of certain soils, possess the maximum absorption capacity. However, as is well known, the percentage of any fraction is dependent on the character of the soil-forming rocks, maturity, profile, and the soil process. Problems relating to the balance of metals in any soil profile therefore should be solved in each specific case, with local conditions taken into account.

The exchange reactions between heavy metals and soil colloids have been studied by Sedletskii [1945], Hill et al. [1953], Painter et al. [1953], Pac et al. [1953], and others. The humus substances with respect to exchange-adsorption reactions are close to montmorillonite clays, but humic acids possess a greater selectivity with respect to individual heavy metals, e.g., they hold ions of cobalt, copper, and uranium better than the mineral part of colloids.

The explanation for this must be found in the capacity of cobalt, copper, and uranium to form extremely close bonds with organic substances of the chemosorption compound type, which is facilitated by the presence of carboxyl and hydroxyl groups in the humic acid molecule (Manskaya et al. [1956, 1960]).

In experiments with exchange cations it has been noted that a certain part of the copper, nickel, and cobalt is not displaced by ordinary neutral solvents such as $NaNO_3$, potassium acetate, etc. The quantity of the extracted form increases proportional to the saturation time. They can be removed only by acids (0.5 normal solution of HNO_3, 0.1 normal solution of HCl) and only with a certain period of contact with the acid. The quantity of absorbed copper and cobalt rigorously corresponds to the displaced calcium (or H^+) and indicates that the reaction on soil colloids has a chemosorption character. In sorption processes it is not impossible that a solid phase will form — hydroxides of metals — cobalt, nickel, copper (pH = 7) or hydrocarbonates and phosphates (Cu, Co), such as in the presence of the anions HCO_3^- and PO_4^{3-}.

In the exchange reactions of copper and cobalt there is noted an affinity to soil fractions enriched with humus and in the case of nickel an affinity to fractions <0.01 mm of clayey minerals, obviously in connection with its entry into the crystalline structures of magnesium silicates.

The study of exchange processes with active Co_{60} has shown that Co^{2+} ions are more difficult to displace from soil colloids than ions of alkaline and alkaline-earth metals. With respect to the rate of removal, cobalt falls in next to the last place in the series: Na > K > Mg > Ca > Co > H.

The closeness of the chemical and physicochemical properties of cobalt, nickel, copper, zinc, and other elements makes it possible to assume that they all should occupy a common place in the series of relative mobilities of ions.

The ions of hydrogen are the most active in displacement of absorbed cations Co^{2+}, Ni^{2+}, and Cu^{2+}. This explains the considerable migration of metals in swampy and podzol soils over ore deposits when the pH is low. The presence of carbonates of alkaline-earth metals leads to a decrease in the mobility of cobalt, nickel, and copper in soils.

The principal forms of cobalt, nickel, and copper forming in the process of adsorption and chemosorption are: 1) easily extracted forms, differing little from absorbed bases; 2) closely sorbed forms, displaced only when there are specific concentrations of hydrogen ions; 3) forms of adsorbed precipitates forming in the presence of the above-lying anions.

The cations and anions in the soil substrate are bonded to one another electrostatically and this safeguards them from excessive mobility, leading in the long run to elutriation and removal with surface water. On the other hand, the ease with which cations are exchanged in the soil absorbing complex make it possible for plants to extract the elements which they require freely.

* * *

The final objective in biogeochemical exploration is the locating of secondary dispersion haloes of ore deposits, the study of their sites at the surface, and the conditions under which they have formed. The concentration and dispersion of mineral elements over ore deposits are determined by the weathering and soil-formation processes under the specific biogeochemical conditions of the ore region. The most important factors in weathering and soil-formation are the moisture conditions of the climate, temperature, and the influence of surface plants and soil organisms.

The soil profile inherits many minerals of the weathered crust, but not all, and in addition it differs by the presence of new formations of a biogenic origin: secondary quartz, calcium carbonates and phosphates, certain characteristic ore minerals, etc. (over deposits). Organic substances in the soil — humic and fulvic acids — are of great importance in the migration of ore elements. Depending on climatic conditions they can facilitate the concentration of metals over ores or their dispersion (fulvic acids). In the study of the processes of migration of chemical elements in soils, water, and plants, it is necessary to take into account their behavior in the colloidal-dispersive systems of the soil, such as the ease with which cations are exchanged in the soil-absorbing complex.

CHAPTER IV

ORE DEPOSIT DISPERSION HALOES

The geologist equipped with a lens, hammer, compass, and aneroid barometer now has but few chances of discovering a new deposit. Everything which could assist him in his work – traces of past hydrothermal activity (carbonatization, silicification, etc.), ancient mine workings – have long been noted by his predecessors and plotted on prognostic maps. The footsteps of geologists and mineralogists have been followed by geophysicists with their more modern apparatus. These geophysicists have covered extensive areas with magnetic, electric, and seismic surveys. Their work has led to the discovery of many deposits of iron, manganese, titanium, nickel, and other minerals both in the USSR and abroad. However, modern technology requires the production of those metals (especially rare and dispersed) which were only produced in relatively small quantities before the Second World War: V, W, Mo, Sn, Hg, Ge, Be, Zr, Nb, Ta, RE, and others. At the same time, it is well known that the majority of these elements do not possess sufficient physical characteristics for detection by geophysical methods. This has required specific new exploration methods.

Halo methods now fill this gap: the gas survey, the metallometric survey, the biogeochemical indication method, and others. The development of these methods is entirely legitimate, because, at the present stage of development of the natural sciences an ever-increasing need is being felt to use such methods as make it possible to penetrate more deeply into the world of small quantities. The methods of study of the dispersion haloes of ore deposits is an example.

"Russian and Soviet geologists, especially geochemists and geophysicists," wrote V. I. Smirnov [1954], "long have appreciated the importance of the study of the dispersion haloes of ore deposits, and have taken the first steps in this new direction. A. E. Fersman distinguished various genetic types of dispersion haloes and has pointed out ways in which they can be studied and used in geological exploration work. A. P. Vinogradov and his colleagues have done considerable work in determining the patterns of distribution of microelements in soils in areas of ore deposits." The study of dispersion haloes is a means which makes it possible to prospect for rare and dispersed chemical elements.

Dispersion haloes are zones of high concentration of metals over ore deposits (in comparison with the surrounding geochemical background). They are localized in rocks of the weathered crust (alluvium, residual material) and disseminated in the soil, in ground water, and in plants.

Depending on the character of the dispersion haloes (primary, secondary) and the method used in their formation (mechanical, chemical, gas) it is necessary to employ different methods for their detection and delimitation (Safronov [1936], Sergeev [1941], Sokolova [1948], and others). Halo methods of exploration for metals have come to be known as metallometric surveying.

In the exploration of ore deposits the geologist first encounters dispersion haloes at the outcrops of a primary deposit in the surface layers of the oxidation zone. The finding of geochemical haloes often is impossible by ordinary mineralogical procedures. The primary ores lose their initial behavior and composition upon entry into a zone in which surface processes (oxidation, hydrolysis, leaching) are active.

Outcrops of the eluvial weathered crust sometimes preserve traces of secondary mineral formation and serve as clues in the exploration for primary ores. However, as leaching progresses they penetrate to greater depths and become inaccessible for visual exploration. Visible signs of mineralization often disappear closer to the surface.

The zone of oxidation of sulfide and other primary deposits is an integral part of geochemical dispersion haloes. It is the oxidation zone which characterizes the direction of the processes of migration of ore elements under specific conditions prevailing in the province studied. In addition, the oxidized zone gives a key to the understanding of the

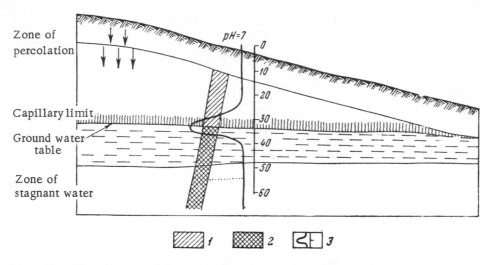

Fig. 16. Diagram of the zone of oxidation of a sulfide deposit (according to Solovov [1959]). 1) Oxidized ores; 2) sulfide ores; 3) change of pH with depth.

character of the primary deposit, which is hidden at depth, often below the ground water level. The study of the oxidation zone, especially sulfide, sulfide-arsenide, and other similar deposits, is an extremely timely problem, as was repeatedly pointed out by S. S. Smirnov (1936).

In the process of the oxidation of sulfide deposits there are radical changes in the mineralogical and chemical composition of primary ores and country rock, which are brought about in part by numerous natural weathering factors, which have been discussed at length above.

A characteristic of the oxidation zone of sulfide deposits is the formation of extremely aggressive sulfuric acid. This acid develops in the process of oxidation of sulfides: $FeS_2 + 7O + H_2O = FeSO_3 + H_2SO_4$.

The chemical effect of free sulfuric acid on the surrounding rock and ore decreases as the weathered crust develops by leaching, since there is a gradual neutralization of the acid by constantly present bases and the formation of sulfates. Figure 16 shows a schematic profile of an oxidation zone characteristic of many sulfide deposits.

The history of development of the zone of oxidation of ore deposits is much more complex than the formation of the weathered crust on ordinary igneous, metamorphic, or sedimentary rocks as a result of the great variety of geochemical processes of mineral formation (and salt formation): the formation of oxides, hydrolyzates, secondary sulfates, etc.

We will now discuss a specific example of the development of an oxidation zone in a sulfide-arsenide copper-nickel-cobalt deposit in the Tuvinskaya ASSR.

1. Oxidation Zone of a Sulfide-Arsenide Deposit in Tuva

The sulfide-arsenide deposit which we studied is a typical example of the profound modification of primary ore minerals of hydrothermal origin. The deposit was formed in the process of contact-skarn metamorphism in a region of tectonic dislocations in Silurian schists and limestones due to a Taconian granitic intrusion. Great masses of acidic rocks rose and partially broke through the more ancient cover of Cambrian and Silurian rocks and created a system of dislocations and faults. Several successive phases of hypogene mineralization can be distinguished in the formation of the deposit: 1) early arsenides of cobalt and nickel, smaltine-chloanthite (1st generation), and niccolite-rammelsbergite; 2) late arsenides of cobalt and nickel, smaltine-chloanthite (2nd generation), and safflorite-skutterudite; 3) sulfides of iron, copper, zinc, and, in part, lead (pyrite, chalcopyrite, bornite, sphalerite, and galenite).

The sequence of the phases and the formation of the deposit can be judged on the basis of unmodified and little-modified hypogene minerals of nickel, cobalt, and copper. The most widely disseminated of these are sulfides of copper and iron, arsenides and sulphoarsenides of cobalt and nickel. The index supergene minerals of the oxidation zone of the arsenide deposit are of equal significance in the reconstruction of the initial composition of the ore zone. Among these, mention should be made of sulfides of copper and iron (pyrite, chalcosite, covellite), arsenates (erythrite, adamellite, scorodite), carbonates (azurite, malachite), sulfates (jarosite, morenosite), oxides (limonite, psilomelane-

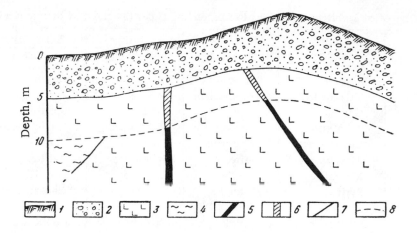

Fig. 17. Weathered crust on a copper-nickel-cobalt deposit. 1) Soil layer; 2) residual material; 3) skarnified limestones with intercalated aleurolites; 4) aleurolites with intercalations of sandstones and limestones; 5) unoxidized ore; 6) oxidized ore; 7) fault line; 8) boundary of oxidized zone.

wad), and others. However, the principal objective or our investigation was a study of the patterns associated with dispersion haloes of an ore deposit.

The nonhomogeneous geological structure of the deposit and the complex topography were the factors responsible for the extremely irregular development of the oxidation zone. Other important factors were the numerous joints in the skarn rocks and nonuniform solubility of primary minerals. The minerals of nickel and cobalt most subject to solution, and therefore susceptible to oxidation, are smaltine, chloanthite, and safflorite. Nevertheless, due to peculiarities in the climate and the sharply dissected relief, the thickness of the oxidation zone in the deposit is small, for the most part not exceeding 10-20 m. To be sure, this does not exclude the deep penetration of oxidation processes in individual cases, to 100 m or more, due to the extremely low water table.

Figure 17 is a schematic geological profile, along profile 6 (southern part of the deposit). It can be seen that in the oxidation zone profile an important part has been played by talus deposits and highly modified skarn limestones and siltstones. On the basis of precise determinations of the content and ratio of the index elements of a particular paragenesis, Fe, Co, Ni, or Cu, an attempt was made to reconstruct the history of these elements in supergene processes and establish the geochemical outcrops of the oxidation zone. All these problems constitute part of the study of the dispersion haloes of ore deposits. There is no question of the importance of this part of geochemistry in theory or exploration; it also is a part of the biogeochemical method of prospecting for minerals.

The combination of conditions determining the direction of geochemical processes in the zone of oxidation of arsenide and sulfide-arsenide deposits includes a great many factors: geological, climatic, geochemical, and biogeochemical. We will concentrate attention only on those processes which directly involve chemical and biogeochemical reactions in the supergene process.

Hypogene Minerals of the Deposit

The primary minerals of copper, nickel, cobalt, and iron in the deposit which we studied are rather varied, 40 in all. The following primary minerals of nickel and cobalt are found in the deposit: smaltine $CoAs_{3-2}$, chloanthite $NiAs_{3-2}$, niccolite $NiAs$, rammelsbergite $NiAs_2$, safflorite $CoAs_2$, skutterudite $CoAs_3$, gersdorffite $NiAsS$. Among the iron minerals we will mention arsenopyrite $FeAsS$ and pyrite FeS_2.

The most common minerals of copper are: chalcopyrite $CuFeS_2$, bornite Cu_5FeS_4, chalcosite Cu_2S, and covellite CuS. In a copper deposit the primary minerals of copper very often form so-called tennantite $Cu_3As(Sb)S_3$, which apparently includes Zn, Fe, Ni, and Co as an isomorphic admixture.

The minerals of cobalt, nickel, and copper which make up the ore body form veins in the form of more or less dense masses, or are scattered in the country rock.

TABLE 12. Degree of Stability of Sulfides in Descending Order (as given by different authors)

Wells	Nischihara	Nischihara	Ellin	Zeiss, Ellin et al.
H_2SO_4	H_2SO_4	$Fe_2(SO_4)_3$	$Fe_2(SO_4)_3$	$CuSO_4$
Pyrrhotite	Pyrrhotite	Pyrrhotite	Chalcocite	Galena
Sphalerite	Tetrahedrite	Tetrahedrite	Bornite	Pyrrhotite
Galena	Galena	Galena	Pyrite	Sphalerite
Chalcopyrite	Sphalerite	Arsenopyrite	Marcasite	Chalcopyrite
Pyrite	Chalcopyrite	Sphalerite	Covellite	Bornite
"	Arsenopyrite	Pyrite	Sphalerite	Pyrite
—	Marcasite	Enargite	Chalcopyrite	Covellite
—	Pyrite	Marcasite	—	Chalcocite

Certain of the mentioned minerals of copper, nickel, and cobalt characterize a quite well-defined and apparently late phase in the development of the hydrothermal process (bornite and others). A peculiarity of this phase is the relatively small content of primary minerals of iron. Naturally, this phenomenon was reflected in some way in all subsequent processes of oxidation of ore minerals.

For example, it is known that pyrrhotite, the most widespread primary mineral of iron, is the most unstable in the oxidation zone. With respect to the rate of decomposition, pyrrhotite stands in first place among the sulfides and sulfoarsenides in the stability series of various sulfides prepared by Wells (1914), Nischihara [1914], and other investigators. The oxidation reaction of pyrrhotite can be represented by the following equations:

$$FeS + 2O_2 = FeSO_4;$$
$$12FeSO_4 + 6H_2O + 3O_2 = 4Fe_2(SO_4)_3 + 4Fe(OH)_3;$$
$$Fe_2(SO_4)_3 + 6H_2O = 2Fe(OH)_3 + 3H_2SO_4.$$

The iron sulfate $Fe_2(SO_4)_3$ and sulfuric acid developing as a result of the oxidation of pyrrhotite change the degree of the stability of the sulfides, as can be seen easily from the data in Table 12.

The data in Table 12 show that pyrite in an acidic medium is the least reactive. Moreover, the presence of ferric sulfate in the solution greatly increases the oxidability of pyrite in comparison with other sulfides — sphalerite, chalcopyrite, etc. Apparently this explains the unsuccessful attempt of individual authors (Gottschalk and Buchler [1912]) to arrange the sulfides by degree of stability as a function of potentials (opposite a copper wire in distilled water). In the series of voltages of sulfides there is the following sequence, characterizing the increase of oxidability from the highest potentials to lower (in volts):

Gottschalk and Buchler Series

Marcasite	+0.37	Bornite	+0.17
Argentite	+0.23	Galenite	+0.15
Chalcopyrite . . from	+0.18	Chalcocite	+0.14
to	+0.30	Niccolite	+0.02
Molybdenite	+0.20	Copper	0.0
Covellite	+0.20	Sphalerite . from	−0.20
Pyrite	+0.18	to	−0.40

A comparison of the data in Table 12 and the Gottschalk and Buchler series reveals the absence of correlation in the series between the stability of sulfides and potentials. This can be attributed to the great complexity of the electrochemical systems created during the simultaneous presence of several minerals. Factors of importance here can include the nature of the solution, the degree of polarization, and the influence of gases, among others.

From the example of the data shown in Table 12, it is possible to see the influence of the products of oxidation of iron sulfides on the relative stability of the minerals of copper, zinc, and lead. The corresponding data for nickel and cobalt are unfortunately missing, but the example for copper is sufficiently convincing for drawing the conclusion that the greater part of the iron is freed more rapidly from primary ore sulfides. After oxidating, the iron is accumulated at the tops of the deposit (iron hats), whereas the nickel, cobalt, and copper are concentrated in the zone of

TABLE 13. Sequence of Mineral Formation in the Zone of Oxidation of a Sulfide-Arsenide Deposit

Sulfides and arsenides	Bornite Cu_5FeS_4, chalcopyrite $CuFeS_2$	Pyrite FeS_2	Arsenopyrite FeAsS	Niccolite NiAs	Smaltine $CoAs_{3-2}$
Secondary sulfides	Zone of enrichment. Chalcocite Cu_2S, covellite CuS				
Sulfates	Brochantite $CuSO_4 \cdot 3Cu(OH)_2$	Jarosite $KFe_3[SO_4]_2 \cdot (OH)_6$			
Arsenates			Scorodite $Fe_3[AsO_4] \cdot 2H_2O$	Annabergite $Ni_3[AsO_4]_2 \cdot 8H_2O$	Erythrite $Co_3[AsO_4]_2 \cdot 8H_2O$
Oxides and hydroxides	Tenorite CuO	Limonite $nFeO_2 \cdot$ aq	Limonite $nFeO_2 \cdot$ aq	Bunsenite NiO	Asbolan $n(Co, Ni)O \cdot MnO_2 \cdot nH_2O$
Carbonates	Azurite $2CuCO_3 \cdot Cu(OH)_2$, malachite $CuCO_3 \cdot Cu(OH)_2$	Siderite $FeCO_3$	Siderite $FeCO_3$		Spherocobaltite $CoCO_3$
Silicates	Chrysocolla $CuSiO_3 \cdot nH_2O$				

cementation. The relatively low content of iron sulfides in the ore stratum of the sulfide-arsenide deposit is indicative of the phenomenon of secondary enrichment of the ore zone with sulfides of copper, nickel, and cobalt (chalcosite, bornite, and millerite). The process of formation of secondary sulfides correlates with the lower horizons of the zone of percolation of meteoric water (the upper level of stagnant water) and transpires when there is an inadequate supply of oxygen.

A reaction of the following type can serve as a typical example of the process of oxidation of chalcopyrite in the presence of copper sulfate:

$$5CuFeS_2 + 11CuSO_4 + 8H_2O = 8Cu_2S + 5FeSO_4 + 8H_2SO_4$$

or

$$CuFeS_2 + CuSO_4 = 2CuS + FeSO_4.$$

The forming chalcosite and covellite remain stable for some time, because they can be transformed into one another depending on the pH conditions, the redox potential, etc. However, they cannot exist for a long time in the oxidation zone and are transformed into sulfates in accordance with the following scheme:

$$CuS + 2O_2 = CuSO_4;$$
$$5CuS + 3CuSO_4 + 4H_2O = 4Cu_2S + 4H_2SO_4;$$
$$2Cu_2S + 5O_2 + 4H_2O = CuSO_4 \cdot 3Cu(OH)_2 + H_2SO_4.$$
(brochantite)

The presence of secondary minerals of nickel and cobalt in the oxidized zone of a sulfide-arsenide deposit is a sure indicator of the closeness of primary sulfides and arsenides of these elements. Simple sulfates, such as pentlandite $(FeNi)_9S_8$ or linneite Co_3S_4 are formed by the oxidation of nickel, cobalt, and iron sulfides. The composition of the oxidation products is considerably more complex when arsenides and sulfoarsenides are present. The sulfates will be accompanied by nickel and cobalt arsenates: annabergite $Ni_3(AsO_4)_2 \cdot 8H_2O$, erythrite $Co_3(AsO_4)_2 \cdot 8H_2O$, and others. Despite the constant presence of arsenopyrite FeAsS and enargite Cu_3AsS_4 among the primary minerals, the oxidation products are virtually free of copper arsenates [trichalcite $Cu_3(AsO_4)_2 \cdot 5H_2O$] and iron arsenates (scorodite $Fe^{3+}AsO_4$

· $2H_2O$). The apparent reason for this phenomenon is the low stability of the copper and iron arsenates. As a result of these differences there is a dissimilarity in the direction of mineral formation of copper, nickel, cobalt, and iron in the weathered crust of the sulfide-arsenide deposit, as can be deduced from the scheme (Table 13).

In Table 13 the minerals encountered most frequently in the oxidation zone of the sulfide-arsenide deposit have been enclosed in boxes. The scheme shows that there are two important concentrations of copper in the cementation zone — in the form of secondary sulfides and in the form of carbonates, especially widespread in the second copper deposit.

Copper sulfate compounds, on meeting with calcium and magnesium carbonates, form azurite and malachite. Their formation can be represented by the following equations:

$$3CuSO_4 + 3CaCO_3 + H_2O = 2CuCO_3 \cdot Cu(OH)_2 + 3CaSO_4 + CO_2;$$

$$2CuSO_4 + 2CaCO_3 + H_2O = CuCO_3 \cdot Cu(OH)_2 + 2CaSO_4 + CO_2.$$

In tracing the mineralogy of the oxidation zone of the studied deposit, it can be noted that the iron is almost entirely in limonite and only to an insignificant degree in carbonates and arsenite.

The possibility of the formation of secondary minerals of nickel and cobalt in the oxidation zone is indicated by the presence of annabergite in the ore, and especially erythrite. The latter is a rich ore mineral here, found throughout the deposit. In exactly the same way, analyses of the black manganese encrustations forming in ores and in the country rock reveal high contents of cobalt, apparently due to the presence of the mineral asbolan. Analyses show that they contain nickel and copper.

The most abundant minerals of copper, nickel, and cobalt in the oxidation zone are annabergite, erythrite, and malachite. They constitute a substantial part of the ore minerals of the deposit. These minerals possess an extremely noticeable coloring and are detected easily at first glance. Blue and green fragments of copper minerals and rose encrustations of erythrite often are encountered in ancient mines and indicate hidden zones of mineralization. However, the presence of these minerals is not always discovered above the ore (in the soil layer). The well-developed process of oxidation of the ore stratum has caused a general scattering of the ore components, among which there has been an inevitable formation of easily soluble compounds of copper, nickel, cobalt, and other elements. The ore and mine waters also are known to contain sulfates,* chlorides, bicarbonates, and other dissolved compounds.

Meteoric water, penetrating through the ore stratum of the deposit without encountering stagnant or ground water along its path, sometimes travels to considerable depths. It penetrates into fissures, flows from roofs into drifts, and is easy to collect for analysis. The composition of this water indicates the presence of anions SO_3^-, HCO_3^-, Cl^-, and cations Ca^{2+}, Na^+, Cu^{2+}, Ni^{2+}, Co^{2+}, as well as iron (Table 14).

The data in Table 14 show a considerable enrichment of mine waters with cobalt, nickel, and copper in comparison with natural surface waters (Malyuga [1946]). For example, the cobalt content in sample 54 exceeds the mean cobalt content in natural surface waters ($2 \cdot 10^{-7}\%$) by a factor of almost 50. It has been established that the mine waters of drift No. 1 are fed by the waters of drift No. 4, situated at a higher horizon. This explains the almost equal quantity of nickel and copper in the waters of drifts Nos. 1 and 4. The appreciable enrichment of the water from drift No. 1 with cobalt can be attributed to its passage through a stratum of oxidized ores, greatly enriched with mobile cobalt. The waters taken from the mineralization zone contain a relatively high quantity of cobalt and show a very acidic reaction (samples 101, 102). The deep waters (sample 57) and waters taken from beyond the zone of mineralization (sample 103) are noticeably alkaline and are low in ore-forming elements.

The surface waters penetrating through ore minerals of different composition are not enriched with soluble compounds to an identical degree. The most abundant solution occurs in sulfide pentlandite and linneite ores. There is a less significant loss of nickel and cobalt from ores represented by arsenites, which are not easily soluble. However, the constant presence of ions of sulfuric and arsenic acids creates conditions under which nickel and cobalt are in considerable part transformed into a solution, primarily in a sulfate form. Experience shows that bicarbonates are of considerable importance, which for the most part is responsible for their vertical and horizontal migration in the biogeochemical profile.

_____
*The solubility of $NiSO_4$ at 22°C is 274.8 g/liter; for $CoSO_4$ at 20°C it is 268.8 g/liter.

TABLE 14. Cobalt, Nickel, and Copper Content in Mine Water of Deposit

Sample No.	Origin of water	Date of sample	pH	Content, %			Ratio	
				Co	Ni	Cu	Ni:Co	Cu:Co
53	Dripping, drift No. 4, 160 m from exit at a depth of 29 m, southern sector	8/10/59	—	$2.5 \cdot 10^{-6}$	$5 \cdot 10^{-6}$	$6 \cdot 10^{-6}$	2	2.4
54	Dripping, drift No. 1 (seeping along rock from drift No. 4), 70 m from exit, southern sector	8/10/59	—	$9.3 \cdot 10^{-6}$	$4.3 \cdot 10^{-6}$	$5.8 \cdot 10^{-6}$	0.5	0.6
57	Deep hole in drift No. 11-h, northern sector	7/13/59	8.8	$6.8 \cdot 10^{-6}$	$1.2 \cdot 10^{-6}$	$0 \cdot 10^{-6}$	0	0
56	Hole along profile No. 8, southern sector, ore-free zone	8/6/59	—	$8.5 \cdot 10^{-7}$	$1.7 \cdot 10^{-6}$	$1.1 \cdot 10^{-6}$	2	1.3
101	Dripping, drift No. 2, 50 m from exit, southern sector	8/6/59	2.4	$8.9 \cdot 10^{-6}$	$1 \cdot 10^{-6}$	$3.3 \cdot 10^{-6}$	0.12	0.4
102	Hole 159 along profile No. 6. Depth 107 m, southern sector	8/6/59	2.6	$5 \cdot 10^{-5}$	—	$2.9 \cdot 10^{-5}$	1	0.6
103	Dripping, drift No. 4b along profile 6a, 150 m from exit, southern sector, ore-free zone	8/6/59	8.2	$2.4 \cdot 10^{-7}$	$4.7 \cdot 10^{-7}$	$6.6 \cdot 10^{-7}$	2	2.5

In reviewing the hydrogeological conditions of the studied region, we noted the relative lack of meteoric water and the total absence of ground water at reachable depths in the deposit. A study of the soil-geological profiles shows, however, an absence of conditions for an excessively high accumulation of heavy metals in the surface horizon of the soil, similar to that which is observed, for example, in certain soils in the Southern Urals over nickel deposits. It is obvious, nevertheless, that there is a descending seepage of solutions here; these solutions are enriched with heavy metals. The descending flow exceeds the ascending flow. The only exception to this rule is on the well-warmed southerly steppe slopes of hills (chestnut soil complex). Profiles obtained in forested areas are under less favorable conditions because, in this case, there is a tendency to podzolization of the soil. This matter will be discussed in greater detail below.

2. Secondary Dispersion Haloes

Dispersion haloes are classified as primary or secondary. Primary dispersion is associated with deeper processes in the history of formation and further development of an ore deposit, syngenetic or epigenetic with the country rock in high- and low-temperature stages of ore formation (Ginzburg [1957]; Polikarpochkin [1957], Mukanov [1957], and others), than is secondary dispersion.

According to the observations of Cooper and Huff [1954], Morris and Lovering [1954], and others, the impregnation of ore elements of Cu, Pb, and Zn in dense limestone and dolomite country rock is very limited: from 1 to 5 m from the boundary of the ore deposit. The concentration of metals attenuates logarithmically in accordance with the rate of diffusion of ions in aqueous solutions. The dispersion curves therefore resemble diffusion curves, as is shown quite well in Fig. 18, which illustrates the degree of penetration of lead and zinc into undisrupted limestones. As the diagram confirms, the depth of penetration amounts to several feet. The conditions of diffusion (concentration, time, rock porosity) can increase the dispersion haloes of metals in rocks, but they are not large and there is not a great probability for their detection. The secondary haloes in a zone of oxidation of ore deposits are the most extensive and accessible to study. The distribution of metals in the secondary haloes is dependent on the relief, the depth of the vein, and the thickness of the soil layer and its stability. According to E. A. Sergeev [1941], L. S. Huff [1951], and others, the content of metals (Cu, Pb, Zn, and others) in secondary dispersion haloes is distributed in accordance with the mechanical movement of the soil and residual material downslope, and can be expressed in the form of the diagram shown as Fig. 19. The diagram shows that the maximum concentrations of metals are found in the upper horizon of the soil near a vein, and downslope. Upslope, in the immediate vicinity of the vein, the metal content drops off and soon attains the background value. The anomaly at the surface is more extensive in area than in the deeper layers, but the intensity in these layers is greater.

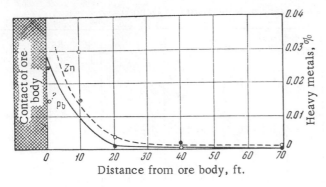

Fig. 18. Dispersion of lead and zinc in the primary dispersion halo (according to Finlayson (1910) and Morris [1954]).

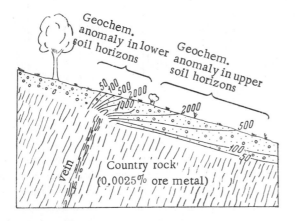

Fig. 19. Secondary dispersion halo in vertical profile (according to Sergeev et al. [1941]).

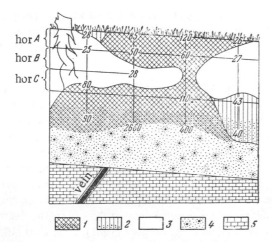

Fig. 20. Dispersion halo of cobalt in soil-geological profile of a sulfide-arsenide deposit (Tuva). Cobalt content: 1) < 50 mg/kg; 2) > 40 mg/kg; 3) < 40 mg/kg; 4) residual material; 5) skarnified limestones and shales.

The regularity of the pattern of distribution of metals in a mechanical halo is disrupted by the influence of chemical and biochemical processes. Solutions enriched with ore elements — e.g., Ni, Cu, Zn, Mo — rise to the surface by virtue of diffusion and capillary action. They enrich the soils and friable rocks and completely change the initial configuration of the mechanical dispersion halo. The secondary haloes therefore acquire a mixed character.

New data show that the localization of a salt dispersion halo in a sialic (moderately moist) weathered crust occurs in two planes: upper — corresponding to the humus layer of the soil, and lower — lying closer to the ore zone, the layer of illuvium and residual material (Fig. 20). Between these planes there is a zone from several centimeters to 1 m or more in thickness, impoverished of metals. This phenomenon also is observed both in symmetric haloes on plains and in asymmetric haloes on mountain slopes. On the basis of depth, haloes are classified as open (emerging at the surface) and closed (lying below later alluvium).

The formation of open dispersion haloes and their intensity at the surface is dependent on the climatic conditions of the region, temperature, and humidity (aridity). "In areas where there is a sharp predominance of the annual precipitation over evaporability," notes A. P. Solovov [1959], "the upper horizons of unconsolidated deposits are greatly elutriated, and as a result, under conditions of slackened denudation there can be an acidic reaction of the medium (pH < 7), corresponding to a sialic stage of weathering." As is well known, under such conditions there is some metallic enrichment of residual material at depth (Fig. 21a). In the case of a small quantity of precipitation and considerable evaporability, as occurs in the steppe zone, there are favorable conditions for the accumulation of metals in the soil layer (pH > 7) and in the ash of steppe vegetation (Fig. 21c). Finally, in the wooded-steppe and meadow-steppe zone, characterized by a certain intermediate precipitation and evaporability level, there are intermediate migration conditions (pH = 7), with an almost uniform distribution of metal salts in the soil profile (Fig. 21b).

Recent and ancient deposits (moraines, alluvial deposits), which cover ore bodies, change the direction and character of the migration of heavy metals in the salt dispersion halo. Depending on the thickness of the cover, to one degree or another there is an attenuation of the intensity of the anomaly in the direction of the surface. With respect to the character of the migration of ore elements, they approach primary dispersion haloes, which are developed in accordance with the laws of diffusion of solutions in porous and fractured rocks. Under favorable geological and climatic conditions of this type, closed haloes are discovered quite easily by the biogeochemical method, such as in exploration for ore-bearing

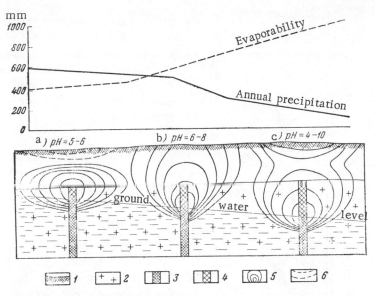

Fig. 21. Diagram of the dependence of the dispersion halo on climatic conditions (according to Solovov [1957]). 1) Unconsolidated deposits; 2) bedrock; 3) primary ores; 4) secondary ores; 5) probable isoconcentrations; 6) possible isoconcentrations.

zones, covered by morainal and aeolian clayey loams, in the case of nickel and chromium ores lying under Tertiary clayey loams of moderate thickness (Southern Urals), etc. However, closed dispersion haloes are virtually inaccessible to exploration by means of an ordinary metallometric survey.

3. Principle in Exploration for Secondary Dispersion Haloes

The choice of the most effective method for use in the search for secondary dispersion haloes (lithochemical, biogeochemical, hydrochemical) depends on the character of the dispersion halo and the conditions under which it was formed, and those under which it is found. In this case it is necessary to take into account the quantitative aspect in the migration of ore components, that is, the predominant significance of the mechanical, chemical, or biogeochemical migration factor.

Salt dispersion haloes are related morphologically to mechanical haloes, that is, to the unconsolidated products of weathering over the zone of oxidation. The migration of metal salts in the stratum of unconsolidated new formations conforms entirely to the physicochemical laws of diffusion, selective sorption, crystallization, etc. In the process of formation of a salt halo, the hydrochemical halo becomes mixed, and superposed on a mechanical halo, as a result of which the concentration of metals increases in the lithochemical sample. This process naturally is dependent on the pH of the solutions, the character of the metals, etc. It has been noted that the acidity of solutions in the zone of oxidation of sulfide deposits facilitates their enrichment with metals and removal beyond the limits of the zone of mineralization, which leads to an expansion of the haloes to the limit of total neutralization of water. In this case, as already mentioned, there will be a hypergene separation of copper and lead (Ginzburg et al. [1960]), lead and zinc, etc. Because of their high migration properties the dispersion haloes of copper and zinc greatly exceed the haloes of lead.

Lithochemical and biogeochemical methods can be used successfully in the search for mixed dispersion haloes. For example, in mountainous region with a highly developed alluvial process, in most cases it is necessary to deal with open mixed dispersion haloes. This apparently is explained by the following words of A. P. Solovov: "All the principal practical results of metallometric surveys in the USSR (apparently in Kazakhstan — D.M.), leading to the discovery of new deposits of nonferrous and rare metals of commercial importance, until now have been associated with the discovery of dispersion haloes of a complex type, with a sharp predominance of the mechanical phase and a subordinate role of the salt dispersion." It is known that open dispersion haloes are not always detected by a lithochemical survey, since their structure is dependent on climatic conditions and other factors.

It should be noted that the proponents of the lithochemical method put too much hope on mechanical dispersion haloes. However, these conclusions are based on experience with exploration for a rather limited number of metals

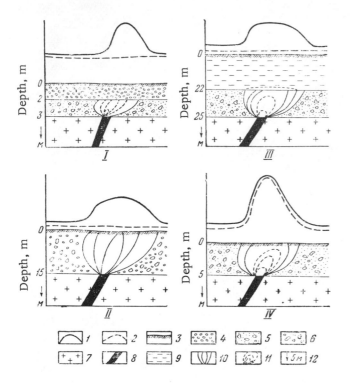

Fig. 22. Comparative effectiveness of the lithochemical and biogeochemical methods in different dispersion haloes. I) Mixed, covered with moraine (tundra zone); II) open, leached (podzol zone and others); III) covered with thick deposits of sand and clayey loams (desert and semidesert zone); IV) open, mixed (found in different zones). 1) Maximum metal content in soil humus and plant ash; 2) maximum metal content in residual material; 3) soil; 4) moraine; 5) residual material; 6) lower residual material; 7) mother rock; 8) ore; 9) clayey loam; 10) chemical dispersion halo; 11) mechanical dispersion halo; 12) thickness of horizon, m.

yielding stable (not in all zones) minerals — Sn, Mo, W, and Pb. The authors are often so carried away that they attempt to relate haloes of biogenic origin to mechanical haloes (Solovov [1959]). However, the role of biogenesis in the formation of dispersion haloes consists primarily in the concentration of ore elements in the humus horizon.

Without discussing the significance of any particular method in geochemical exploration for ore elements, we will note the principal cases where the biogeochemical method is most effective in the exploration for ore deposits.

Biogenic Dispersion Haloes

The role of biogenesis in the formation of "chemical" dispersion haloes has not been appreciated adequately by geologists. However, the importance of this process has been noted repeatedly by the leaders in geochemistry — Vernadskii [1926], Goldschmidt [1938], A. E. Fersman [1931], Vinogradov [1957], among others. It is sufficient to recall that surface vegetation mobilizes mineral nutrients from a stratum of considerable thickness, attaining 22 m (black haloxylon), and on the average (for all surface vegetation) is equal to 3-5 m.

As already mentioned, the concentrating role of surface plants and other soil organisms involves the fixing of chemical elements in the form of humates. The mechanism of this process involves the deposition of organic substances in the upper part of the profile from the plant, forest, and meadow litter, and most importantly — humification of root systems. The scale of this process will be discussed below. We should note here that biogenic processes actively participate in the formation of the dispersion haloes of ore deposits: 1) in a meadow-steppe zone the vegetation, with the participation of all organisms populating the soil, facilitates the migration of ore elements to the surface; the formation of the humus layer favors the accumulation and retention of many heavy metals, including Fe, Co, Ni, Cu, Zn, Mo, and others; 2) in the moist forest zone the ore elements are extracted actively by woody and shrubby vegetation. They are included in the small biogeochemical cycle and with difficulty escape from it, since they are intercepted by higher and lower vegetation and retained over the zone of mineralization. This is the nature of the high accumulation of uranium in the trees and mosses in the swampy areas of the northern regions of the Soviet Union and this is the way in which radium is accumulated by higher and lower plants; 3) in deserts and semideserts there are "high-content" haloes of Cu, Mo, and U in the ash of xerophytic vegetation (haloxylon, Syrian rue, and others). As a result of the activity of this vegetation on anchored sectors of the soil, there will be haloes with a high metal content in the humus (from rocks, under the roots of trees and shrubs). Thus, the conditions are defined under which biogenesis plays a predominant role in the formation of anomalies over ore deposits. The biogeochemical method should be of primary importance in the search for such anomalies.

Figure 22 shows cases of the preferential application of the biogeochemical method in the case of complex — leached and overlapping — dispersion haloes. The biogeochemical method can be applied successfully in the case of leached open haloes where the lithochemical methods do not give positive results (II — podzol zone), and also in the case of closed haloes in tundra and desert zones (I and III). In chernozem and chestnut zones in the steppe it is possible to employ a combined lithochemical and biogeochemical method (IV).

Thus, depending on the character of the dispersion haloes and the properties of the studied metals, the choice of the halo method should differ. For example, a metallometric survey based on sampling of alluvium has given good results in exploration for Sn and W, elements yielding stable minerals at the surface. Exploration for uranium is being carried on successfully by hydroradiometric and biogeochemical emanation methods. In the exploration for easily mobile elements, Co, Ni, Cu, Zn, Mo, Pb, U, and others, the use of the biogeochemical method is promising, especially in the zone of occurrence of gray forest and podzol soils. The biogeochemical method can render great assistance to other methods, and as noted by A. P. Vinogradov, this is especially true in regions covered by a thick mantle of sediments (morainal deposits and desert sands).

By their nature, dispersion haloes reveal the inevitable natural depletion of an ore deposit in conformity to the laws of migration of chemical elements in the zone of hypergenesis. However, this depletion does not set in immediately as a result of the contradiction in the processes of dispersal and concentration, which are observed constantly in the biosphere. Biogeochemical investigations of the dispersion haloes of ore deposits show that the climate and soil processes are not capable of changing the geochemical conditions to such an extent as to bring the level of the elements in soils and plants to the "background" content. This is prevented by the influence of the great masses of elements migrating from the ore body into the surrounding unconsolidated rocks. Such a situation prevails until the enriched rocks or ores are completely modified.

The study of secondary dispersion haloes constitutes an important problem for geologists, mineralogists, geochemists, and others. The theoretical importance of this problem is clear from the large scale of practical use of dispersion haloes in the geochemical search for ore deposits.

The biogeochemical or lithochemical exploration method is used, depending on the character of the halo. The biogeochemical method is used successfully in the case of leached open haloes, and also in the case of closed haloes in the tundra zone and in the desert zone, where the lithochemical method is inapplicable.

CHAPTER V

PATTERNS OF DISTRIBUTION OF HEAVY METALS IN SOILS

There is a rigorous dependence in the distribution of chemical elements in the biosphere, that is, in soils, natural waters and plants, on: 1) their content and ratio in igneous, metamorphic, and sedimentary bedrocks, and 2) the character of weathering and soil-formation processes (Vinogradov [1937], Ivanov [1950], Glazovskaya [1952]).

A study of the zonal soils of the USSR, which has been made over a period of some years at the Institute of Geochemistry of the Academy of Sciences of the USSR, has shown that for the most part the content of ore elements in soils is determined by their content in the recent and ancient sedimentary formations of the Russian platform, West Siberian and Caspian Lowland, and other areas covered by a thick mantle of sedimentary deposits.

The problems which we are concerned with can be reduced to the following: 1) study of the migration of copper, nickel, cobalt, and other chemical elements in the soils of all the principal soil zones of the USSR for the purpose of establishing the mean content of metals in soils; 2) determination of geochemical soil provinces, enriched with or lacking in copper, nickel, cobalt, and other elements; and, 3) study of the patterns of development of soils over deposits.

The data used in this work were those obtained by the latitudinal soil sampling expeditions organized by the Biochemical Laboratory of the Academy of Sciences of the USSR, as early as 1936. The soil samples were obtained in virgin lands and reserved areas by genetic horizons in regions of the Soviet Union typical for each zone in accordance with the zonal soil map prepared by L. I. Prasolov [1932]. The study of the content of chemical elements was made using the most sensitive and precise chemical and physicochemical methods — colorimetric, polarographic, etc. We will discuss the results of these investigations briefly.

1. Content of Certain Ore Elements in Soils

Almost all the principal zonal soils of the Soviet Union were represented in the studied soils from meridional samples from the tundra regions on the north, to subtropics in the south, and desert in the southeast. Table 16 gives the names of these soils and their content of certain ore elements.

There is a conspicuous quantitative predominance of manganese and iron among the ore elements entering into the composition of zonal soils: chromium, cobalt, nickel, etc. The content of manganese and iron in various soils reflects the zonal character of the soil quite well, that is, a correspondence to the conditions of loss or accumulation of these elements. For example, in podzols there is a decrease in the content of manganese and iron, while in chernozems and chestnut soils there is an accumulation in comparison with the soil-forming rock. In laterites it is iron that is accumulated to the highest degree, whereas in steppe soils it is manganese. In many cases it is possible to observe a certain tendency to the accumulation of manganese and iron in chernozem and chernozem-like soils. This can be attributed to the precipitation of sesquioxides by humic acids (pH = 5.86-3.38), an important component of dispersive colloidal soils systems (Ermolenko [1960]).

Heavy metals other than manganese and iron are separated out in the form of humates; these include chromium, cobalt, nickel, zinc, copper, molybdenum, and lead. In these cases there is a different ratio of metals to humic acids: humic, crenic, and apocrenic.

Variations in the content of ore elements in zonal soils — chernozems, chestnut soils, podzols, etc. — are characterized, as in the case of manganese and iron, by the relative mobility of these elements under different bioclimatic conditions. Especially great variations are observed in the content of cobalt, nickel, and copper (Fig. 23). This

TABLE 15. Distribution of Heavy Metals in Zonal Soils by Horizons

Soil	Horizon	Depth from which sample was taken, cm	Content, %					
			Cr	Co	Ni	Cu	Zn	Pb
Peaty-gley, tundra	A_0	0—15	$4 \cdot 10^{-3}$	$4.9 \cdot 10^{-4}$	$2.6 \cdot 10^{-3}$	$2.3 \cdot 10^{-3}$	$7.6 \cdot 10^{-3}$	—
" "	A_1	15—25	—	$1.5 \cdot 10^{-4}$	$1 \cdot 10^{-3}$	$1.1 \cdot 10^{-3}$	—	—
" "	B	25—50	$5 \cdot 10^{-4}$	$2.2 \cdot 10^{-4}$	$1.2 \cdot 10^{-3}$	$1.3 \cdot 10^{-3}$	$7.4 \cdot 10^{-3}$	—
Podzol, clayey loam	A_1	0—18	$1.8 \cdot 10^{-2}$	$1.4 \cdot 10^{-3}$	$2.4 \cdot 10^{-3}$	$8.3 \cdot 10^{-4}$	$3.3 \cdot 10^{-3}$	$1.5 \cdot 10^{-3}$
" "	A_2	18—34	$6.5 \cdot 10^{-3}$	$9.3 \cdot 10^{-4}$	$2.2 \cdot 10^{-3}$	$5.5 \cdot 10^{-4}$	$2.5 \cdot 10^{-3}$	$1 \cdot 10^{-3}$
" "	B_1	34—60	$2.9 \cdot 10^{-2}$	$6.6 \cdot 10^{-4}$	$1.6 \cdot 10^{-3}$	$5.4 \cdot 10^{-4}$	$2.5 \cdot 10^{-3}$	—
" "	B_2	60—110	$2.2 \cdot 10^{-2}$	$8.3 \cdot 10^{-4}$	$2.2 \cdot 10^{-3}$	$6.8 \cdot 10^{-4}$	$3.4 \cdot 10^{-3}$	—
Gray forest	A_1	0—5	$5.7 \cdot 10^{-2}$	$8.1 \cdot 10^{-4}$	$2.7 \cdot 10^{-3}$	$1.2 \cdot 10^{-3}$	—	—
" "	A_2	20—25	$1.4 \cdot 10^{-2}$	$6.4 \cdot 10^{-4}$	$1.7 \cdot 10^{-3}$	$1 \cdot 10^{-3}$	$2.8 \cdot 10^{-3}$	—
" "	B_1	40—45	$3.1 \cdot 10^{-3}$	$6.7 \cdot 10^{-4}$	$2.2 \cdot 10^{-3}$	$9.4 \cdot 10^{-4}$	$2.6 \cdot 10^{-3}$	—
" "	B_2	75—80	$4.4 \cdot 10^{-2}$	$7.8 \cdot 10^{-4}$	$2.2 \cdot 10^{-4}$	$8.4 \cdot 10^{-4}$	$3 \cdot 10^{-3}$	—
" "	C	100—105	$2.7 \cdot 10^{-3}$	$7.2 \cdot 10^{-4}$	$2.1 \cdot 10^{-3}$	$7.6 \cdot 10^{-4}$	$4.7 \cdot 10^{-3}$	—
Clayey chernozem (ordinary)	A_1	0—5	$4 \cdot 10^{-2}$	$6.7 \cdot 10^{-4}$	$3.9 \cdot 10^{-3}$	$1.7 \cdot 10^{-3}$	$9 \cdot 10^{-3}$	$9 \cdot 10^{-4}$
" "	A_2	24—32	$6.3 \cdot 10^{-2}$	$5.6 \cdot 10^{-4}$	$3.3 \cdot 10^{-3}$	$1.2 \cdot 10^{-3}$	$9 \cdot 10^{-3}$	$8 \cdot 10^{-4}$
" "	B	80—82	$2.2.15 \cdot 10^{-2}$	$7.5 \cdot 10^{-4}$	$3.5 \cdot 10^{-3}$	$1.9 \cdot 10^{-3}$	$6.3 \cdot 10^{-3}$	$6 \cdot 10^{-4}$
" "	C	128—144	$2 \cdot 10^{-2}$	$1.2 \cdot 10^{-3}$	$4.8 \cdot 10^{-3}$	$1.6 \cdot 10^{-3}$	—	$1.1 \cdot 10^{-4}$
Gray soils of deserts	A	0—5	$5.7 \cdot 10^{-2}$	$3.4 \cdot 10^{-4}$	$1 \cdot 10^{-3}$	$5.1 \cdot 10^{-4}$	$3.9 \cdot 10^{-3}$	—
" "	B	65—70	$5.7 \cdot 10^{-2}$	$6.1 \cdot 10^{-4}$	$2.8 \cdot 10^{-3}$	$8.4 \cdot 10^{-4}$	$4.1 \cdot 10^{-3}$	—
" "	C	160—170	$3.5 \cdot 10^{-2}$	$8.8 \cdot 10^{-4}$	$2.9 \cdot 10^{-3}$	$1.2 \cdot 10^{-3}$	—	—

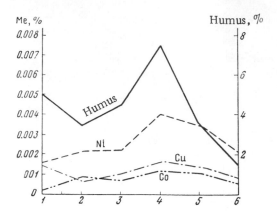

Fig. 23. Correlation of cobalt, nickel, and copper with humus in the zonal soils of the USSR. 1) Tundra soils; 2) podzols; 3) gray forest soils; 4) chernozems; 5) chestnut soils; 6) gray semidesert soils.

apparently explains the surface impoverishment of the dispersion haloes of nickel, copper, and lead in the podzol zone, as well as the formation of soil provinces on the territory of the USSR with an inadequacy of biologically active elements (biogeochemical provinces).

There is a very remarkable, virtually uniform distribution of zinc in all the zonal soils of the USSR. Its content in soils differs little from the mean values known for igneous and sedimentary rocks. The phenomenon of the high stability of zinc in soils taken from different zones apparently is associated with the ability of zinc to form stable compounds with clayey dispersive minerals of the soil absorbing complex.

There is no clear pattern in the distribution of uranium. This apparently can be attributed to the inaccuracy of data on uranium in zonal soils, since there is an apparent sharply expressed noncorrespondence of the uranium content in the soils of the USSR in comparison with the mean value. The uranium content in the soils of the USSR is very high, and, therefore, the ratio derived on the basis of all available data does not correspond to the Th:U ratio in the soils of the USSR. Our data reveal that the normal content of uranium in the soils does not exceed $1 \cdot 10^{-4}\%$ which, with a mean content of thorium in soils of $1 \cdot 10^{-3}$, corresponds to the ratio Th:U = 10:1. A decrease in the Th:U ratio should be expected in predominantly uranium deposits, as we confirmed in one case.

The Ni:Co ratio is of equal importance in exploration work. The mean value of this coefficient in zonal soils is 4:1. However, the Ni:Co ratio in soils over nickel deposits varies from 10:1 to 30:1 and averages 15:1. Thus, the high values of the Ni:Co ratio in soils is evidence of nickel-bearing rocks (serpentinites) or nickel ores being present.

It should be noted that the Ni:Co ratio in soils over nickel-cobalt sulfide-arsenide deposits drops off sharply and on the average does not exceed unity. Consequently, the coefficients of the ratios of ore elements are a good indicator during exploration for deposits.

The figures for the normal content of ore elements in soils cited in Table 16 have a relative, rather than an absolute value. With an increase in the number of analyses of zonal soils these figures can change, but not to such an extent as to change the order of numerical values. However, over ore deposits there is often an increase in the level of these elements by a factor of ten in comparison with the mean values for soils.

Merely by a comparison of the figures derived in the process of a biogeochemical survey (from a soil analysis) and the data in Table 16 it is possible to detect the presence of an anomaly associated with the zone of mineralization.

As already noted, an extremely important criterion for the detection of anomalies is the value of the local normal geochemical background of ore elements in soils. This value is determined on the basis of an analysis of soil samples from the humus layer (from the surface to 10 cm), collected beyond the limits of known and surmised ore zones.

2. Distribution of Metals in the Profile of Zonal Soils

A study of the samples selected from the entire soil profile from 0 to 120-150 cm was made to obtain a complete description of the distribution of metals in zonal soils. All genetic horizons were represented in each of the studied profiles, including soil-forming rocks. Experience has shown that the content of metals in individual soil horizons is dependent on a whole series of factors: 1) the composition of the soil-forming rocks, 2) physical geography and soil-biological conditions, 3) individual chemical and physicochemical properties of metals, and 4) maturity of the soil profile.

In this chapter we will attempt to demonstrate the dependence of the distribution of heavy metals in the soil profile on bioclimatic conditions, the most important factor in the sound devising of a rational biogeochemical method for the exploration of ore deposits. We will discuss several specific examples of the distribution of cobalt, nickel, copper, etc. in the profile of zonal soils obtained outside the limits of ore deposits. Certain data on this problem have been given in Table 15 and in Fig. 24; these reveal a regular accumulation of chromium, cobalt, nickel, and copper

TABLE 16. Content of Certain Ore Elements in the Zonal Soils of the USSR in % * (According to Vinogradov [1957])

| Element | Soil | | | | | | | | Mean | |
	tundra	podzol	gray forest	chernozem	chestnut	gray soil	red soil	in soils	in sedimentary rocks	in earth's crust
B	$2 \cdot 10^{-4}$	$4 \cdot 10^{-4}$	$2 \cdot 10^{-4}$	$1 \cdot 10^{-3}$	$1 \cdot 10^{-3}$	$1.3 \cdot 10^{-3}$	$4 \cdot 10^{-4}$	$1 \cdot 10^{-3}$	$1.2 \cdot 10^{-3}$	$3 \cdot 10^{-4}$
Cr	$4 \cdot 10^{-3}$	$2 \cdot 10^{-2}$	$2 \cdot 10^{-2}$	$3 \cdot 10^{-2}$	$4 \cdot 10^{-2}$	$5 \cdot 10^{-2}$	$1 \cdot 10^{-2}$	$2 \cdot 10^{-2}$	$1.6 \cdot 10^{-2}$	$2 \cdot 10^{-2}$
Mn	$1.8 \cdot 10^{-1}$	$7.0 \cdot 10^{-2}$	$2 \cdot 10^{-1}$	$1.0 \cdot 10^{-1}$	$1.0 \cdot 10^{-1}$	$1.0 \cdot 10^{-1}$	$7 \cdot 10^{-2}$	$8.5 \cdot 10^{-2}$	$6.7 \cdot 10^{-2}$	$9 \cdot 10^{-2}$
Fe	2.5	1.5	2	3.8	3.5	2	8	3.8	8.33	5.1
Co	$5 \cdot 10^{-4}$	$6 \cdot 10^{-4}$	$8 \cdot 10^{-4}$	$1 \cdot 10^{-3}$	$1.2 \cdot 10^{-3}$	$3 \cdot 10^{-4}$	$1 \cdot 10^{-3}$	$1 \cdot 10^{-3}$	$1 \cdot 10^{-3}$	$1 \cdot 10^{-3}$
Ni	$2.5 \cdot 10^{-3}$	$2 \cdot 10^{-3}$	$2.7 \cdot 10^{-3}$	$4 \cdot 10^{-3}$	$5.9 \cdot 10^{-3}$	$1 \cdot 10^{-3}$	$2.7 \cdot 10^{-3}$	$4 \cdot 10^{-3}$	$4 \cdot 10^{-3}$	$6.5 \cdot 10^{-3}$
Cu	$2 \cdot 10^{-3}$	$8 \cdot 10^{-4}$	$1 \cdot 10^{-3}$	$1.7 \cdot 10^{-3}$	$1.5 \cdot 10^{-3}$	$1.5 \cdot 10^{-3}$	$1 \cdot 10^{-2}$	$2 \cdot 10^{-3}$	$4.1 \cdot 10^{-3}$	$7 \cdot 10^{-3}$
Zn	$5 \cdot 10^{-3}$	$3.5 \cdot 10^{-3}$	$5 \cdot 10^{-3}$	$7 \cdot 10^{-4}$	$4 \cdot 10^{-3}$	$4 \cdot 10^{-3}$	$5 \cdot 10^{-3}$	$5 \cdot 10^{-3}$	$8 \cdot 10^{-3}$	$5 \cdot 10^{-3}$
Mo	$3.5 \cdot 10^{-4}$	$2 \cdot 10^{-4}$	$2 \cdot 10^{-4}$	$2.5 \cdot 10^{-3}$	$2 \cdot 10^{-4}$	$2 \cdot 10^{-4}$	$3 \cdot 10^{-4}$	$2.5 \cdot 10^{-4}$	$2 \cdot 10^{-4}$	$3 \cdot 10^{-4}$
Pb	—	$5 \cdot 10^{-4}$	$1 \cdot 10^{-3}$	$2 \cdot 10^{-3}$	$1.5 \cdot 10^{-3}$	$5 \cdot 10^{-4}$	$1 \cdot 10^{-3}$	$1 \cdot 10^{-3}$	$2 \cdot 10^{-3}$	$1.6 \cdot 10^{-3}$
U	$3 \cdot 10^{-4}$	$3 \cdot 10^{-4}$	$3.2 \cdot 10^{-4}$	$4 \cdot 10^{-4}$	$3 \cdot 10^{-4}$	—	$4 \cdot 10^{-4}$	$1 \cdot 10^{-4}$	$3.2 \cdot 10^{-4}$	$3 \cdot 10^{-4}$
Th	$8 \cdot 10^{-4}$	$1.1 \cdot 10^{-3}$	$1.2 \cdot 10^{-3}$	$1.0 \cdot 10^{-3}$	$1 \cdot 10^{-3}$	—	$1 \cdot 10^{-3}$	$6 \cdot 10^{-4}$	$1.1 \cdot 10^{-3}$	$8 \cdot 10^{-4}$
Th : U	2.7	3.3	3.8	2.5	3.3	—	2.5	6	3.4	2.7
Ni : Co	5	3.3	3.4	4	5	3.5	2.7	4	4	6.5

* The table gives the metal content in the upper humus horizon of the soil, from 0 to 10-15 cm.

55

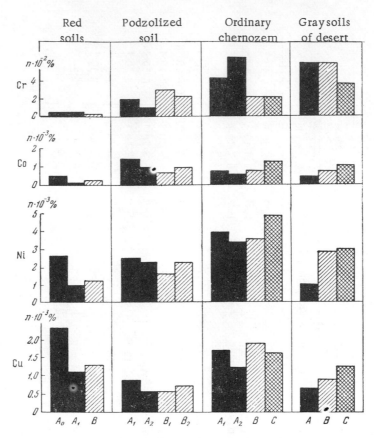

Fig. 24. Distribution of chromium, cobalt, nickel, and copper
by soil horizons.

in the upper humus horizon of peaty-gleyey soil, ordinary chernozem, gray forest soil, and podzol. In almost all cases, except for steppe soils, the A_2 and B_1 horizons are noticeably lacking in metals as a result of their loss into the lower-lying horizons. In certain cases the B_2 horizon of podzolized soil is therefore enriched with metals to a greater extent than the above-lying A_1 and B_1 horizons.

In gray forest soils there is a slight tendency to a loss of metals into the B_2 horizon (a similarity to a podzol soil). On the whole, the distribution of metals in the profile of gray forest soils is relatively regular, resembling their distribution in ordinary chernozem (Cu, Zn).

The distribution of metals in chestnut soils, not shown in Table 15, resembles that which is observed in chernozem soil (Vinogradov [1957]).

The distribution of heavy metals in the gray soils of semideserts is extremely unusual. In contrast to other zonal soils, in gray soils the upper horizon is very lacking in cobalt, nickel, copper, and zinc, which apparently is related to the process of deflation of clayey and organomineral particles, usually enriched with metals. It should be remembered that such a phenomenon can be observed in a zone in which ore deposits are found. The customary use of the upper horizon of gray soil in biochemical exploration therefore becomes inapplicable.

A study of the diagrams in Fig. 24 reveals an extremely complex distribution of cobalt, nickel, and copper in the profile of zonal soils. This can be attributed to the similar chemical and physicochemical properties of these elements in different soil processes. The most important of these are the following: 1) the solubility of organometallic and mineral compounds, 2) the capability of ions of metals to concentrate in soil colloids. This capacity of individual elements (Co, Cd, Al) has been studied by K. K. Gedroits [1955]. The adsorptive properties of metals in colloids were studied by I. N. Antipov-Karataev [1947] and others. The differing behavior of copper, mercury, and lead to absorption by montmorillonite clays has been established. For example, whereas the absorption of lead and mercury ions is fully reversible, the absorption of copper ions is to a considerable extent irreversible. In exactly the same way, cobalt and nickel are for the most part accumulated in the silty fraction of soils enriched with ferromagnesian minerals of the montmorillonite type (Painter et al. [1953], Hill et al. [1953]).

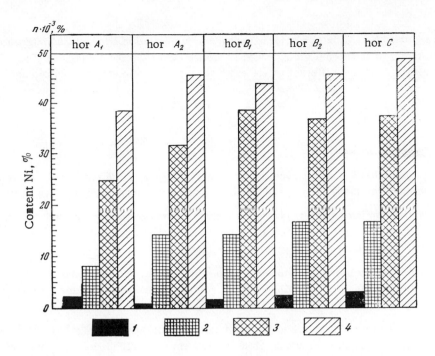

Fig. 25. Distribution of nickel in different fractions in different horizons
in brown forest soil (according to Painter et al. [1953]. 1) 2.00-0.05 mm;
2) 0.05-0.02 mm; 3) 0.02-0.002 mm; 4) less than 0.002 mm.

The distribution of nickel by fractions of the mechanical composition of brown forest soil has been shown graphically in the form of the diagrams in Fig. 25. These diagrams show that the greatest quantity of nickel is found in the fraction smaller than 0.002 mm. This fraction includes not only minerals and organominerals, but humic substances as well. An important peculiarity of the dispersive fractions of a soil is their considerable mobility in the soil profile, especially in acidic and saline soils. In the steppe soils the migration of the silt-clay fractions downward in the profile leads to the crumbling of clayey and loamy steppe soils. In eluvial soils with a completely formed profile there is a clearly defined distribution of silt-clay fractions, characterizing the zonal and age peculiarities of the soil. Thus, we have the complete loss of dispersive fractions into the lower horizons in the mature profile of a podzol (see Fig. 14), and on the other hand, the even distribution of mechanical fractions in the profile of most steppe soils.

The process of migration of colloidal solutions downward in the profile of chestnut soils (Kimpersai, Aktyubinskaya Oblast) can be judged on the basis of dark brown streaks which penetrate to a depth of as much as 1.5 m. They can be distinguished easily from the surrounding brighter loam not only due to their brown color, but also from the effervescence of $CaCO_3$, carried from the carbonate horizon, situated closer to the surface. Thus, the importance of clay-silt formations in the distribution of heavy metals in the profile of zonal soils becomes completely obvious.

With respect to the conditions under which separation occurs — sorption and desorption of metals in soil colloids— we only can add to what has been said before, i.e., that this problem is being transformed more and more from a purely "agricultural" one, which usually is considered in relation to the study of the absorption capacity of plants, to a problem of geochemistry, playing a role of the greatest importance in the theory of formation of dispersion haloes over ore deposits. In this connection we will discuss certain regularities in the distribution of the ions of heavy metals in soil colloids.

The principal colloidal carriers of metal ions in soils are: 1) clayey minerals of the montmorillonite and kaolinite types, 2) humic acids, 3) oxides and hydroxides of aluminum, iron, manganese, and others. They all differ with respect to capacity and specificity of absorption of cations and anions.

As already noted, the presence and relationship of these dispersive substances is a zonal peculiarity of the soil. For example, it is known that chernozem soils are rich in humus, montmorillonite minerals accumulate for the most part in alkaline soils, and kaolin in acidic and neutral soils, etc.

We now will note certain peculiarities in the absorption mechanism of soil colloidal systems (a soil absorbing complex).

The absorption capability of humic acids is dependent on absorption capacity, which in turn is determined by the number and character of functional groups. The latter are easily taken into account if we adopt the following scheme for the combination of the different groups entering into the composition of humic acid:

$$C_{60}H_{35} \begin{cases} -(COOH) & 4-6 \\ -(OH) & 3-5 \\ -(OCH_3) & 1-2 \\ -CH=COH \end{cases}$$

It follows from this scheme that for each molecule of humic acid there are 4 to 6 carboxyl groups, from 3 to 5 phenolhydroxyl groups, 1-2 methoxy groups, and 1 carbonyl group (the enol form is shown in the scheme).

A larger or smaller number of active groups is involved in the exchange reactions, depending on the pH of the solution and the aggregate state of the soil humus. The humus of chernozem soils, saturated with exchange bases — ions of Ca and Mg and certain heavy metals — possess the least activity.

The mechanism of activation of the processes of sorption and desorption of ions in colloids can be expressed in the simple action of meteoric water containing carbonic acid, in accordance with the following scheme: (humate) $> Ca^{2+} + (H_2^+ \rightleftharpoons 2HCO_3^-) \rightarrow$ (humic acid) $= H_2 + (Ca \rightleftharpoons 2HCO_3^-)$.

As a result of such an interaction of humates with carbonic acid, the ions Ca^{2+} and Mg^{2+} are exchanged for hydrogen ions, and the alkaline-earth elements migrate in the form of bicarbonates. The hydrogen ions in the colloids can be replaced easily by ions of heavy metals, after which the system becomes inert for some time.

The mineral part of the soil silt-clay colloids (the soil absorbing complex) includes not only montmorillonite, but also haluasites and kaolinite, sesquioxides, and silicic acid. When evaluating the adsorption properties of organic, organomineral, and mineral colloidal systems it is therefore necessary to take into account the charge of the particles. N. F. Ermolenko [1960] assumes that "the organomineral complex of soils usually has a negative charge" and this for the most part is determined by the negative charge of humates. During the interaction of positively charged hydroxides of heavy metals with negatively charged organomineral particles, an isoelectric state of the system can set in, under which there will be a coagulation of soil colloids.

The sequence of replacements of cations, including the ions of heavy metals in colloidal systems, was discussed briefly in the preceding chapter. The complexity of this process, which involves a great many individual properties of cations — valence, the hydratability of ions, and many others — is still further complicated by the influence of external migration factors. It is therefore necessary to rely here entirely on the empirical data at our disposal. Certain conclusions from these observations have been cited in the book Soil Microelements and Colloids. Essentially these conclusions are as follows:

1) the completeness of ion exchange increases with an increase of the valence of the exchanged ions:

$$Na^+ < Ca^{2+} < Al^{3+} < Th^{4+};$$

2) under these same conditions and a constant valence, the intensity of exchange increases with an increase in the atomic number of the element:

$$Li^+ < Na^+ < K^+ < Rb^+ < Cs^+;$$
$$Mg^{2+} < Ca^{2+} < Sr^{2+} < Ba^{2+};$$

3) the higher the coefficient of activity, the greater is the exchange potential.

According to Mitchell [1945], the energy of absorption of a number of heavy metals by soil colloids is greater than it is for calcium, magnesium, and others. Because of this, many ore elements are stably held by the soil, primarily in an absorbed state in clayey and organic colloids. On the basis of absorption energy such elements fall into the following series with respect to calcium and hydrogen:

$$H^+ > Cu^{2+} > Pb^{2+} > Ni^{2+} > Co^{2+} > Zn^{2+} > Ca^{2+}.$$

The hydrogen ions are in first place with respect to absorption activity. This explains the appreciable migration of a number of metals under conditions of low pH, such as nickel, cobalt, and copper in podzols and other acidic soils. The presence of calcium carbonates in the soils of arid regions lowers the mobility of these elements.

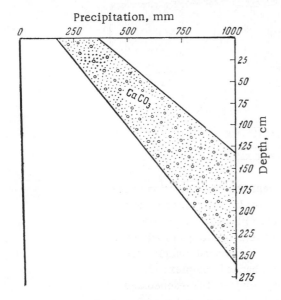

Precipitation, mm

Fig. 26. Dependence of the depth of the carbonate horizon of the soil on precipitation (according to Jenny [1948]).

3. Influence of the Zonality of Soil Processes on the Distribution of Metals in the Profile

The influence of various factors on the distribution of ore elements in the soil profile already has been noted: rocks, the migrational properties of the metal, bioclimatic weathering conditions, and mineral formation. It seemed to us that, depending on the chemical composition of the soil-forming rocks, the character of the soil process, and the "maturity" of the profile, the content of metals in the soil can be greater or smaller than that in the rock. Under conditions of physical weathering (high-mountain regions, the Arctic zone, and the zone of mountainous steppes), the content of metals in the soil differs little from their content in the rock, including in ore-forming rock. The most sharply developed differentiation of the content of metals in the soil profile occurs in humid regions, where podzolization has developed. In such areas, for a number of metals, the upper humus horizon along with the vegetation litter, can be enriched with individual biogenic elements — nickel, copper, and zinc. The lower illuvial B_2 horizon is enriched with iron, manganese, and in part with cobalt.

In the zone with moderately dry and moist steppes with chernozem and chestnut soils there is a general accumulation of ore elements in the soil profile with a certain excess of copper, zinc, and molybdenum and other biogenic elements in the humus horizon.

By tracing the distribution of chemical elements in the horizons of steppe, meadow-steppe, and forest-steppe soils, it is possible to note that the macrocomponents of calcium and magnesium correspond to a particular level, characterizing the precipitation regime. Many researchers have devoted considerable time to the formulation of schemes showing the distribution of carbonate, gypsum, manganese-containing, and other horizons in relation to the amount of precipitation, etc. (Marbut [1928]; Jenny and Leonard [1934], and others).

As an example, Fig. 26 shows the dependence between the depth and thickness of the carbonate horizon in the soil profile and the amount of precipitation along a line extending through the states of Colorado, Kansas, and Missouri (Jenny [1948]). This, to the highest degree an arbitrary extrapolation of the correlation of the amount of precipitation and the depth and thickness of the carbonate horizon, is far from true if we make observations at any specific point on any continent. It is found that the depth of the carbonate horizon is dependent not only on hydrothermal conditions, the amount of precipitation, and the mean annual temperature, but also on the relief, the character of the soil-forming rocks (clay, loam), and even on the depth of plowing (for cultivated areas), etc.

As an example we will discuss one of our investigations, made in the Southern Urals (Aktyubinskaya Oblast). In climatic respects the region studied belongs to the Trans-Ural province with inadequate moisture conditions. Because of this there is a correlation with relief conditions in the distribution of soils and plant associations. Meadow-chernozem soils, along with corresponding vegetation, have developed in the floodplains of rivers and in well-drained and moist ravines. A complex of chestnut soils with soddy grasses (sheep's fescue, feather grass) predominates on the slopes and drainage divides; these are mixed with white wormwood, ground pine, shaggy goldilocks, etc. Saline soils with salt-loving vegetation have developed on uplifted but poorly drained plateaus.

A carbonate horizon is formed as a result of the inadequate moisture conditions in the profile. Its position usually corresponds to horizon B, but the level of the carbonate horizon approaches the surface or withdraws to some depth, depending on the relief and the character of the underlying rocks. A characteristic indicator of the appearance of carbonates at the surface is the specific brownish-gray color of the soil on which salt-loving plants grow, as was noted earlier.

Figure 27 is a schematic soil profile along the line III-III for the Shcherbakovskii deposit. Local soils — chestnut loamy and clayey — have developed on recent and ancient (tertiary) loams and clays which cover the ancient weathered crust on leached serpentinites, kaolinized gabbro-amphibolites, etc. Figure 27 shows the change of relief and indicates the position of the effervescent horizon. In this case the effervescent horizon emerges at the surface in

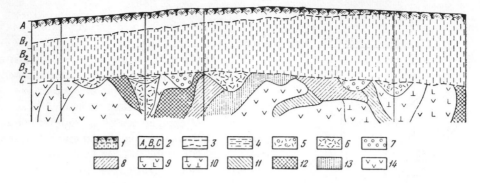

Fig. 27. Diagram of the distribution of the effervescent zone as a function of relief. 1) Soil profile; 2) soil horizons; 3) upper and lower limits of effervescence; 4) sandstones; 5) ochers in rocks of a banded complex; 6) kaolinized gabbro-amphibolites; 7) ochers in serpentinites; 8) nontronitized serpentinites; 9) rocks of a banded complex (serpentinites + gabbroids); 10) rocks of a banded complex (serpentinites + pyroxenites); 11) nontronites in rocks of a banded complex; 12) weakly nontronitized serpentinites; 13) silicified serpentinites; 14) leached and dense undivided serpentinites.

the high soddy part of the relief, whereas it lies at a depth of 25-30 cm in lower areas. The thickness of the carbonate horizon varies from 20 to 150 cm.

The uniformity of the dense clays and loams which cover the ore bodies at depths of 3 to 10 m is disrupted along shrinkage cracks which have a depth as great as 200-250 cm. As a result, relatively dense rocks are easily penetrated by solutions and plant roots.

The carbonate horizon, with a pH of 7 or more, which is common for steppe soils, is a shield which is not easily penetrated by ions of metals with a coefficient of instability of ions with a pH below 7: iron, cobalt, nickel, copper, zinc, lead, and others. This involves ions of metals which move upward and downward. In order to check this phenomenon, which we had noted earlier, a study was made of the distribution of nickel and cobalt in a vertical profile over a shallow ore nontronite in the Shcherbakovskii nickel silicate deposit. The soil-geological profile has the following lithological-morphological composition: 1) a humus eluvial horizon A on brown loam, effervescent with HCl, containing large quantities of nickel and cobalt (thickness of the horizon is 10-25 cm); 2) a carbonate-illuvial horizon B_c, enriched with calcium and magnesium carbonates, containing larger quantities of nickel and cobalt (thickness of the horizon is 10-15 cm); 3) the BC_c horizon consists of a dark gray loam, highly enriched with calcium and magnesium carbonates, conspicuously impoverished in ore metals (thickness of the horizon is 40-50 cm); 4) nontronitized serpentinite with inclusions of gypsum, not effervescent, pH about 7 (thickness 250 cm); 5) bauxitized nontronite, enriched with nickel and cobalt; 6) leached serpentinite, friable, greenish-gray.

Table 17 gives data on the content of nickel and cobalt in the soil and rocks making up the profile. These data show that the upper soil horizon from 0 to 40 cm is considerably enriched with nickel and cobalt. A certain decrease in the content of ore elements at a depth of 30-40 cm in comparison with the above-lying humus layer occurred as a result of their partial loss from horizon B. With increasing depth there is then a decrease in nickel and cobalt.

The impoverishment of the lower-lying soil horizons can be attributed to the mobilization of metals by the roots of grassy vegetation. The decrease in the content of metals in the lower part of the carbonate horizon and under it can also be attributed to the absence of any appreciable seepage of dissolved salts of metals both upward and downward. Upward movement is shielded by the carbonate horizon, whereas the salts of metals do not move downward due to the presence of an alkaline reaction of the circulating solutions. Thus, a rather thick layer of rock is formed (about 3 m) with a relatively low content of nickel and cobalt, although by a depth of 370 cm there is an increase in the content of nickel and cobalt by a factor of almost 10.

In analyzing these data for the purpose of finding a rational method of geochemical exploration in different bioclimatic zones of the country, it is found to be possible to employ in biogeochemical exploration the upper humus layer of the soil, enriched with metals, and the ash of plants, possessing the capability of penetrating through the carbonate shield and reaching the ore layer with their roots.

TABLE 17. Nickel and Cobalt Distribution in Vertical Profile (Prospecting Pit 1, Shcherbakovskii Deposit)

Sample No.	Soil, rock	Depth, cm	Content,%		Ratio Ni : Co	Comments
			Ni	Co		
470	Chestnut, clayey loam	0-10	0.038	0.0020	19	Highly effervescent with HCl
471	The same	30-40	0.030	0.0017	18	The same
472	Greenish-gray clayey loam	70-80	0.015	0.0009	16.5	The same
473	Nontronitized serpentinite	130	0.010	0.0008	12.5	The same
474	The same	170	0.018	0.0010	18	Not effervescent
475	The same	270	0.006	0.0007	8.5	The same
476	Ocherized nontronite	370	0.0075	0.0010	7.5	The same
477	Leached serpentinite	470	0.062	0.0031	20	The same

A study of ore elements in the zonal soils of the Soviet Union has made it possible to determine their mean content in soils for the purpose of delimiting provinces enriched with or lacking in cobalt, nickel, copper, etc. The data thus obtained were used in the mapping of biogeochemical endemic provinces, and also in developing the theoretical principles of a method of biogeochemical exploration of ore deposits.

During a study of the distribution of metals in the profile of zonal soils it was established that their content in individual horizons is dependent on: 1) the composition of soil-forming rocks; 2) physicogeographic conditions; 3) the maturity of the soil profile; 4) the concentrating or scattering role of surface plants and soil animals; and, 5) individual physicochemical properties of metals.

Among the individual properties of ore elements, those which are of greatest importance in their distribution in the soil profile are: the solubility of compounds, and the capability of ions to concentrate on soil colloids.

The principal colloidal carriers of metal ions in soils are: clayey minerals of the montmorillonite and kaolinite types, humic acids, aluminum oxides and hydroxides, iron, manganese, etc.

With respect to the energy of absorption by soil colloids, the ore elements fall into a series in relation to calcium and hydrogen:

$$H^+ > Cu^{2+} > Pb^{2+} > Ni^{2+} > Co^{2+} > Zn^{2+} > Ca^{2+}.$$

The most important factor in the distribution of ore elements in the soil-geological profile is the bioclimatic zonality of soils (vertical and horizontal): the influence of hydrothermal conditions, the distribution of carbonates in the soil profile, and the influence of surface plants and animals populating the soil.

CHAPTER VI

CONDITIONS FOR THE ACCUMULATION OF HEAVY METALS IN PLANTS

There is no more indicative example anywhere in nature of the reciprocal influence of the mineral substrate and organisms than in the soil. We refer to the "close reciprocal dependence between the environmental conditions for plant nutrition and internal processes of the exchange of matter in plants" (Peterburgskii [1959]). Moreover, living organisms, such as surface plants, which possess an extremely perfect mechanism for the absorption of nutrients from the soil, actively influence minerals: they dissolve matter in a solid state, extract sorbed ions from the soil colloids, and selectively assimilate the elements which they require.

An indirect effect of organisms on the soil and rocks also occurs after their death. This is because organic matter, after entering the soil, continues its chemical and biological function. The organic matter accumulating in the soil leads to the development of soil flora and fauna. The humus, organic acids, and other substances which form facilitate the further development of life on the earth's surface. Almost all the known chemical elements are drawn in such a way into the biological cycle through the life functions of plants.

Because of the slowness of the process of mineralization of organic matter many "ash" elements accumulate in the humus; these are derived from plants, and include heavy metals. That is why the soil in a natural state contains all the necessary elements for mineral nutrition. As is well known, the content of these substances is dependent on the character of the rocks and local bioclimatic conditions.

The presence of the same ore elements in soil humus and in plant ash makes it possible to carry out a joint soil-plant survey in exploration work.

1. Mobility and Assimilability of Heavy Metals

Despite the long history of the discovery of heavy metals in organisms, the conditions under which they are assimilated by surface plants has not been clarified entirely and requires further study.

It was assumed that ten chemical elements are necessary for the normal development of higher plants: C, N, P, S, O, H, K, Mg, Ca, and Fe. Electropositive elements are received from the soil in the form of cations, and electronegative elements as simple and complex anions: Cl^-, NO_3^-, PO_4^{3-}, SO_4^{2-}, and others.

The list of chemical elements required by plants now has expanded considerably; this is particularly true of the metals Mn, Cu, Zn, Mo, and others. Certain of them, together with iron, participate in redox reactions in catalytic processes of assimilation and dissimilation (Fe, Mn, Mo), and others enter into enzymes and vitamins (Zn, Co). In addition, it has become clear that many precious and dispersed chemical elements in small quantities are stimulators of growth and development of surface plants, such as Ni, Cr, Pb, Ra, and others. They have a negative effect in large doses (Shkol'nik, [1950], Voinar [1953], Stiles [1950], and others).

Still unexplained is the biological function of heavy metals in plants which are concentrators of Mn, Ni, Zn, Se, and Mo, related to the natural enrichment of metals in rocks, ores, natural waters, etc. Reference is made to zinc flora (Thlaspi calaminare, and others), accumulating more than 10% zinc (in the ash), serpentinite flora (Alyssum bertolonii, and others), whose ash contains more than 10% nickel, and selenium and molybdenum vegetation.

Recent experience with concentrator plants shows how complex the interrelationships between surface vegetation and the "chemical" medium are; these do not fit into the ordinary concepts concerning the requirements of plants for a particular chemical element.

The presence of heavy metals in plants indicates their presence in the soil. However, there is no direct dependence between the content of chemical elements in available, that is, assimilable form, and their total content in soils.

This can be attributed to the fact that many minerals and compounds of silicon, titanium, iron, aluminum, manganese, and many other macro- and microelements are found in soils and underlying rocks in not easily available form: in fragments of silicate and alumosilicate rocks and in the form of not easily soluble minerals (rutile, zircon, pyrolusite, hematite, etc.), or enter into organomineral colloids.

When considering the problem of the presence of heavy metals in soils, which has a direct bearing on another problem — the assimilability of metals by surface plants, it must be taken into account: 1) that metals enter into the lattice of silicates and ore minerals; 2) that there is chemosorption on colloids (oxides and other not easily soluble compounds); 3) that there are exchange forms in organic and clayey colloids; and, 4) that there are water-soluble compounds. The content and ratio of these forms is dependent on bioclimatic weathering conditions, on the depth of destruction of the rocks, the soil-forming process, etc. We already have noted the significance of weathering conditions and soil formation on the migration of ore elements over the zone of oxidation. Mobile or stable forms of a particular ore element develop, depending on the character of the processes of secondary mineral formation and "salt formation." The possibility of absorption of metal ions by plants will be dependent on the ratio of these forms.

The example of manganese can serve as an extremely graphic illustration of the above. With respect to the forms of manganese in the soil, A. P. Vinogradov [1957] writes: "There are at least two forms of manganese in the soil: assimilable, easily mobile, and unassimilable, not mobile. The first form corresponds to compounds of Mn^{2+} and is found in soil solutions in the form of a carbonate or bicarbonate, sulfate, and other easily soluble salts in the acidic zone to pH = 6. When pH = 5.5, as is well known, Fe^{2+} begins to precipitate, and when pH = 8, it is followed by $Mn(OH)_2$, in accordance with the equation:

$$Mn(HCO_3)_2 + 2H_2O \rightleftarrows Mn(OH)_2 + 2H_2CO_3.$$

The hydroxide $Mn(OH)_2$ or $MnO \cdot nH_2O$ very rapidly is heated in the air and becomes a more highly oxidized form — manganite Mn^{3+}, which conventionally can be represented in the form $(OH)_3$ or $Mn_2O_3 \cdot nH_2O$. Further oxidation leads to the formation of hydrous $MnO_2 \cdot nH_2O$, and then to crystalline pyrolusite MnO_2." Consequently, depending on the redox conditions and the pH of the medium, manganese is found in soils in a form (Mn^{2+}) which is easily assimilable by plants, or in a completely inert form. As we already have noted, for each element the forms of the compounds have their specific characteristics in accordance with the geochemical properties of the metal.

The following factors exert a great influence on the rate of overturn of chemical elements in the biogenic cycle: the water regime of the soils, the pH of the medium, the oxidizing potential, and the presence of antagonist metals. The character of this influence has been studied by many authors: W. O. Robinson et al. [1935], E. I. Ratner [1950], M. Ya. Shkol'nik [1950], A. C. Hill et al. [1953], L. I. Painter et al. [1953]).

The number of ions of heavy metals available to plants is dependent on the presence of soluble compounds of metals in soils, chlorides, sulfates, bicarbonates, etc., and also on the presence of exchange forms of metals in soil colloids. Experience shows that the content of water-soluble forms of the majority of heavy metals in soils does not exceed 1% of the total content. However, the quantity of exchangeable forms, that is, completely assimilable forms, attains several tens of percent of the total content of metals. Many therefore assume that the principal sources of inorganic plant nutrition are the exchangeable forms of ions which are sorbed on organomineral soil colloids.

The assimilability of ions of heavy metals by plants is dependent on the ways in which they are bonded to colloids. Judging from the absorption energy of ions, expressed by Mitchell [1957] in the form of the series

$$Cu, > Pb > Ni > Co > Zn > Ca > Mg,$$

the heavy metals form more stable bonds than ordinary exchangeable bases: calcium, magnesium, and others. The reason for this is the ability of the ions of metals to form complex compounds with organic substances, forming an energy series close to the preceding one:

$$Pb > Cu > Ni > Co > Zn > Mn > Mg > Ca$$

(Hasler [1943]), and, in addition, the ability of heavy metals, provided the pH is suitable, to form more stable compounds with soil colloids.

In experiments with tagged cobalt (Co_{60}), Banerjee et al. [1953] demonstrated that a considerable part of the cobalt sorbed on soil colloids is not extracted by ammonium acetate when the pH is from 5 to 7. The remaining stably sorbed part of the cobalt can be separated only when pH = 3, for example, using HCl.

Similarly, the studies of Antipov-Karataev [1947], Kabata [1955], Lucas [1948], and Peech[1941], have established that there is a more stable bonding of nickel, copper, and zinc with soil colloids than with exchangeable bases. The forms of copper ions sorbed by soil colloids are Cu^{2+} and $CuOH^+$.

In contrast to nickel, copper, and zinc, cobalt is capable of forming other kinds of ions because of its ability to change into a trivalent state. This requires appropriate redox conditions, the absence of Fe^{2+} and Mn^{2+} ions, etc. The forming hydroxides can be sorbed on soil colloids in the form of $Co(OH)_2^+$ ions. The poorly soluble forms of cobalt explain its poor assimilability by plants in calcareous soils and during the calcification of soils.

However, this does not preclude the possibility of the absorption of cobalt and other heavy metals present in not easily available form, in the form of minerals and other stable chemical compounds (oxides, hydroxides, carbonates). In this case, as will be mentioned below, plants use the chemical precipitates of the root (H_2O, CO_2, organic acids), acting upon the substrate as ordinary reagents.

Mobile and less-mobile assimilable forms of metals are studied by means of specially developed methods for their extraction by "soft" and "hard" solvents — neutral salts or acids. In addition, in order to clarify the mechanism of absorption and the character of the compounds participating in exchange reactions, it now is the practice to use tagged atoms, such as Co_{60}, P_{32}, and others. In order to determine the percentage of metals in an exchangeable state in soil colloids, it is customary to use a solution of ammonium acetate with a pH = 7 (Mitchell [1957]), a 1 N solution of $NaNO_3$ (Malyuga, [1956]) and other neutral solvents. In addition, it is assumed that acidic solvents more precisely characterize the content of assimilable forms, such as a 1 N solution of HCl (Peive et al., 1953), a 2.5% solution of acetic acid (Mitchell, [1957]), and others.

Specialists recently have begun to use complex mixtures of organic acids and their salts — citric, acetic, and oxalic — for determination of assimilable forms. These mixtures give the solution an acidity close to that which is observed near the root hair (pH = 3). A persistent shaking of the soil with such a mixture makes it possible to extract from 5 to 20% copper, nickel, cobalt, zinc, and molybdenum. It has been established that the acidity of a solvent is the principal agent in the extraction of metals. In the extraction of molybdenum by the salts of organic acids the process is influenced by the formation by the MoO_4^{2-} ion of a complex compound from oxalic, citric, and other acids.

In order to determine the percent of water-soluble and exchangeable forms of cobalt, nickel, and copper (mobile forms) in the general soil balance, we studied soil samples of a gray forest clayey loam soil sampled over a copper-nickel-cobalt deposit in the Tuvinskaya ASSR. For this purpose the soil samples were processed with neutral and weakly acidic solvents: distilled water, 1 N $NaNO_3$ and 1% HCl.

The technique of extracting metals is as follows: a 10-g weighed soil sample was moistened by 50 ml of one of the above-mentioned solvents. After an hour of standing, during the following hour the sample was shaken in an apparatus and then filtered. The resulting solution was analyzed for its content of cobalt, nickel, and copper. The determined quantities were expressed in percent of the weighed soil sample and the total content of metals in the soil. Table 18 gives the results of these investigations.

The data in Table 18 show that the water fraction constitutes a rather small part of the total content of cobalt, nickel, and copper in the soil: for cobalt, $1/70$; for nickel, $1/240$; and for copper, $1/110$. Thus, cobalt is the most mobile and nickel less so, as also indicated by the Ni:Co ratio — 0.4.

The content of water-soluble cobalt, nickel, and copper by horizons of the soil profile is approximately identical. Nickel and cobalt are extracted best with HCl from the humus horizon (A) and the illuvial horizon (B_2). Copper passes best into an HCl solution from the B_2 carbonate horizon, and especially from the C horizon (at a depth of 1 m).

The sum of the H_2O and HCl fractions does not give the total cobalt and nickel content in the soil even approximately (on the average from 10 to 20%). In the case of copper, the extraction attains 75%, although in the humus horizon it is considerably lower. These facts indicate the presence in the soil of compounds which are insoluble in diluted HCl — oxides, organic compounds of metals (humates), etc.

In evaluating the distribution of cobalt, nickel, and copper on the basis of the properties of these elements, it can be postulated that the relative predominance of copper in HCl extracts is associated with the presence in the illuvial horizon of the soil of dispersed carbonates of the malachite type, which is entirely possible if the pH is greater

TABLE 18. Mobile Forms of Cobalt, Nickel, and Copper (Northern Sector of Deposit. Soil Profile Along Linear Profile 561)

Solvent	Soil horizon and depth, cm	Content, %			Ratio	
		Co	Ni	Cu	Ni : Co	Cu : Co
H$_2$O bidistillate	A 0—5	$6 \cdot 10^{-5}$	$3.1 \cdot 10^{-5}$	$1.6 \cdot 10^{-4}$	0.5	2.7
	B$_1$ 30—35	$3.5 \cdot 10^{-5}$	$2.2 \cdot 10^{-5}$	$2.1 \cdot 10^{-4}$	0.6	6
	B$_2$ 50—55	$1.1 \cdot 10^{-4}$	$3.2 \cdot 10^{-5}$	$1.5 \cdot 10^{-4}$	0.3	1.4
	C 100—105	$1 \cdot 10^{-4}$	$2.7 \cdot 10^{-5}$	$1 \cdot 10^{-4}$	0.3	1
	D 200—205	$9.5 \cdot 10^{-5}$	$4.6 \cdot 10^{-5}$	$1.8 \cdot 10^{-4}$	0.5	1.9
	Mean	$8 \cdot 10^{-5}$	$3.2 \cdot 10^{-5}$	$1.6 \cdot 10^{-4}$	0.4	2
1% N HCl	A 0—5·	$1.2 \cdot 10^{-3}$	$1.6 \cdot 10^{-3}$	$2.5 \cdot 10^{-3}$	1.3	2
	B$_1$ 30—35	$4 \cdot 10^{-4}$	$2.3 \cdot 10^{-4}$	$7 \cdot 10^{-3}$	0.6	17.5
	B$_2$ 50—55	$1.6 \cdot 10^{-3}$	$2.2 \cdot 10^{-3}$	$6 \cdot 10^{-3}$	1.4	4
	C 100—105	$3.1 \cdot 10^{-4}$	$6.2 \cdot 10^{-4}$	$1.7 \cdot 10^{-2}$	2	55
	D 200—205	$3.8 \cdot 10^{-4}$	$2 \cdot 10^{-4}$	$2.5 \cdot 10^{-3}$	0.5	6.5
	Mean	$7.8 \cdot 10^{-4}$	$9.7 \cdot 10^{-4}$	$7 \cdot 10^{-3}$	1.2	9
1% N NaNO$_3$	A 0—5	$4.5 \cdot 10^{-5}$	$2.6 \cdot 10^{-5}$	$1.9 \cdot 10^{-4}$	0.6	4.2
Total soil content	A 0—5	$4.1 \cdot 10^{-3}$	$7 \cdot 10^{-3}$	$1.2 \cdot 10^{-2}$	1.7	3
	B$_1$ 30—35	$3 \cdot 10^{-3}$	$3 \cdot 10^{-3}$	$1 \cdot 10^{-2}$	1	3.3
	B$_2$ 50—55	$6 \cdot 10^{-3}$	$8 \cdot 10^{-3}$	$1 \cdot 10^{-2}$	1.3	1.7
	C 100—105	$6 \cdot 10^{-3}$	$6 \cdot 10^{-3}$	$2 \cdot 10^{-2}$	1	3.3
	D 200—205	$8 \cdot 10^{-3}$	$1.5 \cdot 10^{-2}$	$4 \cdot 10^{-2}$	2	5
	Mean	$5.4 \cdot 10^{-3}$	$8 \cdot 10^{-3}$	$1.8 \cdot 10^{-2}$	1.5	3.3

than 7. In the case of cobalt, this form is less probable, due to the ability of cobalt to be oxidized to trivalence when the pH reaches a specific value (above 6.8). The forming hydroxides are sorbed on soil colloids or are deposited in the form of films and incrustations, together with manganese and iron. In either case the cobalt becomes less mobile than nickel and copper. Nickel apparently occupies an intermediate position between cobalt and copper. It follows from the data in Table 18 that nickel, like copper, is capable of forming carbonates which also are destroyed easily by a weak acid, so that both metals pass into solution. Only in this way is it possible to explain the increase of the Ni : Co ratio in the HCl extract in comparison with the H$_2$O extract (from 0.3 to 1-2%). It is not impossible that in the case of both nickel and cobalt there is a formation of oxides and hydroxides, in part sharing the fate of manganese wads. In this case the nickel is bonded to the clayey soil substrate and its hypergene migration is similar to that of cobalt.

If we now turn to the upper A soil horizon, we will see a noncorrespondence of the Cu : Co ratios in the HCl extract and in the soil. The data in Table 18 show that copper is extracted from the humus horizon in lesser quantities than from the lower-lying carbonate horizons. Taking into account the total absence of carbonates in the A horizon, established on the basis of the pH values (6.3) and from the reaction between carbonates and HCl, it can be concluded that the principal form in which copper and other heavy metals are found in the humus horizon is in compounds with organic substances (humates, etc.). For example, the humates of cobalt, nickel, and copper pass into an HCl extract in appreciable quantities and are rather stable in solution. Judging from the different reaction to rubeanic acid, the humates of cobalt and nickel are considerably more stable than the corresponding compounds of copper. For example, if rubeanic acid and ammonia are added to a solution of cobalt, nickel, and copper humates until a weakly alkaline solution is obtained, even after a prolonged period of standing a considerable part of the nickel and cobalt (up to 80%) remains in solution, whereas the copper is separated out entirely in the form of rubeanates. As is well known, the citric acid which is added to hold Fe^{2+}, Mn^{2+}, Pb^{2+}, etc. in solution is no obstacle to the precipitation of the rubeanates of cobalt, nickel, or copper, which characterizes the humates of heavy metals as extremely stable chemical compounds.

The sorbed ions Co^{2+}, Ni^{2+}, and Cu^{2+} are not displaced from the soil absorbing complex by neutral solvents ($HNaNO_3$ and others). The latter indicates that we are dealing with processes of chemosorption on organic colloids, resulting in the appearance of forms of bonds characterized by a high stability in exchange reactions in soils.

In the case of the lower horizons of the soil (pH > 7) it is not impossible that cobalt and nickel enter into the lattice of silicates of variable composition (dispersed minerals of the montmorillonite type), in which they replace Mg^{2+} and Fe^{2+}.

It follows from the above data that the content of mobile forms of ore elements is dissimilar and is dependent on the chemical and physicochemical properties of the metal.

In exactly the same way, the pH of the soil influences the content of mobile forms, as does the pH of the solvent used. According to data published by R. L. Mitchell [1957], the quantity of exchangeable cobalt and nickel extracted by 2.5% acetic acid from the upper soil horizon exceeds by a factor of 10 the values obtained as a result of extraction with 1 N ammonium acetate (pH ~ 7). This difference became less in the lower horizons.

The content of any particular element in a mobile form does not always ensure that it will be available to plants, since the entry of ions into plants is dependent on many factors, especially on soil conditions (Peive and Ivanova [1956], Vlasyuk [1956], and others).

According to the data published by D. N. Pryanishnikov [1952], D. A. Sabinin [1955], A. V. Peterburgskii [1944], and many others, the most important factor governing the entry of ions into plants is the pH — the reaction of the soil medium. It has been established that the most favorable medium for the assimilation by plants of calcium, magnesium, and probably other bivalent chemical elements is a pH of about 7. When the pH < 5 the absorption of calcium by plants decreases sharply, which is associated with the antagonistic influence of ions of hydrogen, aluminum, and manganese, always present in acidic soils (podzols).

It is important to note that the absorption of molybdenum by plants, like the absorption of calcium, decreases with soil acidity. The assimilation of chemical elements is facilitated considerably by soil organisms, among which there are numerous fungi, algae, actinomycetes, and various kinds of fauna and microfauna.

The most active helpers of plants are fungi, molds, and bacteria, which facilitate the mineralization of dead organic residue of surface plants (leaves and stems, roots), and also the synthesis of nitrogen. It is therefore not without reason that the soils best populated by organisms are considered the best supplied with nutrients.

2. Mechanism of Absorption of Ions of Metals by Plants

We already have discussed the problem of the mobility of chemical elements in soils, which is related to the possibility of absorption of the ions of metals by plant roots.

The absorption of ions from the soil solution was regarded for a long time as the only possible means for root nutrition of plants. The rate of extraction of salts therefore was considered on the basis of the conditions for transpiration of solutions from the soil. The observations of E. I. Ratner [1944] and others revealed that the absorption of salts from the soil is not proportional to the quantity of water entering plants. The impossibility of such proportionality is demonstrated by the presence of reverse motion of ions in surface plants and their elimination through the roots, such as ions of Ca^{2+}, PO_4^{3-}, SO_4^{2-}, HCO_3^{-}, and others, as well as the ability of plants to extract ions from the solid phase of the soil, bypassing the soil solution, the so-called contact method (Ratner [1938], Jenny [1934], Peterburgskii [1944]). By This means the plant is capable of using not only the gravitational and capillary water of the soil, but also film and colloidal water, in the presence of which it is still possible for the processes of mineral nutrition of surface plants to take place.

Plants are capable of an independent effect on the substrate of soil colloids by creating around the rootlets spaces with a high concentration of hydrogen ions. The nature of this phenomenon has not yet been explained fully.

As already mentioned, around the absorbing root hairs is formed a sphere with an increased pressure of CO_2, corresponding to a solution with pH = 3-4. As a result, in the zones near the roots the ions of heavy metals, such as cobalt ions, can be exchanged for hydrogen in accordance with the following scheme:

$$2H_2CO_3 \rightleftarrows 2H^+ + 2HCO_3^-.$$

Absorbing	$+ Co$		Absorbing	$- H$
complex	$+ Co + 2H^+ \rightleftarrows 2HCO_3^-$		complex	$- H$
	$+ Co$			$+ Co$ $^+$
				$+ Co$

$$+ Co\,(HCO_3)_2.$$

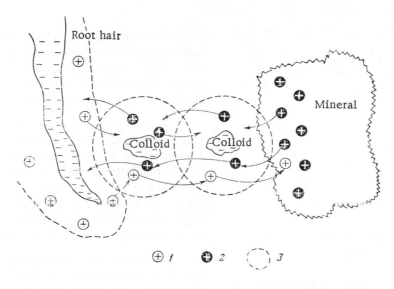

Fig. 28. Diagram of root absorption of cations. 1) H ions;
2) metal ions; 3) sphere of interaction of ions $H^+ \rightleftharpoons Me^+$.

The forming bicarbonates of cobalt (Ni, Cu, and others) are easily caught up by the root hairs of plants and by means of a complex process of ion exchange in the root plasma enter into the exchange cycle of the plant (Fig. 28).

Depending on the physiological function, the metal enters into the plant tissue or is fixed by organic molecules (proteins, vitamins, enzymes). If the plant does not use all the elements entering together with the basic nutrients, it frees itself of them, discarding them into protective and structural tissues, or, finally, into organs and tissues which are being renewed or are dying (leaves, rootlets). Under all conditions there is a certain accumulation of heavy metals in the organic residue of the soil. With the decomposition of the stems, leaves, and dead roots of the plant, the heavy metals, together with the most stable organic compounds, remain in the humus layer of the soil. Observations show that not all metals are retained by the humus to an identical degree. Those which are retained to the highest degree are those used by soil microorganisms, such as iron, manganese, cobalt, copper, zinc, and others.

We will now briefly discuss an example of the study of humus matter which we removed from a dark chestnut soil of a nickel deposit in the Kimpersiskii ore region of Aktyubinskaya Oblast.

After the removal of exchangeable forms of Na, Ca^{2+}, Mg^{2+}, Fe^{2+}, Ni^{2+}, and others by means of 2% HCl, the humus matter was extracted from the soil by 2% sodium acetate at 50°C. Several milliliters of 2% HCl were added to the completely transparent dark brown solution which had been obtained by centrifuging. A dark brown precipitate of humic acids was obtained which was washed carefully with water and dried in a vacuum. The conditions under which the precipitation with the acid was carried out completely excluded the presence of hydroxides (Fe, Al) and carbonates (Ca, Mg). A weighed sample of dry matter was burned and the ash then weighed. There was found to be a considerable ash content — 80.5% of the weighed sample. A quantitative analysis of the ash revealed 12% Si, 10% Ca, 14% Fe, about 4% K + Na, and tenths and hundredths of a percent of Cu and Co. There was a surprising total absence of Ni, although the soil content was about 0.5%. A recalculation of elementary Si, Ca, Fe, and Na into oxides and carbonates (Ca) precisely indicated the weight of the ash, that is, 80.5% of the weighed sample of organic matter. Such a high ash content indicates, in the author's opinion, that there is atomic bonding of the determined elements with carbon and other elements. A further study of the complexes, their composition, and structure is required before drawing final conclusions as to the forms of the bonding of the atoms of metals in the studied organic complex.

3. Selective and Concentrating Capacity of Plants

Data from chemical analyses of the ash of different animals and plants show that the mineral composition is an important (specific or generic) criterion of the organism.

In the process of the life activity of an organism, surface plants, as an example, must wage a struggle for specific elements needed in nutrition, which cannot be satisfied by others. In order to maintain equilibrium in the combination of the necessary components of mineral nutrition, the plants use their capacity of selective absorption of anions and cations.

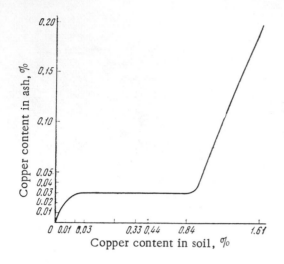

Fig. 29. Dependence between copper content in soil and in the ash of stock (according to Tkalich [1959]).

The bioclimatic affinity of soils and plants greatly facilitates the selective extraction by plants of the nutrients which they require because, as we will see below, the soils in their composition contain mineral compounds introduced by preceding generations of the same plants.

The selective capacity of plants has not been thoroughly explained scientifically. S. Thiessen et al. [1954] relate the phenomenon of selective extraction of the ions of metals to the oxygen respiration of the roots. However, the active assimilation by the plant of anions (HCO_3^-, NO_3^-, SO_4^{2-}) suggested in this theory and the passive implication of cations not only does not explain the selective absorption of individual cations, but quite on the contrary, complicates its explanation.

The use of radioactive isotopes for study of the mechanism of selective absorption of ions by plants has revealed that in addition to the processes of diffusion, ion exchange, and other physicochemical processes, a factor of considerable importance in this process is the phenomenon of "active metabolism" in the living cell of the root with the participation of the molecules of carriers of the ferment type, and others (Epshtein and Henricks [1956]). The ions entering into the cell system are selectively intercepted by carrier-bodies and are directed into the exchange cycle of the plant. Other ions, not entering into contact with the carriers, are located temporarily in the sphere of influence of the root or return to the soil.

Under "ordinary" conditions in the life of a plant, it is easy to regulate the processes of absorption and elimination of anions and cations, since the soil substrate favors the normal process of assimilation and dissimilation. With a change in ecological conditions — temperature, moisture, pH of the soil, or combinations of mobile ions in the soil absorbing complex — the plants experience the effect of competing ions, which are capable of causing a sharp change in the conditions for the absorption of metal ions. In this competition, the advantage is held by ions present in excess, in a mobile state. The behavior of plants in this case is reflected well by a diagram showing, for example, a dependence of the concentration of copper in Matthiola incana on its content in the soil (Fig. 29).

The above-cited case shows that a plant cannot withstand the entry of high, frequently undesirable, quantities of the ions of metals, responding to this process with a corresponding reaction (chlorosis, delayed growth), including possible death of the plant. These phenomena often are observed over ore deposits, especially on old mine workings and on spoil banks. As is well known, mutations of vegetation under the influence of an excess of elements is used in exploration for different metals.

However, as A. P. Vinogradov has written [1952], "In the course of a long time species of organisms adapt to a specific level of the content of chemical elements in the environment, to the character of their compounds, to their forms of accumulation, etc." A comparative study of the soils and plants sampled in the climatic zones of the Soviet Union, and many other data, show that plants do not reflect precisely the composition of the soil substrate on which they grow. The greater part of the mass of the plant ash consists of those elements which under the conditions prevailing in the biosphere form easily mobile compounds in large quantity and provide for the life functions characteristic of a particular zone of surface vegetation (Vinogradov [1945]).

A simple comparison of the content of individual chemical elements in soils and plants shows that some are concentrated more in soil and others more in plant ash. The first group includes elements with low mobility — Al, Si, Ti, Fe, Zn, Sn — forming minerals which are not easily soluble; the second group includes active migrants, among which there are one alkaline and alkaline-earth elements and many bivalent metals: Li, Be, B, P, S, K, Mn, Zn, Se, Mo, Ra, and others. In addition, many elements occupy an intermediate position. These include elements which form stable compounds with humus: V, Cr, Co, Cu, and others.

When comparing the mean contents of chemical elements in rocks and in plant ash, there is found to be an extremely important regularity — the relative accumulation of mobile (biogenic) elements in surface plants. As a graphic illustration of this regularity we have compared the mean content of chemical elements in plants* (see Table 5) with

---

*In this comparison the content of elements in the ash was calculated in dry weight.

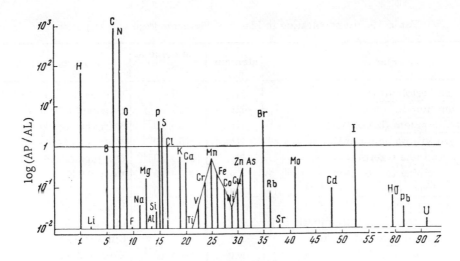

Fig. 30. Abundance ratio of chemical elements in plants.

their mean content in rocks (abundance) using the formula AP/AL = A; where AP is the mean content of the element in plants, AL is the lithosphere, and A is the abundance, expressed logarithmically.

The derived numerical values (logarithms of the ratios) have been used for the construction of appropriate diagrams, as shown in Fig. 30. The logarithms of the ratios (AP/AL) have been plotted along the y axis and the sequence numbers of the chemical elements have been plotted along the x axis.

Figure 30 shows that many "biogenic" elements – P, S, Br, I – have coefficients of the ratios greater than unity and lie above the separating line; others, including B, Mg, K, Ca, Mn, Fe, Cu, Zn, Ag, and Mo – are close to the dividing line, which indicates a biogenic function in organisms in common with the first-named elements. Elements (Pb, Sr, Hg, and others) with a low value of the coefficient of the ratio are potential "poisons." These apparently also include Cr and Ni which, according to data published by Robinson et al. [1947] and Hill et al. [1953], when present in high concentrations are poisonous to surface plants.

Experience shows that elements with a high coefficient of the ratio are accumulated in plants over ore deposits (Mn, Mo, Zn, Cu) to a higher degree; on the other hand, metals with a low coefficient are present in plants in relatively smaller quantities.

Thus, the coefficients of the ratios make it possible to foresee the behavior of individual elements in plants over deposits, which is of considerable importance in determining the effectiveness of biogeochemical exploration for any particular metal.

With respect to the problem of the concentration of chemical elements by plants, A. P. Vinogradov distinguishes selective (specific, generic) and group concentration of chemical elements. Selective concentration has been discussed in considerable detail at the beginning of this study. The group concentration involves all the vegetation of a particular geochemical region. All the chemical elements, with the exception of a few which are found in high quantities in rocks and ores are accumulated to one degree or another by plants.

The accumulation of chemical elements in plants is unquestionably associated with a general high level in soils. Conformity to this regularity also has made it possible to use soils and plants simultaneously as indicators of ore deposits. However, as pointed out by A. P. Vinogradov, the value of the method is not identical for different elements, For example, for Si, Al, Na, Ca, Mg, and other elements, the method at this time is of little value; for elements such as Zr, Ti, and Th, which have little mobility, it is completely inapplicable; and for other elements, such as Ga, Ge, Tl, In, (RE), Nb, Ta, and others, it has been studied very little.

The biogeochemical method now has been tried out for a whole series of chemical elements: B, Cr, Mn, Fe, Co, Ni, Cu, Zn, Se, Nb, Mo, Ag, Sn, Au, Hg, Pb, Ra, U, and others. In the determination of the sensitivity of the method, it is necessary to distinguish elements which are common in plants: Cr, Fe, Mn, Co, Ni, Cu, Zn, Mo, and those which are rarer: Ag, Au, Pb, Hg, U, and others. As has been shown by means of diagrams of the logarithms of the ratios (Fig. 30), the level of elements of the first and second groups in plants is dissimilar; however, the sensitivity

Table 19. Concentration in Plants of Elements from Ore Deposits

Plant	Element	Ash content, %	Author, year
Alyssum bertolonii (L.)	Ni	10	Minguzzi et al. [1948]
Alyssum murale	Ni	>10	Doksopulo [1961]
Pulsatilla patens (L.) Mill.	Ni	$3 \cdot 10^{-2}$	Storozheva [1954]
Linosyris villosa Benth et Hook	Ni	$6 \cdot 10^{-2}$	Malyuga [1950]
Alnus glutinosa Gaerth (leaves)	Ni	$2.3 \cdot 10^{-2}$	Malyuga (1946)
Viscaria alpina (L.) G. Don	Cu	$5 \cdot 10^{-2}$	Vogt (1949)
Cicuta virrosa (L.)	Cu	$1 \cdot 10^{-2}$	Malyuga (1946)
Melandrium dioicum (L.)	Cu	$5 \cdot 10^{-2}$	Vogt (1949)
Viola lutea Huds var. Calaminaria Lej	Zn	>1	Linstow [1929]
Thlaspi calaminare Lej et Cur	Zn	>1	Linstow [1929]
Trifolium pratense (L.)	Mo	$>1 \cdot 10^{-1}$	Vinogradova*
Sanguisorba officinalis (L.)	Mo	$1 \cdot 10^{-1}$	Vinogradova*
Astragalus declinatus (roots)	Mo	$>1 \cdot 10^{-1}$	Malyuga et al. [1958]
Juniperus monosperma	U	$1 \cdot 10^{-2}$	Cannon [1952]
Pinus edulis (L.)	U	$8.3 \cdot 10^{-3}$	Cannon [1952]
Polygonum hydropiper (Z.)	U	$2 \cdot 10^{-3}$	Malyuga [1952]
Equisetum palustre (L.)	Au	$6.1 \cdot 10^{-2}$	Babichka [1954]
Juncus Gerardi Hois (roots)	U	$2 \cdot 10^{-2}$	Malyuga [1961]

*These data are being published for the first time.

of the method is adequate in both cases. The relatively low biogeochemical background of Au, Hg, and U in soils and plants makes it possible to detect anomalies even when there is a relatively low accumulation of these elements over ore deposits. For example, the normal content of uranium in soils and in the ash of plants is $5 \cdot 10^{-5}$%, that is, much lower than the abundance in igneous rocks. Therefore, even the most insignificant increase of uranium in soils and plants over ores (from $1 \cdot 10^{-4}$ to $1 \cdot 10^{-3}$%) already can be detected clearly on the general low background of uranium and can be used as an indicator in exploration work.

We already have noted the importance of plants in exploration work, as concentrators of ore elements; a classical example is galmei flora. Plants have now been found which are concentrators of nickel, copper, molybdenum, and other elements. A list of certain of these plants and their content of ore elements is given in Table 19.

The data in Table 19 show a considerable content of rare and dispersed chemical elements in the ash of plants, sometimes measured in several percents. Finding plants which are concentrators makes it possible to improve present-day field techniques. By employing sensitive micromethods for the determination of nickel, cobalt, lead, molybdenum, uranium, and radium in concentrator plants (drop color reactions, autoradiography, plant histochemistry), it will be possible to make a closer evaluation of the relative content of microelements in plants (soils) directly in the field. By plotting the derived values on a map it will be possible to evaluate the resulting data in the field and appropriately change the field work plan.

4. Influence of Ecological, Seasonal, and Age Phenomena on the Accumulation of Metals by Plants

Among the ecological factors influencing the accumulation of ore elements in surface plants are soil-geological and climatic conditions: the composition of the soils and underlying rocks, the temperature and moisture of the surrounding medium, etc.

Among the soil-geological conditions for the accumulation of ore elements in plants are also the character of the secondary dispersion haloes — the depth of the ore body, the conditions for penetration by plant roots, and the rocks covering the ore.

Under specific bioclimatic conditions (tundra, forest, steppe zone, etc.), the permeability of rocks could be characterized by the depth of penetration of plant root systems.

TABLE 20. Depth of Root Systems in Different Zones
(according to Malyanov [1937], Viktorov [1960], Rateenko [1952], Dadykin [1952], and others)

Zone	Plant	Depth of roots, cm	Comments
Tundra	Dwarf birch Betula nana L.	28	Permafrost at a depth of 50 cm
	Larch Larix sibirica Ledb.	40	The same, at a depth of 130 cm
	Wood reed Calamagrostis Langsdorfii Trin	60	The same, at a depth of 60 cm
	Sedge Carex globularis L.	104	The same, at a depth of 57 cm
	Horse tail Equisetum silvaticum L.	150	The same, at a depth of 60 cm
Forest podzol	Birch Betula verrucosa	350	Podzol clayey loam soil
	Fir Picea excelsa Link	200	Moskovskaya Oblast
	Pine Pinus silvestris L.	250	Age of trees from 30 to 90 years
	Aspen Populus alba L.	300	
Forest-steppe and steppe	Birch Betula verrucosa	402	Gray, forest, sandy soil
	Pine Pinus silvestris L.	380	Buzulukskii pinewood
	Elder Sambucus sp.	350	Heavy clayey loam
	Sow thistle Sonchus arvensis L.	200	Calcareous chernozem, and others
	Quack grass Agropyrom repens L.	200	Southwestern Ural foothills
	Cornbind convolvulus arvensis L.	180	
	Clover Trifolium repens	200	
Desert and semidesert	Haloxylon Haloxylon aphyllum	1000	Deserts and semideserts of Central Asia
	Tamarisk Tamarix ramosissima	500	The same
	Camel's thorn Alhagi pseudoalhagi	1500	The same
	Itsechek Anabasis aphylla	500	Southeastern Armenia
	Golden milk vetch Astragalus aureus	1000	The same

The normal activity of any species of plant is ensured by adequate permeability and aeration of the soil, optimum moisture conditions, and the presence of nutrients in the soil. Disruption of these conditions results in excessive activity of the roots. This activity is dictated by the need for deepening the root system in the case of inadequacy of moisture in the soil, a broader extension of the root system in the soil volume in the case of inadequate soil nutrients, or, finally, intensified transpiration in moist and warm climates. In all cases the plant is specialized in the direction of increase in the function of absorption of chemical elements, and therefore in the direction of an increase in the effectiveness of the biogeochemical exploration method.

We will now discuss the problem of the significance of root systems in the mineral sustenance of plants. "At the present time the roots of woody plants have acquired great significance not only as organs of absorption and movement of water and nutrients, but also as the most important organs in which are concentrated the specific reactions of formation and exchange of substances, extraordinarily important for the life activity of plants" (A. I. Akhromeiko, from the foreword of the book by I. N. Rateenko [1952]).

The root systems of trees, bushes, and grassy plants are specific zonal organs of plants which ensure their sustenance under specific conditions of the medium. The penetration of roots in depth, it is found, facilitates the effective depth of the biogeochemical method. For this reason the method is zonal in the sense that its primary applicability is in specific bioclimatic zones.

The study of root systems, reported in hundreds of studies, shows that individual species of plants have different abilities to send their roots deep into the ground. In the wooded steppe zone the woody species with the deepest root system are: oak, 5.6 m (at an age of 47 years); birch and aspen, 3-3.5 m (at an age of 90 years); the Siberian pea tree and elder, 4 m; and pine in a mixed forest, 3-3.5 m (Rateenko [1952]). The depth of the root systems of grassy vegetation of moderately moist steppes does not exceed 1.5-2 m. In many cases the roots of certain plants penetrate to a depth of 2.5-3 m in clayey soil in mole hills and fractures.

In the case of regions with a constant moisture deficit, e.g., deserts and semideserts, many plants are known which have a root system from 5.5 to 15 m or more in length, such as camel's thorn, black haloxylon, and others (Viktorov [1960], Iordanskaya [1960]). Root systems of nearly equal depth are observed in our country in the milk vetch in the dry mountainous regions of Transcaucasia (Armenian SSR). In taiga regions, where there is no permafrost, woody and shrubby vegetation has a root system from 1.5 to 3 m in length.

An area of the greatest interest is the permafrost zone which spreads over an enormous area in the eastern and northern regions of the Soviet Union. As a result of the work of V. P. Dadykin [1952], it is known that the penetration of the root systems of individual plants is not limited to the active layer of the soil, but also extends into the permafrost. Most trees (warty birch, dwarf birch, Siberian cedar, etc.) have roots penetrating as deep as 50 cm, with an extensive development along a surface at a depth of 5 m or more. Wood reed and rose penetrate deeper, sending roots deeper than the permafrost surface and attain depths of 60 cm or more. Sedge, cloudberry, and horsetail possess the ability to penetrate into the permafrost to a depth of 100-150 cm from the surface when the upper limit of the permafrost is at a depth of 50-60 cm.

Table 20 shows the dependence of the depth of the root systems of plants on physicogeographic and climatic conditions. The data cited show a decrease in the depth of root systems of zonal vegetation in a latitudinal direction from the Central Asiatic deserts and semideserts to the tundra zone. Consequently, the effective depth, i.e., the effective use of the biogeochemical survey method based on plant sampling, obviously will decrease with an increase in latitude. However, experience shows that the effective depth of the biogeochemical method is not limited strictly by the depth of penetration of plant roots in the direction of ore and almost always exceeds the latter. Additional factors increasing the effective depth of the method are the capillary rise of ground water, the seasonal change of the ground water table and topographic conditions, making it possible for the root systems of plants to come into contact with fissue and other tectonic waters which in turn are in contact with ores at a greater depth, from 30 to 60 m or more.

Among the soil-geological factors involved in the accumulation of metals by plants is the distribution of metal ions in the dissolved and sorbed phases, the concentration of salts, and the character of metal ions. For example, it is known that the absorption of ions occurs most actively from weak solutions. Bivalent manganese and iron are assimilated better than trivalent ions. On the other hand, it is easy for plants to assimilate metals forming complex anions — e.g., chromium and molybdenum — in higher degrees of oxidation. At the same time, as already mentioned, the most important factor is the pH of the medium.

In this connection one should note the influence of the pH on the capacity of the root for cation exchange (Sabinin [1955]), and the influence of soil moisture and temperature, and the temperature and humidity of the surrounding air, on the assimilability of metal ions by plants. A thorough study has been made of the phenomenon of the seasonal change of the content of ash elements, especially in the organs of growth — leeves, needles, and young shoots.

It has been established through the work of the Biogeochemical Laboratory of the Academy of Sciences of the USSR (Malyuga [1939, 1946]) that, toward autumn, the content of nickel, cobalt, and copper in the leaves of trees increases by a factor of 2-3 in comparison with the content in the spring. These data have been confirmed by tens of new observations.

According to data collected by V. S. Chebaevskaya [1960], the content of the microelements Co, Ni, Cu, and others in plants increases toward the time of the appearance of the reproductive organs. The distribution of individual elements by phases of growth differs. Mn, Fe, and Co appear in the early phase and Cu, Ni, and others in later phases. Data are available on the accumulation of other microelements during the blossoming period. Most authors conclude that the content of heavy metals in the leaves (needles) of trees increases rapidly toward the second half of the growing season and more slowly before defoliation. Summer, autumn, and winter (needles) vegetation samples, as well as the dry stems of grassy vegetation which have experienced winter conditions are equally suitable for use in a biogeochemical survey.

Fear that dry stems and leaves which have experienced winter conditions have lost metals obviously is without basis. Analyses of the stems of chicory and St. Johnswort which have experienced winter conditions reveal that there is a full retention of the copper and molybdenum, as indicated by the data in Table 21.

In a number of cases the data in Table 21 show a high content of copper in the ash of plants from the preceding year which have experienced winter field conditions, attaining 1%. The increase in comparison with plants freshly harvested in August varies from 1 to 7 times. Approximately the same situation is observed in the distribution of

TABLE 21. Molybdenum and Copper Content in the Ash of Fresh Plants and Those of the Preceding Season (in %) *

Sample No.	Plant	In fresh plants		In plants of preceding season	
		Mo	Cu	Mo	Cu
202	Chicory Cichorium intybus L.	0.0037	0.043	0.0400	0.075
106	The same	0.0040	0.030	0.0138	0.033
108	The same	0.0033	0.017	0.0190	0.032
325	Variegated figwort Scrophularia variegata M. B.	0.0075	0.180	0.0080	1.01
332	St. Johnswort Hypericum perforatum L.	0.009	0.025	0.130	0.180
340	The same	0.079	0.0127	—	—
384	The same	0.0085	0.0430	—	—

* Kadzharan, 1958. Our data.

molybdenum. The reason for the increase in the copper and molybdenum content in plants which have experienced winter conditions has not been explained. A comparison of the data shown in Table 21 shows the following noncorrespondence in the content of copper and molybdenum: the higher the copper content, the lower the molybdenum content, and vice versa. An attempt to attribute the increase of the metal content in plants from the preceding season to a decrease in ash content due to the leaching of the mobile chemical elements K, Na, Ca, and P was unsuccessful, since the ash content of fresh plants and those from the preceding season is approximately identical.

Thus, the data available in the literature on the influence of rain on the leaching of heavy metals from leaves and stems (Mn, Ti, Cu, and Fe) are not confirmed. Some decrease in the content of iron after heavy rainfall in potato leaves obviously can be attributed to the washing of contaminations from the surface of the leaves, always more enriched with iron than the plant itself.

Differing distributions of metals in the organs and tissues of plants also has been noted. Available data show that the maximum content of metals is in the growing parts of plants: in the leaves and branches. There is an intermediate content in the roots and bark, and a minimum content in the wood. Concentrator plants accumulate individual metals in the leaves and stems (Ni, Zn, Mn), in the roots (Mo, U, Pb), in the bark, and very rarely in the wood.

In a survey much care is given to the sampling of plants in order to obtain comparable results. Our investigations in the copper-molybdenum deposits in Armenia and in the nickel deposits in Kazakhstan (Aktyubinskaya Oblast) have established a very important regularity which consists of a certain equalization of the content of metals in plants over ore deposits (Malyuga [1958]). The results obtained in the analysis of plants collected in the region of the Shcherbakovskii nickel deposit in the Aktyubinskaya Oblast are shown in Table 22.

TABLE 22. Nickel Content in the Ash of Plants from the Shcherbakovskii Deposit
(Reference section 2, hole 863, over ore, August 3, 1960)

Sample No.	Plant	Nickel content, %	Concentration coefficient
2	Sheep's fescue	0.015	3
3	Hoary speedwell	0.033	6.6
4	Spiraea	0.040	8
5	Common yarrow	0.030	6
7	Shaggy goldilocks (abnormal)	0.020	4
8	Shaggy goldilocks (normal)	0.012	2.4
9	Tatar goldilocks	0.023	4.6
10	Summer cypress	0.048	9.6
11	Russian globe thistle	0.026	5.2
12	True bedstraw	0.015	3
13	Austrian wormwood	0.040	8
	Mean	0.027	5.4
	Mean in plant ash	0.005	

The data in Table 22 show an appreciable nickel enrichment in almost all the plants sampled over the zone of mineralization. Despite differing contents of nickel in individual species, without exception all plants accumulate nickel when the soils and the underlying rocks and ores are enriched with it. Exactly the same observations have been made in the case of copper, molybdenum, etc. Consequently, when making a biogeochemical survey, in case of necessity it is possible to replace certain species by others.

When making a biogeochemical survey, the principal vegetation types used are trees, shrubs, and perennial grassy plants. It is known that the depth of its root systems is dependent on the age of the plant. The older the plant, the deeper its roots penetrate into the ground, and therefore the greater the probability that the root systems will come into contact with ore or a dispersion halo. It has been noted that the depth of the root systems of trees does not change after reaching the age of 30 years, and it therefore is possible to obtain samples from young trees and shrubs. Observations show that shrubs and trees with weaker root systems use paths followed by dead roots, and thus penetrate to a great depth.

The influence of illumination in a closed forest is without importance and therefore should not be taken into account in a survey. Likewise, it is without importance when making a survey in open areas.

5. The Biogeochemical Role of Plants in the Accumulation of Ash Elements in Soils

As already mentioned, the formation of secondary minerals in soils occurs with the direct participation of surface plants and soil organisms. In the process of the mineralization of vegetation residue the soil annually receives tons of mineral matter: SiO_2, Al, Fe, Ca, Mg, and others entering into the so-called small biological cycle. However, there is a paucity of data concerning the quantity of the products of mineralization of plant residue in the soil. The work of N. I. Bazilevich [1955, 1958] and V. A. Kovda [1956] on the study of the cycle of ash elements in the different bioclimatic zones of the USSR is therefore worthy of considerable attention.

The quantity of ash matter entering into the soil during the mineralization of litter fall, that is, the dead parts of plants — leaves, stems, and roots — is dependent on bioclimatic conditions and the character of the vegetation cover. The increment of ash matter in meadow-steppe soils attains 1400 kg/hectare, in the moderately dry steppes it is 600 to 1000 kg/hectare, but in the dry steppes it does not exceed 200-250 kg/hectare. In deciduous forests the quantity of ash components returning to the soil is 670 kg/hectare, while in coniferous forests it approaches 300 kg/hectare. The minimum increment of ash matter in the soil occurs in the deserts — 70-100 kg/hectare. "At the basis of these phenomena lies both the selectivity of absorption of chemical elements by plants and the relationships in the litter fall of the green component and the root residue" (Basilevich [1958]).

According to data collected by V. A. Kovda [1956], the surface parts of grassy plants contain 500-700 kg of mineral matter per hectare, and the dead root system 300-400 kg/hectare. This matter is also a source of material for the formation of calcium and magnesium sulfates and carbonates in soils and the formation of clayey minerals, sesquioxides, etc.

The investigations of Bazilevich [1958] in the virgin steppe and meadow-steppe associations of Western Siberia, the Altai and Novosibirskaya Oblast, have revealed that 70% of the Ca, K, P, and S in the meadow-steppe associations enters the soil with the litter fall of the green part of grasses and from root residue.

During the mineralization of organic matter there is often observed an increase in the soil content of SiO_2, R_2O_3, CaO, and MgO and, on the other hand, a decrease of the mobile elements K, P, Na, Cl, and N. In this case the SiO_2 to R_2O_3 ratio in living plants, equal to $50:1$, changes in the litter fall to $10:1$, and in the mineralized residue to $4:1$, which indicates the predominant accumulation of stable clayey minerals in the meadow-steppe soil process.

It has been noted that the mean ash content of the litter fall (surface and underground parts) increases from north to south: from 1% in coniferous forests and 1.6-7.5% in deciduous forests to 7-8% in the litter fall of meadow-steppe regions. The ash content decreases to the south due to the relatively high percentage in desert and semidesert litter fall of ligneous surface and underground organs and tissues with a lesser ash content.

The cited data reveal that secondary biogenous compounds in soils are an important source of mineral sustenance of surface plants. At the same time, if we take into account the relative accessibility to plants of the elements included in these new formations (in comparison with rock minerals), it is possible to appreciate fully the importance of the biological factor in the concentration of chemical elements in soils, including ore elements.

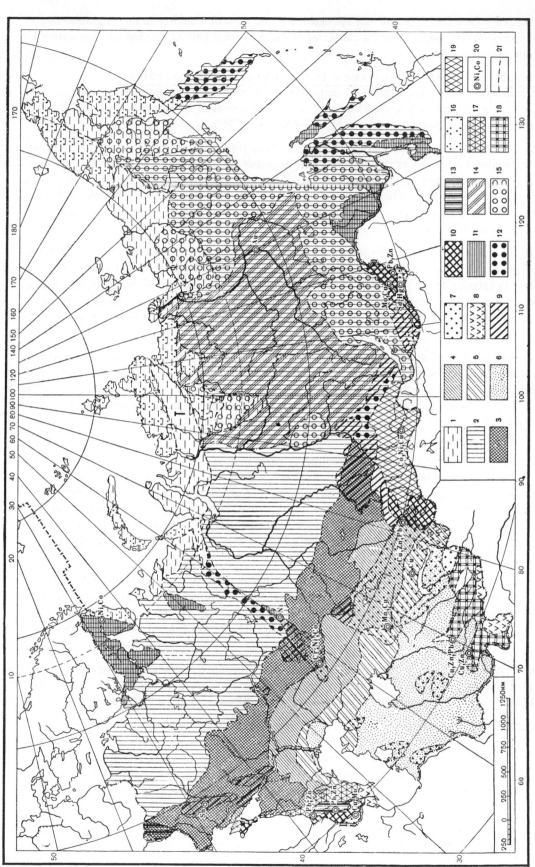

Fig. 31. Schematic map of the application of a biogeochemical survey in different zones in the territory of the Soviet Union. Soil zones with characteristic conditions for the migration of chemical elements. 1) Tundra; 2) podzol zone; 3) chernozem zone; 4) chestnut soil zone; 5) brown soil zone; 6) zone of gray soils of deserts and semideserts; 7) dry steppes and foothills of Transcaucasia, Kazakhstan, Southern Siberia, and the deserts of Central Asia; 8) zones of moderately high and high mountains in Central Asia and Southern Siberia; 9) moderately moist steppes and wooded steppes of the Ukraine, Caucasus, and Southern Siberia; 10) mountain-steppe regions of the Crimea, Caucasus, Southern Urals, and Southern Siberia. Provinces of acidic and neutral soils and waters: 11) Lowland and hilly taiga regions; 12) mountainous taiga regions; 13) mountain-forest regions of the Carpathians and Lesser Caucasus; 14) taiga plateaus of Eastern Siberia; 15) mountainous regions of Eastern Siberia; 16) tundras of the Far North. Provinces with a sharply expressed vertical zonality: 17) Caucasus; 18) Central Asia; 19) Altai-Sayan; 20) regions of biogeochemical exploration work; 21) boundaries of biochemical provinces.

75

The foregoing discussion makes clear the role and importance of bioclimatic zonality in the migration of metals in soils over ore deposits, which imparts special character to the new geochemical method for exploration for ores on the basis of soil and plant sampling.

6. Bioclimatic Zonality and Its Importance in Geochemical Exploration

In studying the influence of various biogeochemical factors on the migration and accumulation of chemical elements in soils and plants, it is possible to note the affinity of individual geochemical processes to natural zones, delimited as environmental-geographic zones (Dokuchaev [1949]; Polynov [1946]).

Polynov has written: "Recently there has been noted a completely legitimate aspiration in different branches of the earth sciences to regionalization of the earth's surface. Soil scientists are not satisfied with zones alone, but define soil provinces (an idea advanced by L. I. Prasolov) while geochemists aspire to define geochemical provinces; the desire has been expressed for special biogeochemical provinces (Vinogradov [1949]), etc." On his part Polynov has formulated the study of geochemical environments, proposing the investigation of the migration of chemical elements within a geochemical environment.

It should be remembered that the most important factor in the migration of chemical elements in the environment is the regional bioclimatic factor, although much depends on the mineralogical and chemical composition of the rocks, water, and plants in relation to the properties of active and less active migrating elements (H, Ca, Al, Fe, Si). It therefore becomes understandable why geochemists desire to delimit in the territory of the USSR provinces with identical behavior of ore elements for the purpose of developing rational geochemical methods for the exploration for ore deposits.

Experience in the compilation of environmental-geochemical maps (Perel'man and Sharkov [1957]) consisted of the delimitation within the metallogenetic zones of the USSR of provinces characterized by identical conditions for the migration of metals as a function of relief, pH of soil and water, and the character of the soil and vegetation, for example: 1) provinces with alkaline and neutral reactions of the soil and water; 2) provinces with an acidic or neutral reaction; 3) provinces with a clearly expressed vertical zonality — the mountainous regions of the Caucasus, Central Asia, Altai, Tuva, etc.

We plotted the data from the environmental map compiled by Perel'man and Sharkov on a soils map in order to represent clearly the position of the delimited provinces on the background of the latitude zonality of the USSR. A review of the map (Fig. 31) makes it possible to perceive the possible variety of natural conditions encountered when making lithochemical and biogeochemical surveys. However, this map, like any other sketch map, is far from being usable for work under specific conditions in a particular area. For such work it is necessary to dispense with generalized maps and compile detailed geochemical maps of the area in which it is proposed that a geochemical survey be made.

The following factors influence the rate at which chemical elements pass through the biogenic cycle: the water regime of the soil, the pH of the medium, the oxidation potential, and the presence of antagonistic metals. The quantity of ions of heavy metals accessible to plants is dependent on the presence of soluble compounds — chlorides, sulfates, bicarbonates, etc. — in soils and also on the presence of exchangeable forms of metals in the soil absorbing complex.

Plants are capable of assimilating with their roots metals in the soil which are of difficult access, in the form of minerals and other stable chemical compounds (oxides, hydroxides, carbonates), using various kinds of root chemical secretions, e.g., carbonic acid, organic acids, all of which act on the soil substrate as ordinary chemical reagents.

The content of any chemical element in mobile form is no proof of the accessibility of this element to plants, since the entry of ions into plants is dependent on a whole series of factors — the character of the soil cover, pH, and others. The most favorable medium for the assimilation of calcium, magnesium, and other bivalent chemical elements is one with pH $\sim$ 7. When pH < 5 the absorption of calcium and other elements decreases sharply, which can be attributed to the antagonistic influence of ions of hydrogen, aluminum, and manganese, always present in solution in acidic soils.

The absorption of salts from the soils is not proportional to the quantity of water transpired by plants, as indicated in plants by a reverse movement of ions and the elimination through the roots of Ca^{2+}, PO_4^{3-}, SO_4^{2-}, HCO_3^-, and others.

When there is a considerable content of a particular element in the medium (soil, solution) the plants are not able to resist for long the entry of high quantities of chemical elements, often unnecessary to the plant, with the result that there is a corresponding biological reaction (chlorosis, delayed growth), as is observed in ore deposits, and especially in ancient mine workings and on spoil banks.

The content of various elements in soils and plants is different: the content of some is higher in soils, while the content of others is higher in plants. The first group includes Al, Si, Ti, Fe, and Sn, forming compounds which are of difficult access, and the second group includes actively migrating elements, which are alkaline and alkaline-earth elements, many bivalent metals, and Li, Be, B, P, S, K, Mn, Ln, Se, Mo, and Ra.

In a comparison of the mean content of chemical elements in rocks and plants one notes a relative accumulation of biogenic elements in surface plants, which can be expressed by the ratio AP/AL — the abundance of the element in the plant divided by the abundance of the element in the lithosphere. This coefficient is a criterion which can be used to classify a particular element as biogenic or nonbiogenic. This is of appreciable importance in determining the effectiveness of biogeochemical exploration with respect to a particular element.

Root systems are a zonal criterion for plants, ensuring the sustenance of plants under specific ecological conditions. The penetration of plants in depth facilitates a greater effective depth, that is, the effectiveness of the biogeochemical method.

The metal content in plants increases appreciably toward the second half of the growing season. Summer, autumn, and winter sampling of vegetation, as well as sampling of plants from the preceding season (dry grasses), is equally suitable in a biogeochemical survey.

The most important factor in the migration of chemical elements in the environment is the bioclimatic factor, although much depends on the character of the rocks, soils, and ground water, and on the individual properties of individual elements. For this reason it is most urgent to define provinces in the USSR which have identical conditions of behavior of ore elements in order to be able to develop a rational geochemical method for exploration for metals.

CHAPTER VII

EXPERIENCE WITH THE APPLICATION OF THE BIOGEOCHEMICAL
EXPLORATION METHOD IN DIFFERENT ZONES OF THE USSR

A very great amount of experience in geochemical and biogeochemical investigations in different environmental and geochemical zones of the earth's surface has been accumulated, but the material has remained uncollected and ungeneralized. A major step in the generalization of data on the geochemical zonality of exploration work in the USSR was the preparation of environmental and geochemical maps by A. I. Perel'man and Yu. V. Sharkov [1957] at a scale of 1 : 5,000,000.

It is known that the environmental-geochemical zonality of a studied area is related to the physicogeographic location of the country, geological structure, latitudinal, and vertical zonality, especially the orographic structure of the studied area, the influence of adjacent landscape regions, the orientation of ranges, the nearness of the sea or deserts, etc.

Experience has shown that the practical use of the proposed environmental-geochemical maps at a scale of 1 : 5,000,000 or smaller does not yield the desired results because of the great diversity of bioclimatic and other conditions (relief, microclimate), even within the limits of sometimes relatively small areas of land, especially in mountainous regions.

Taking into account the considerations mentioned above, in each new region it is necessary to carry out systematic experimental geochemical investigations for the purpose of determining the conditions for the migration of chemical elements over the mineralization zone: the nature of the stratification of the rocks, the origin and depth of the ground water, and the conditions for the formation of secondary minerals and salts, especially the formation of a carbonate horizon in the soil profile. The precipitation regime, the character of weathering and soil formation, the pH, and the character of the vegetation are of great importance.

The geochemical and biogeochemical data obtained for one deposit can be used to great advantage in organizing exploration work in adjacent sectors under similar landscape conditions. As an example we will discuss the experience obtained during biogeochemical investigations which we made in individual bioclimatic zones of the Soviet Union: in the Southern Urals, in Tuva, in Transcaucasia, and elsewhere. These investigations were made in zones with a dry steppe environment, in the mountainous steppe, and in forested areas, in moist forested mountains, in a desert landscape, and elsewhere. We will now give a discussion of these results.

1. Nickel and Chromium Deposits in the Southern Urals

The behavior of the triad of elements Fe − Co − Ni in igneous rocks and their relationship to magnesium and silicon has been shown in the form of curves in Fig. 32. This diagram shows that in rocks rich in magnesium, in dunites, and peridotites, and partially in gabbros and basalts, the distribution of iron, nickel, and cobalt reveals a proportionality to the magnesium content. This regularity in the distribution of nickel and cobalt gradually disappears when the content of magnesium in the rock is less than 4%. In the above-mentioned triad, iron is the key element during the entire differentiation process. Its content rarely drops to 1%, whereas nickel and cobalt decrease sharply in acidic and ultra-acidic rocks, attaining a maximum dispersion of $1 \cdot 10^{-4}\%$. It is known that in the process of differentiation of magma, iron is set free in considerable quantities in the form of ore minerals: pyrrhotite, chromite, ilmenite, magnetite, etc. Other elements set free with the iron are Ti, V, Cr, Mn, Ni, Co, and Cu. However, the content of nickel, cobalt, and copper in these minerals is low and rarely exceeds hundredths or thousandths of 1%.

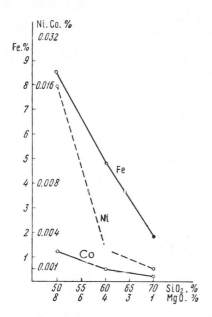

Fig. 32. Distribution of iron, cobalt, and nickel in igneous rocks.

The high affinity of copper, nickel, and iron to sulfur links these elements in deep processes. Nickel and iron are the principal components of magmatic sulfides in the paragenesis of the ore minerals pyrrhotite-pentlandite. In many cases the sulfide ores have been enriched with copper, primarily by chalcopyrite (Sudbury, Ontario, Canada) and contain cobalt. In these early sulfides the nickel clearly predominates over cobalt. The mean content of nickel in primary sulfides is about 3%, and the cobalt content is $2 \cdot 10^{-1}\%$; the Ni : Co ratio is 1 : 15. In the hydrothermal process there are new paragenetic relationships between nickel and cobalt in sulfide, arsenide, and sulfide-arsenide minerals.

The geochemistry of nickel and cobalt in the upper part of the earth's crust in the biosphere differs appreciably from the geochemistry at depth. For example, in a weathered crust of ultrabasic rocks, cobalt is associated with manganese in asbolans $m(Co, Ni)O \cdot MnO_2 \cdot nH_2O$ and psilomelane-wad, whereas nickel is masked by ferromagnesian silicates of nontronitic ores, or forms independent siliceous minerals $(NiO + SiO_2 \cdot nH_2O)$, garnicrite, nepoite, etc.

In the long run, the weathering of rocks and ore deposits leads to the dispersion of nickel and cobalt in the biosphere. The scale of this process can be judged from the mean content of nickel and cobalt in recent and ancient sedimentary formations, in natural water, and in soils and organisms, as shown in Table 23. The data are evidence of the unusually high dispersion of nickel and cobalt in natural surface water. Their content in soils and sedimentary rocks approaches the mean for the lithosphere.

The distribution of nickel and cobalt in soils has a relationship to climatic zonality and is influenced by the character of clayey and organic colloids. The content of nickel and cobalt in rocks associated with granites, basalts, serpentinites, limestones, etc., is the most variable. As might be expected, soils developed on granites contain extremely small quantities of nickel and cobalt, only ten-thousandths of 1%. Soils with serpentinites always are enriched with nickel; the nickel and cobalt in soils formed on calcareous rocks is more abundant by a factor of 10 than in the rock.

The distribution of nickel, cobalt, and other chemical elements in the upper part of the earth's surface, primarily in soils and surface plants, forms the background on which anomalies associated with ore deposits become apparent. A preliminary study of the content of individual elements in soils and plants makes it possible to recognize more easily anomalies on the background of oreless or unpromising areas.

Many nickel silicate deposits of the Southern Urals (Kimpersaiskii ore region of Aktyubinskaya Oblast) are associated with outcrops of the ancient weathered crust of the Kimpersaiskii ultrabasic complex. The deposits sometimes lie close to the surface and therefore are easily detected by the presence of iron ochers and other characteristic weathered products. For detection of deeper deposits the local geological exploration party now, as before, uses the method of drilling into anomalies discovered by a magnetic survey and by electrical exploration, in such areas as zones of contact between serpentinites and gabbro-amphibolites, etc., no geochemical survey is made.

The region of the Kimpersaiskii ultrabasic complex has now been well studied. In the opinion of local geologists, there is absolutely no possibility of discovering new ore deposits in this area. However, the possibilities of studying the effectiveness of geochemical methods in drilled, but unexploited, deposits are essentially unlimited. This made it possible for us to make studies for the solution of a number of theoretical problems involved in the application of the biogeochemical method to regions in which the physical geography is similar to that in Northwestern Kazakhstan.

Purposes of the Study and Problems Involved

A study of the effectiveness of the biogeochemical method under the conditions prevailing in the steppe zone of chestnut soils is of great importance because this zone extends over immense areas of the Soviet Union, and because it occupies an intermediate position between the forested zone and the zone of gray soils of the semideserts.

TABLE 23. Nickel and Cobalt Distribution in the Earth's Crust*

| Contained in | Content, % | | Ratio |
	Co	Ni	Ni : Co
Lithosphere	$1.1 \cdot 10^{-3}$	$6.6 \cdot 10^{-3}$	6
Sedimentary rocks	$1 \cdot 10^{-3}$	$3.2 \cdot 10^{-3}$	3
Natural surface water	$2 \cdot 10^{-7}$	$3 \cdot 10^{-7}$	1.5
Ground water	$1 \cdot 10^{-6}$	$3 \cdot 10^{-6}$	3
Soils (mean)	$1 \cdot 10^{-3}$	$4 \cdot 10^{-3}$	4
Soddy-podzol soils	$8 \cdot 10^{-4}$	$2 \cdot 10^{-3}$	2.5
Chernozem soils	$1 \cdot 10^{-3}$	$4.5 \cdot 10^{-3}$	4.5
Chestnut soils	$9.5 \cdot 10^{-4}$	$3.5 \cdot 10^{-3}$	3.7
Plants (in ash)	$1.5 \cdot 10^{-3}$	$5 \cdot 10^{-3}$	3.3

*According to Malyuga [1946, 1947b, 1947c, 1952], Petterson and Rotschi [1951],
Mitchell [1945], and others.

We are concerned with the following practical and theoretical problems:

1. The influence of zonal climatic factors — temperature, humidity, and pH — on the geochemical distribution of nickel, cobalt, chromium, and other elements in the soil-geological profile over ore;

2. The conditions of accumulation of nickel and cobalt in soils separated from the ore by a considerable thickness of overburden, the influence of the character of the covering rock, the thickness of the rocks, and the importance of the thickness of the carbonate horizon (effervescence zone), etc.;

3. A comparative study of the effectiveness of the biogeochemical method and a metallometric survey in the exploration for nickel silicate ores in the zone of chestnut soils;

4. Problems relating to the selective concentrating capacity of plants growing above the ore, with respect to nickel, cobalt, and chromium, and the discovery and possibility of using endemic plant species in preliminary exploration of ore deposits;

5. The practical and theoretical checking of the biogeochemical method under specific conditions when carrying out exploration work in new areas of promise.

The region of the Kimpersaiskii ultrabasic complex is exceptionally favorable for the solution of most of the formulated problems. The following factors facilitated a good study of this region: a great many explored but still unexploited deposits, the shallow position of the ore zones within the limits of sensitivity of the biogeochemical method, and the wide variety of geological and geomorphological conditions making it possible to study the different aspects of the geochemical migration of ore elements from the ore to the surface and back.

In the study of the problems listed we made use of all available geological, hydrogeological, and geochemical data, exploiting the extensive archives of the Kimperskaiskii and Donskaya geological exploration parties, and in addition to exploiting the general geological data on the studied ore deposits we also used graphic materials (profiles, geological maps, etc.). The work was done at different times, beginning in 1949 in the Taiketkenskii, Chugaevskii, Oktyabr'skii, Shcherbakovskii, and other deposits of siliceous ores, and also in the "Viktorovskoe" chromite deposits in the Donskoe region (see the schematic map of the area, Fig. 33).

The exploration work was carried out on the northern continuation of the Kimpersaiskii ultrabasic complex near Kherson; the survey in this area covered an area of 2.5 km². Data obtained in this exploration work were submitted to the Kimpersaiskii Geological Exploration Party for checking against borehole data. A total of more than 5000 samples of soils, natural water, and plants were collected and in large part were studied by the chemical method for the presence of nickel, cobalt, chromium, and copper.

Geological and Bioclimatic Characteristics of the Kimpersaiskii Ultrabasic Complex

The Kimpersaiskii ultrabasic complex is situated within the Or'-Ilekskii uplift in the form of a zone 90 km in length and about 50 km in width, and has a N-S orientation. The region is a hilly plain, dissected by a system of deep river valleys and ravines with an elevation between 400 and 500 m above sea level. The complex is made up of dunites and peridotites, which have been transformed into serpentinites at top and to great depths. In the eastern part the

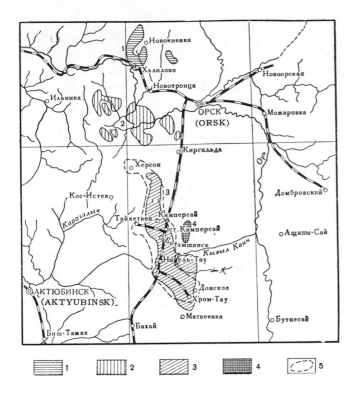

Fig. 33. Map of ultrabasic complexes in the Kimpersaiskii ore region. Ultrabasic complexes: 1) Khalilovskii; 2) Khabarninskii; 3) Kimpersaiskii; 4) Mamytskii; 5) region of biogeochemical investigations.

ultrabasites are bounded by extrusive rocks, Silurian tuffs, and Cambrian shales; on the west there are gabbro-amphibolites. The complex is riddled by a system of gabbro-diabase dikes, and serpentinization processes have developed with particular intensity at the contact with these dikes. The age of the complex is Middle and Late Devonian.

As is well known, deposits of nickel silicate are found in an ancient weathered crust of Jurassic and pre-Jurassic age, covered with a mantle of more recent sedimentary formations of Cretaceous and Tertiary age.

The weathered crust on serpentinites has the following composition (from top to bottom): 1) ochers and ocherized serpentinites; 2) nontronites and nontronitized serpentinites; 3) leached serpentinites; 4) carbonatized serpentinites on fresh serpentinites. The weathered crust is not uniform in structure and not in all cases is there a complete profile of the rocks mentioned.

As already noted, the structure of the roof of the nickel deposits includes sedimentary deposits of Cretaceous and Tertiary age — varicolored clays, marls, and loams of variable thickness: from 1 to 10-15 m.

The thickness of the weathered crust, together with the overlying sedimentary rocks, varies from one to several tens of meters. With the passage of geological time, the ancient weathered crust has been subjected to the influence of chemical and mechanical processes occurring at the earth's surface. These processes are continuing at the present time, as is indicated by the erosion of the surface of the crust and the processes of leaching, replacement, and mineral formation. Therefore, the geochemical relationship between the weathered crust, and consequently the ore deposits, and surface processes is still an active one.

The intensity of the geochemical processes of migration of ore and other chemical elements in the mineralization zone, and the formation of secondary dispersion haloes are dependent to a considerable degree on the hydrochemical and bioclimatic conditions of the region. In a moist and warm climate the removal and dispersion of ore elements takes place more rapidly than in a dry climate with a relatively hot summer and a cold winter, such as is characteristic of the northern part of Kazakhstan (Aktyubinskaya Oblast).

We therefore will discuss the climatic peculiarities of the region.

Climate

In climatic respects the studied region belongs to the Trans-Ural steppe province with inadequate precipitation. Because of this, the distribution of soils and vegetation associations are closely related to the microrelief. Chernozem-meadow soils and corresponding vegetation have developed on the floodplains of rivers and in well-drained and moist ravines. On the slopes and drainage divides there is a chestnut soil complex with soddy grasses (sheep's fescue, feather grass, butterwort), mixed with white wormwood, ground pine, shaggy goldilocks, etc. Saline soils with salt-loving vegetation have developed on high, poorly drained plateaus.

The climate of the region is characteristically continental and dry: there is a considerable range of daily and annual temperatures (hot summer and severe winter), dry winds of hurricane force in summer and winter, and considerable freezing of the soil (to 2.1 m). There is no rain in August at all. The mean annual precipitation usually is 250 mm, but it sometimes drops to 105 mm. The greater part of the precipitation, more than half, falls in the summer and fall. It evaporates rapidly or flows into streams and ravines without adequately moistening the soil.

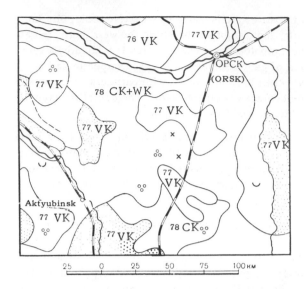

Fig. 34. Geobotanical map of the Southern Ural ore region. 76VK) Volga-Kazakhstan grass-sheep's fescue — feather grass steppes and agricultural lands; 77UK) Volga-Kazakhstan sheep's fescue — feather grass steppes and agricultural lands; 78CK) Caspian-Kazakhstan wormwood — sheep's fescue — feather grass and wormwood — sheep's fescue steppes; 78WK) Western Kazakhstan wormwood — sheep's fescue — feather grass and wormwood — sheep's fescue steppes.

As a result of the severe desiccation of the soil, especially in the clayey substrate, cracks up to 5 cm wide and more than 1 m deep form in the soils. When showers occur, the cracks become filled with humus matter, resulting in the formation of humus streaks which sometimes can be traced in local soils to a depth of 2.5 m. These breaks in the clayey ground are used by the root system of plants for penetrating to greater depths, closer to the moistened zone.

As a result of the inadequate moisture in the steppes (and deserts) the soils have a carbonate layer which prevents the loss of ions of heavy metals to greater depths. The position of the carbonate horizon in the soil-geological profile is a zonal criterion: in a chernozem steppe zone it usually corresponds to the B_2 horizon, while in the zone of chestnut soils, where we made our study, the level of the carbonate horizon approaches the surface and often reaches it.

Hydrogeology

The ground water of the region of the ultrabasite complex can be classified as (a) water in the serpentinite joints and (b) water in alluvial deposits. The water in the joints is of primary significance; the quantity of this water decreases with depth, as does the number of joints filled with carbonates.

The ground water originates as precipitation. The depth of the ground water table is dependent on the relief and varies from 10 to 30 m or more. The joints below 40-50 m usually are cemented with secondary minerals.

The covering deposits, clays, loams, and ocherous-clayey formations are of different permeability. Clays are considered the least permeable. However, when the clays and clayey loams become desiccated they acquire a platy structure with a great many large and small joints. Rain and snow water, therefore, easily reach the underlying ochers and nontronitized serpentinites. Due to the unconsolidated structure and the great number of joints, the latter constitute no obstacle to the vertical and horizontal circulation of solutions. The direction of the ground water flow must be taken into account when interpreting the data from a biogeochemical survey, although it is not of particular importance in areas with a relatively level relief.

The upper horizons of most nickel silicate deposits of the Kimpersaiskii region usually are located above the ground water level, although in certain years with heavier precipitation they become moister to a greater degree. The seasonal variations of ground water are not great and apparently do not exceed 1-2 m.

In studying the hydrogeology of a region from the point of view of its influence on the effective depth of the biogeochemical method, it should be noted that when ground and stratum water come into contact with an ore, there is a definite effect on the enrichment of the upper soil horizons with ore elements. The roots of plants penetrate into the moisture zone, sometimes to a depth of 3-5 m. Taking into account the capillary rise of ground water to a height of 5-6 m, it can be asserted that the effective depth of the biogeochemical method is 10-15 m.

It should be noted that the reverse loss of metals is difficult due to their bonding to soil humus, and also to the shielding capacity of the carbonate horizon of the soil.

While defining the effectiveness of the method to be 10-15 m, at the same time we actually have obtained better results — 20-25 m. The mechanism by which the humus layer is enriched by ore elements from such a great depth for the time being remains unclear.

Soils and Plants

The region has chestnut soils of a heavy composition, lying atop covering clays and loams. The general carbonaceous salinization has resulted in the formation of ordinary solonetz and solonetzic soils which are easily determined from the effervescence of the upper A horizon and their structural characteristics. The surface outcrop of varicolored clays, serpentinites making up the weathered crust, and rocks of the gabbroid type has led to the formation of groups of clayey, ocherous, and stony, primarily siliceous soils.

The most common soil types in the nickel silicate deposits of the Kimpersaiskii region are chestnut and light chestnut soils on recent and ancient clays and loams. As an example we will illustrate a profile obtained by A. I. Makarova on a gentle south slope in the Shcherbakovskii nickel deposit. The profile was obtained 30 m to the south of borehole 1723 in nontronitized and silicified serpentinites. In this area there was an almost continuous grassy sod. On the surface the chestnut soil was covered with fragments of silicified rock.

Horizon A was loamy, moist after rains, soft, chocolate colored, permeated with roots, contained stone fragments, did not effervesce, and had a depth of 0-16 cm.

Horizon B_1 was loamy, dense, dirty brown in color, lumpy, effervesced strongly, and was 16-35 cm thick.

Horizon B_2 was clayey, very dense, brown, lumpy, had brown streaks along the sides of cracks, effervesced, and was 35-60 cm thick.

Horizon B_3 was clayey, yellowish-brown in color, less dense than B_2, had white spots and lenses of calcium carbonates and iron hydroxides in the lower part, with a mixture of nontronitized serpentinites downward to a reddish-brown clay; effervescence decreased downward.

The frequent alternation of the underlying rocks in each case creates new conditions for the formation of soil horizons. Without being able to describe even the most important of them, we nevertheless have noted their general features. The principal feature of virgin chestnut soils is their relative paucity of humus. It was noted that cultivated soils are enriched with humus, which leads to a general increase in their productivity. This apparently can be attributed to the greater mortality of the roots of annual cultivated grasses and their greater humus yield in comparison with perennial wild steppe plants.

The zonal types of vegetation of the studied region (the northwestern part of Aktyubinskaya Oblast) are sodded-grassy steppes: mixed grasses − sheep's fescue − feather grass, sheep's fescue − feather grass and wormwood − sheep's fescue (Fig. 34).

The ultrabasic Kimpersaiskii complex is situated within the confines of the wormwood − sheep's fescue and wormwood − sheep's fescue − feather grass steppes. In this area the typical white-wormwood associations on gravelly soils typical of the desert are accompanied by desert-steppe associations with Lessing's wormwood.*

The principal members of the desert steppe associations are drought resistant soddy grasses: sheep's fescue (Festuca sulcata Hack) and feather grass, primarily Stipa Lessingiana, with the addition of Stipa capillata and Agropyrum Sibiricum on lighter soils. These edaphic plants are accompanied by subedaphic plants: white wormwood, Pyrethrum, yarrow, summer cypress, ground pine, Austrian wormwood, and Polyanthus yurineya.

The makeup of the associations is greatly influenced by the relief and the character of the soil cover. For example, solonetzic plant complexes develop along alluvial river terraces and on low-lying steppe plains where drainage is poor; among these plants are sheep's fescue, summer cypress, white wormwood, and matricary. On crusted solonetz soils there are associations of black wormwood, kok-peka, and ground pine. Associations with the white wormwood Artemisia Lercheana predominate on low plains between elevated drainage divides.

On outcrops of Cretaceous rocks the predominant vegetation is subshrubs and "Cretaceous" species − endemic plants: stock Mathiola fragans, toadflax Linaria cretacea, etc.

The following are noted on rocky outcrops: Anabasis cretacea, catchfly Silene suffrutescens, Gypsophila Patrinii, hoary madwort Borteroa spathulata, Alyssum tortuosum, etc.

Steppe associations often contain an abundance of soil lichens, such as Parmelia vagans, Cladonia, and others, as well as the blue-green algae Stratonostoc, and sometimes the mosses Tortula.

---

*Determined by N. C. Petrunina.

TABLE 24. Nickel and Cobalt Content in the Ash of Alyssum tortuosum

Plant and sampling site	Content, %		Ni : Co ratio
	Ni	Co	
Alyssum tortuosum from the spoil banks of the open pit of the Eastern Kimpersaiskii deposit	1	0.0125	80
Alyssum tortuosum samples over leached serpentinites (outside the deposit)	0.037	0.0046	8

TABLE 25. Nickel and Cobalt Content in Mine and Other Waters of Nickel Silicate Deposits

Origin of water	Content, %		Ni : Co ratio
	Ni	Co	
Spring from deposit, Novaya Akkermanovka	0.062	–	–
Well in serpentinites, Kimpersai	0.027	0.0072	3.8
Hole in serpentinites of the Batamsha nickel deposit	0.021	0.0029	7
From serpentinites from a hole in the Donskoi chromium deposit	0.032	0.011	3
Hole. Nickel deposit, mine water from a depth of 17 m	0.044	0.0077	6

In biogeochemical mapping on the basis of plant samples in areas of virgin steppe in most cases it is necessary to use perennial plants — the principal edaphic species, which are: feather grass, steppe sage, sheep's fescue, white wormwood, black wormwood, shaggy goldilocks, Tatar goldilocks, mourning bride, yarrow, spirea, summer cypress, ground pine, etc. A comparative analysis of the nickel content in these plants, sampled in the same area, revealed the possibility of replacing one plant by another, since the nickel content in all was approximately the same.

Alyssum tortuosum occupies a special place in the local vegetation. This plant is similar to other species of alyssum — steppe alyssum A. murale W. et H., dispermous allysum A. biovulatum N. Busch — in that it is characterized by a very high capacity for concentrating nickel. The concentration of nickel and cobalt in the ash of Alyssum tortuosum, sampled on soils with different nickel content, is shown in Table 24.

These are the general features characterizing the environmental-geochemical features of the Kimpersaiskii ultrabasic complex. We now will proceed to an exposition of data concerning individual deposits of the Kimpersaiskii ore region.

Taiketkenskii Nickel Deposit

This deposit is found in the Kimpersaiskii peridotite complex, falling in the northern part of Aktyubinskaya Oblast. The region of the deposit rises more than 450 m above sea level and for the most part consists of serpentinites. The formation of this deposit, as well as almost all the siliceous nickel deposits of the Southern Urals, is related to the development of the ancient weathered crust. In many places the ultrabasic rocks are covered with gabbro-amphibolites which are entirely ocherized or kaolinized. The presence of more stable basic rocks disrupts the continuity of the ore body, resulting in the formation of ore pockets, separated by products of modified gabbro. The deposit includes sedimentary deposits of Cretaceous and Tertiary age — varicolored clays, marls, sands, etc. Alternating with gabbroic ochers, they form the top of the shallow-sited nickel ores. These rocks, together with leached and partially nontronitized serpentinites, are the parent rocks from which the soil was formed.

In almost all parts of the deposit the nickel ore is close to the surface, so that the average thickness of the overburden does not exceed 10-15 m.

A characteristic of most of the Kimpersaiskii nickel deposits is the low level of the ground water table, which is situated at a depth of 10-20 m, and sometimes 30 m below the ore level.

Due to the high permeability of the gabbroic ochers and unconsolidated Tertiary deposits, covering the ore body, there is a constant connection between the ore and the soil layer by means of the capillary rise of solutions. Under the conditions prevailing in the arid Trans-Ural steppe province in which our studies were made, we considered this connection to be responsible for the considerable accumulation of heavy metals (Fe, Ni, Cr, Co, Cu) in the soils and plants, in complete correlation with the content of these elements in the below-lying ores.

The most important minerals in the nickel silicate deposits in the Southern Urals are nontronite, serpentine, and garnierite. They are accompanied by an extremely complex group of hydrous silicates — ferrimontmorillonites $Fe_2(Al_2)O_3 \cdot 2SiO_2 \cdot 2H_2O \cdot nH_2O$, ferribeidellites, and many others. These quite unstable compounds are characterized by an ability to absorb immense quantities of bonded water; as the top dries out, this water can be freed and migrate upward, carrying along dissolved compounds of nickel, cobalt, and other metals.

Among the mobile compounds of nickel, cobalt, iron, manganese, and copper in such deposits, the most important are bicarbonates, followed by chlorides and sulfates. According to data supplied by I. I. Ginzburg [1947], the ground water of the Kimpersaiskii peridotite complex is of the carbonate-chloride or carbonate-sulfate-chloride type in which HCO_3 ions (in milligram equivalents) clearly predominate over $SO_4^{=}$ and Cl^-. Salts of the corresponding acids are contained in the soils of the nickel deposit in considerable quantities, which often leads to their salinization and the formation of typical solonetz soils: ordinary, crustal, and deep-structured. A fractional analysis of the soils has shown that the heavy metals, in contrast to alkalis and alkaline earths, are stably bonded in the humus complex of the soil as soon as they enter the soil layer, and are not washed away by ordinary neutral aqueous solvents. This fact has made it possible to explain the gradual accumulation and retention of nickel in soils above deposits in quantities exceeding 0.5%.

The concentration of nickel in soils is not dependent on the character of the roof, be it of leached serpentinites, kaolinized gabbro-amphibolites, or Tertiary varicolored clays differing in nickel content. Precisely the same constant Ni:Co ratio (12:1) remains in the soil, despite the appreciable difference in the rocks making up the roof. Observations have shown that the Ni:Co ratio in unmodified serpentinites averages 20:1. As the serpentinites become increasingly weathered and nontronitized, the Ni:Co ratio changes in the direction of a relative increase in the nickel content, reaching 40:1 or better. The latter closely resembles the Ni:Co ratio in nickel silicate ores. What is the explanation of such a low ratio of nickel to cobalt in soils (and plants)? Table 25, which gives a water analysis, clearly shows that mine water, as well as water from serpentinites and other minerals characteristic of nickel deposits, indicates a shift in the direction of cobalt, with the Ni:Co ratio being 5:1.

The noted change of ratios indicates that in the process of the weathering of basic and ultrabasic rocks the nickel is retained almost intact in the initial products of rock modification in the form of isomorphic admixtures to the already mentioned complex ferrosilicates. In this case, the cobalt and copper partially move downward in the profile of the modifying stratum. This apparently accounts for the closer equalization of the content of nickel and cobalt in the ground water observable in the soils and plants of nickel deposits.

As the ferrosilicates become increasingly oxidized and the pH of solutions changes from 8-10 to lower values, the nickel is set free from the iron and cobalt and begins to migrate together with SiO_2, filling joints in which there often are found nickel hydrosilicates and chalcedonies (Ginzburg [1947]).

We will now proceed directly to an analysis of data obtained in the biogeochemical study of the nickel deposit. In the summer of 1948 work was undertaken in this area by a complex expedition organized by our institute in collaboration with the Institute of Biology of the Ural Branch of the Academy of Sciences of the USSR. The objective of the expedition was to study the biogeochemical provinces in the southern Urals in the vicinity of the nickel deposit. The most important aspect of the study was the solution of problems associated with the theoretical soundness of the soil-plant exploration method and the possibilities for its practical application. This was done, for example, in outlining a part of the deposit.

The work was done in the following manner. Soil profiles were obtained in the ore field and beyond its boundaries; soil and vegetation samples were taken at these points. They subsequently were studied by the polarigraphic method for their content of nickel, cobalt, and copper. Table 26 gives a part of the data which we obtained in the analysis of soils obtained at sites scattered over the entire area of the deposit in such a way that they would reflect the presence or nearness of the ore body fully. The soil in sample 1 was obtained at a certain distance (400 m) from the ore field from kaolinized gabbro-amphibolites. The samples selected from the soil horizons revealed a moderate content of nickel, cobalt, and copper, but the abundance ratios did not exceed 3-4.

The derived ratios between cobalt, nickel, and copper closely resemble the abundance ratios, that is, values unrelated to the dispersion haloes of nickel and cobalt deposits. In the soil taken considerably closer, 3 m from the ore field (sample 2), there was an appreciable increase in the nickel content, which was reflected in the abundance ratio

TABLE 26. Content and Ratio of Cobalt, Nickel, and Copper in Soils of the Taiketkenskii Deposit

Soil and its origin	Soil horizon and depth, cm	Content in dry soil, %			Ratio		Abundance ratio		
		Co	Ni	Cu	Ni:Co	Ni:Cu	Co	Ni	Cu
Light chestnut, solonetzic, clayey loam on gabbro-amphibolites, profile No. 22, outside ore field	A 0-10	$3\cdot10^{-3}$	$1.3\cdot10^{-2}$	$3\cdot10^{-2}$	4.3	4.3	3	3	4
	B 20-30	$3.7\cdot10^{-3}$	$1.3\cdot10^{-2}$	$9\cdot10^{-3}$	3.5	1.4	4	3	4
	C 30-40	$3\cdot10^{-3}$	$1.4\cdot10^{-2}$	$7.6\cdot10^{-3}$	4.7	1.8	3	4	4
Common solonetz, clayey loam, 3 m from ore field, profile No. 13	A 0-10	$6.8\cdot10^{-3}$	$5.7\cdot10^{-2}$	$9.6\cdot10^{-3}$	10	6	6	14	5
	B 35-45	$3.9\cdot10^{-3}$	$5.7\cdot10^{-2}$	$6\cdot10^{-3}$	14	10	4	14	3
	C 45-55	$4\cdot10^{-3}$	$5.7\cdot10^{-2}$	$6.2\cdot10^{-3}$	14	9	4	14	3
Dark chestnut, clayey loam, from ore field, profile No. 14	A 0-17	$2.3\cdot10^{-2}$	$3.5\cdot10^{-1}$	$1\cdot10^{-2}$	15.2	35	23	90	5
	B 17-34	$1.2\cdot10^{-2}$	$2.6\cdot10^{-1}$	$6.4\cdot10^{-3}$	12.5	40	12	60	3
	C 34-44	$5.8\cdot10^{-3}$	$1.2\cdot10^{-1}$	$3.0\cdot10^{-3}$	20	40	6	30	2

TABLE 27. Content and Ratio of Cobalt, Nickel, and Copper in Ash of Plants from Nickel Deposit

Plant and its origin	Ash content, %			Ratio		Abundance ratio		
	Co	Ni	Cu	Ni:Co	Ni:Cu	Co	Ni	Cu
Stipa Johannis Czel (feather grass) from gabbro amphibolites, area No. 5, 500 m from ore field	$1.3\cdot10^{-4}$	$5.9\cdot10^{-4}$	$8.6\cdot10^{-4}$	4.5	1	1	1	1
Stipa Johannis Czel, ore field, area No. 8	$2.6\cdot10^{-4}$	$2.1\cdot10^{-3}$	$2\cdot10^{-3}$	9	1	1	3	3
Avena desertorum (desert oats) from gabbro amphibolites, area No. 5	$3.2\cdot10^{-4}$	$2\cdot10^{-3}$	$1.6\cdot10^{-3}$	6.5	1.5	1	2.7	1
Avena desertorum, ore field, area No. 8	$3.5\cdot10^{-4}$	$9\cdot10^{-3}$	$1\cdot10^{-3}$	26	9	1.5	13	1
Pulsatilla patens (L.) Mill. (pasqueflower), normal form, area of deposit	$2.6\cdot10^{-4}$	$7.8\cdot10^{-4}$	$1.3\cdot10^{-3}$	3	1	1	1	2
Pulsatilla patens (L.) Mill. Endemic form (leafless), ore field, contour XXIX	$1\cdot10^{-3}$	$2.5\cdot10^{-2}$	$8\cdot10^{-3}$	25	3	4	36	12
Pulsatilla patens (L.) Mill. Endemic form (white), ore field, contour XXIX	$1.4\cdot10^{-3}$	$3.7\cdot10^{-2}$	$1.3\cdot10^{-2}$	26	3	6	53	20
Linosyris villosa (shaggy goldilocks)	$1.7\cdot10^{-3}$	$1.9\cdot10^{-2}$	$8.3\cdot10^{-3}$	11	1.5	7	27	14

and in its ratio to cobalt. Thus, the nearness of the ore body already was indicated in this sample, but the indications were still insufficiently clear to assert definitely the presence of nickel ore.

The most characteristic data were obtained in an analysis of the soil sample taken directly over the deposit, where the nickel concentration to the soil clarke increased by a factor of almost 100.

It is of equal interest to trace how plants are affected in this respect. The data in Table 27 are given as a characterization of this property of plants. The table contains a comparison of the content of nickel, cobalt, and copper in plants growing directly over the ore body and at a certain distance from the deposit. In each of these cases it is possible to see the peculiarities, both with respect to the content of chemical elements and their ratios. The content of nickel, cobalt, and copper in Stipa Johannis Czel., Festuca ovina, etc., collected in the area of gabbro-amphibolites, that is, beyond the boundaries of the ore field, is virtually the same as the usual content known for these and other plants obtained in regions having no relationship to the dispersion haloes of ore deposits (Malyuga [1947]). The above-cited ratios fully confirm this. However, the nearness of the ore body is sensed immediately from the content of nickel, cobalt, and copper. It is easy to see that the plants collected in the ore field do not concentrate nickel and other chemical elements to an identical degree. An exceptionally high nickel content is noted in endemic forms of

TABLE 28. Cobalt, Nickel, and Copper Content in Soils Sampled Along Exploration Lines A and B

Soil and its origin	Sample No.	Content, %			Ratio		Abundance ratio		
		Co	Ni	Cu	Ni:Co	Ni:Cu	Co	Ni	Cu
Light chestnut, solonetzic, clayey loam soil from gabbro-amphibolites, profile No. 22, beginning of lines A and B	–	$3 \cdot 10^{-3}$	$1.3 \cdot 10^{-2}$	$8.2 \cdot 10^{-3}$	4.3	1.6	3	3.3	4
Line A									
Solonetz, deep structure, clayey loam, 100 m	36	$2.4 \cdot 10^{-3}$	$9.1 \cdot 10^{-3}$	$8.7 \cdot 10^{-3}$	3.7	1	2.4	2.2	4.4
Common solonetz, clayey loam, 200 m from profile 22	37	$1.9 \cdot 10^{-3}$	$7.8 \cdot 10^{-3}$	$8.1 \cdot 10^{-3}$	4.1	1	2	2	4
Solonetz, deep structure, clayey loam, 300 m	38	$3 \cdot 10^{-3}$	$4.25 \cdot 10^{-2}$	$1.2 \cdot 10^{-2}$	14	3.5	3	10	6
The same, 350 m	39	$2.8 \cdot 10^{-3}$	$3 \cdot 10^{-2}$	$3 \cdot 10^{-2}$	10	1	28	50	15
Common solonetz, clayey loam, 400 m	40	$4.2 \cdot 10^{-3}$	$3 \cdot 10^{-2}$	$6.6 \cdot 10^{-3}$	7.1	4.5	4.5	7.3	3.3
The same, 450 m	41	$4.5 \cdot 10^{-3}$	$4 \cdot 10^{-2}$	$9.5 \cdot 10^{-3}$	9	4	4.5	10	4.8
The same, 500 m	42	$6.7 \cdot 10^{-3}$	$7.4 \cdot 10^{-2}$	$8.75 \cdot 10^{-3}$	11	8.4	6.7	20	4.5
The same, 525 m	43	$1.2 \cdot 10^{-2}$	$1.5 \cdot 10^{-1}$	$7.2 \cdot 10^{-3}$	12.5	20	12	40	3.4
The same, 500 m	44	$1.53 \cdot 10^{-2}$	$2 \cdot 10^{-1}$	$1.9 \cdot 10^{-2}$	10	1.3	15.3	50	8.5
Dark chestnut, clayey loam, 575 m	45	$2.2 \cdot 10^{-2}$	$2.5 \cdot 10^{-1}$	$1.3 \cdot 10^{-2}$	12.5	20	20	62	6.5
The same, 603 m	–	$2.3 \cdot 10^{-2}$	$3.5 \cdot 10^{-1}$	$1 \cdot 10^{-2}$	15.2	35	23	90	5
Line B									
Solonetz, deep structure, clayey loam, 100 m	25	$1.7 \cdot 10^{-3}$	$4.4 \cdot 10^{-3}$	$3.5 \cdot 10^{-3}$	2.5	1	1.7	1	1.8
The same, 200 m	26	$1.6 \cdot 10^{-3}$	$4.5 \cdot 10^{-3}$	$3.1 \cdot 10^{-3}$	2.8	1.5	1.6	1	1.5
The same, 300 m	27	$1.8 \cdot 10^{-3}$	$1.36 \cdot 10^{-2}$	$7 \cdot 10^{-3}$	7.5	2	1.8	3.4	3.5
The same, 350 m	28	$2 \cdot 10^{-3}$	$2.26 \cdot 10^{-2}$	$7 \cdot 10^{-3}$	6.3	3	2	3.2	3.5
Solonetz, deep structure, 400 m	29	$2.6 \cdot 10^{-3}$	$2.6 \cdot 10^{-2}$	$1 \cdot 10^{-2}$	10	2.6	2.6	8.5	5
The same, 450 m	30	$3 \cdot 10^{-3}$	$4.2 \cdot 10^{-2}$	$8.8 \cdot 10^{-3}$	7	5	3	11	4.4
The same, 525 m	32	$5 \cdot 10^{-3}$	$5.9 \cdot 10^{-2}$	$5.9 \cdot 10^{-3}$	11.3	10	5	15	3
The same, 550 m	33	$5.3 \cdot 10^{-3}$	$7.6 \cdot 10^{-2}$	$6.5 \cdot 10^{-3}$	12.5	11	5.3	19	3.2
The same, 575 m	34	$2.4 \cdot 10^{-3}$	$9.1 \cdot 10^{-3}$	$8.7 \cdot 10^{-3}$	4	1	2.4	2.5	4

Pulsatilla patens (L.) Mill. collected in the ore field. These preliminary data made it possible to seek more "sensitive" species, among which the most significant is Pulsatilla patens (L.) Mill.

Making use of the experience accumulated while checking the soil-plant exploration method, we attempted to apply it to the solution of specific problems, such as the following: more precise determination of the northwestern boundaries of the nickel deposit. The inadequate number of boreholes and the extremely irregular outline of the deposit required additional geological exploration work, and this unquestionably would involve a loss of time and considerable cost. In this case, as well, it was possible to demonstrate the advantage of the soil-plant method, which requires no complex technical equipment and can be applied quickly and simply.

Without being able to employ the usual rectangular sampling grid, we drew several radial lines from a single point located beyond the boundaries of the ore field in such a way that they intersected the northwestern boundary of the deposit. Soil profile No. 22, situated in an area of gabbro-amphibolies 500 m from the ore field, was selected as the initial point. The distance between profiles was gradually increased as the boundary of the deposit was approached. This method makes it possible to note the boundary of a sometimes large sector of the deposit without the necessity of an excessively large number of soil and plant samples. The sampling interval was decreased gradually at the same time.

TABLE 29. Cobalt, Nickel, and Copper Content in Linosyris villosa Along Exploration Lines A and B

Distance from soil profile No. 22 on gabbro, m	Sample No.	Ash content, %			Ratio		Abundance ratio		
		Co	Ni	Cu	Ni:Co	Ni:Cu	Co	Ni	Cu
Line A									
100	36	$2.3 \cdot 10^{-3}$	$7.3 \cdot 10^{-3}$	$1 \cdot 10^{-2}$	3.2	1	10	10	1.6
200	37	$3 \cdot 10^{-3}$	$1 \cdot 10^{-2}$	$1.2 \cdot 10^{-2}$	3.3	1	11	13	20
300	38	$1.3 \cdot 10^{-3}$	$1.5 \cdot 10^{-2}$	$9.8 \cdot 10^{-2}$	9	1.5	7.5	21	16
350	39	$2.7 \cdot 10^{-3}$	$1.5 \cdot 10^{-2}$	$9.8 \cdot 10^{-3}$	8	1.6	11	30	21
400	40	$1.6 \cdot 10^{-3}$	$1,85 \cdot 10^{-2}$	$8.7 \cdot 10^{-3}$	11.5	2.1	7	26.4	14.5
450	41	$2 \cdot 10^{-3}$	$2.1 \cdot 10^{-2}$	$1.5 \cdot 10^{-2}$	10	1.4	8.3	30	20.5
500	42	$1.5 \cdot 10^{-3}$	$2 \cdot 10^{-2}$	$8.6 \cdot 10^{-3}$	13.3	2.3	6.2	30	14.3
515	43	$2.1 \cdot 10^{-3}$	$2.3 \cdot 10^{-2}$	$1.1 \cdot 10^{-2}$	11	2	9	33	18
550	44	$1.3 \cdot 10^{-3}$	$1,36 \cdot 10^{-2}$	$1 \cdot 10^{-2}$	11	1.4	6	20	16
575	45	$2 \cdot 10^{-3}$	$2.1 \cdot 10^{-2}$	$2.1 \cdot 10^{-3}$	10.4	10	8.5	30	13.5
600	—	$1.2 \cdot 10^{-3}$	$1.8 \cdot 10^{-2}$	$8.7 \cdot 10^{-3}$	15.7	20	5	26	14.5
Line B									
100	25	$1.6 \cdot 10^{-3}$	$6.3 \cdot 10^{-3}$	$8.4 \cdot 10^{-2}$	4	1	7	9	14
200	26	$1.3 \cdot 10^{-3}$	$8.2 \cdot 10^{-3}$	$9.8 \cdot 10^{-3}$	6	1	5.5	12	16
300	27	$1.7 \cdot 10^{-3}$	$1.6 \cdot 10^{-2}$	$7.4 \cdot 10^{-3}$	9.4	2	7	23	12
350	28	$1.4 \cdot 10^{-3}$	$2 \cdot 10^{-2}$	$1 \cdot 10^{-2}$	14.3	2	6	30	16
400	29	$1.3 \cdot 10^{-3}$	$1.6 \cdot 10^{-2}$	$8 \cdot 10^{-3}$	12.3	2	5.4	13	13
450	30	$1.65 \cdot 10^{-3}$	$1.4 \cdot 10^{-2}$	$1.1 \cdot 10^{-2}$	8	1.3	7	20	18
500	31	$2.24 \cdot 10^{-3}$	$2.6 \cdot 10^{-2}$	$1.1 \cdot 10^{-2}$	11.3	2.3	9	37	18
525	32	$1.8 \cdot 10^{-3}$	$2 \cdot 10^{-2}$	$9.4 \cdot 10^{-3}$	11	2	7.5	30	15.6
550	33	$1.4 \cdot 10^{-3}$	$1.4 \cdot 10^{-2}$	$6.1 \cdot 10^{-3}$	10.2	2.3	6	20	10
575	34	$2.3 \cdot 10^{-3}$	$1.87 \cdot 10^{-2}$	$9.0 \cdot 10^{-3}$	8	2	9.5	27	15
600	35	$1.7 \cdot 10^{-3}$	$1.9 \cdot 10^{-2}$	$8.3 \cdot 10^{-3}$	11	2.2	7	27	14

The schematic map shown as Fig. 35 shows two profiles which hereafter will be referred to as exploration lines A and B. The sampling points were laid out along these lines (from soil profile No. 22) each 100 m, then each 50 m, and finally each 25 m. The plotted points are shown as circles with dots inside. The circles represent the relative concentration of nickel in the soil investigated, and the dots the relative concentration in plants sampled near this same point. The data used have been indicated in Tables 28 and 29. The uppermost part of soil horizon A was investigated from the surface to a depth of 5 cm. Plants were sampled at the same points as the soil and were analyzed without the roots.

By a study of the data in Table 30 it is possible to note that the cobalt and copper content in soils changes very little along the entire length of profiles A and B. At the same time, there is a sharp jump in the nickel content, especially in the samples taken over the nickel deposit. All this is well illustrated by the ratios and abundance ratios of cobalt, nickel, and copper. Thus, whereas the relative concentration of cobalt and copper rarely attains 5:1, in the case of nickel there are times when its content is higher than the soil clarke by a factor of tens. Thus, the distribution of cobalt, nickel, and copper in the investigated soils characterizes not only the presence of a deposit, but also specifically identifies it as a nickel deposit.

An almost identical pattern is obtained when studying the data from an analysis of plants collected at the same time the soils were sampled. As shown by Table 29, the content of cobalt and copper is almost uniformly distributed along the entire length of the exploration lines A and B. At the same time, the nickel content increases as the ore field is approached (samples 38 and 39) and then becomes constant, varying in a rather narrow range.

By a comparison of the data in Tables 28 and 29 it can be established that the content of cobalt and copper in soils and in plant ash is almost identical. However, the nickel concentration in soil ash is smaller by a factor of six than in the soils. This is evidence that plants assimilate cobalt and copper better than nickel and thus probably is related to the earlier noted pathological influence of nickel, expressed in the appearance of endemic forms of Pulsatilla patens (L.) Mill. and Linosyris villosa on soils enriched with nickel. We have expressed the numerical data in the form of diagrams to give a graphic representation of the distribution of nickel in soils and plants. In Fig. 36 the concentration

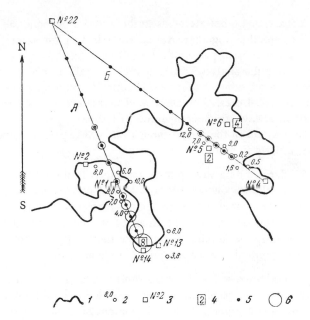

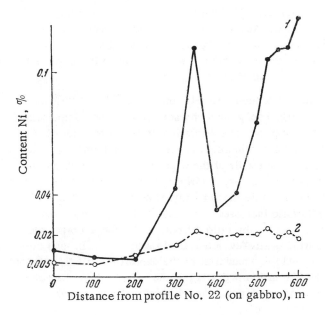

Fig. 35. Distribution of nickel in the soils of the Novo-Tayketkenskoye deposit. Prospects of ore finds along exploration lines A and B. 1) Boundary of ore body according to geological data; 2) thickness of cover, in meters; 3) soil profiles; 4) work areas; 5) relative concentration of Ni in plants; 6) relative concentration of Ni in soils.

Fig. 36. Relative content of nickel in the soils and plants of the Chugaevskii deposit. 1) In soil; 2) in plants.

of nickel in percent has been plotted along the y axis; the points along profile A from soil profile No. 22 to the ore field have been plotted along the x axis, adhering to scale. Figure 36 shows that the nickel content in plant ash is considerably lower than in soils, which more precisely reflect the true presence or nearness of a nickel deposit. It is easy to confirm this by comparing the derived data with the schematic map of the investigated part of the deposit (see Fig. 35).

In this case, it is possible to see the extremely interesting phenomenon of intensification or slackening off of the nickel concentration in the soil (large and small circles) as a function of the closeness to the boundary of the deposit. It might be mentioned that in other deposits there was a clearer correlation between the nickel content in soils and plants, but this will be discussed below.

During the plotting of the nickel content on the map, a comparison was made between the data obtained by the soil-plant method and data obtained by geological exploration. At this time it was established that the precision of the initial boundaries of the deposit was inadequate. For example, the high concentrations of nickel in soils along line A lie beyond the boundary of the deposit with which we associated the presence of an ore field. In actuality, this fact was confirmed by additional drilling. It was established at the same time that the depth of the ore, at least in cases when it does not exceed 10-15 m, is not reflected in the nickel content in the soil. Likewise, it does not influence the character of the soil.

Problems of the correlation of the chemical composition between nickel ores covered by rocks, soils, and plants, required a more detailed check in a number of other deposits which differed from one another in the thickness of the ore body, the depth of the ore body, the character of the rocks separating the ore from the surface, the hydrological conditions (ground water level, direction of movement of pressure water), etc. For a proper solution of these problems, it would be necessary to compare the biogeochemical and geological profiles for all these deposits, that is, plot data on the content of, for example, nickel, cobalt, and copper in soils and plants on a geological map of the nickel deposit, together with all the data required for this case. The Chugaevskii, Oktyabr'skii, and other deposits were used for this purpose.

Chugaevskii Nickel Deposit

This deposit in its characteristics closely resembles the Taiketkenskii deposit. We studied it in 1949 and 1950. In the geochemical investigations we took samples of soils and plants along all geological exploration profiles of the deposit at boreholes and at intervals between them. The soils were sampled from the surface to a depth of 10 cm, that is, the uppermost layer, the most enriched, so it was found, with heavy metals. In addition, soil profiles were obtained to a depth exceeding 2 m, and deeper profiles also were obtained to the depth of the ore body. A study of these samples made it possible to determine the content of

TABLE 30. Relative Content of Nickel, Cobalt, and Copper in Soils of Deposit

Content, %	No. of samples		
	Ni	Co	Cu
0.5	3	—	—
0.1 −0.5	99	—	—
0.05 −0.1	35	—	—
0.01 −0.05	12	74	40
0.005−0.01	1	50	85
0.005	—	26	25

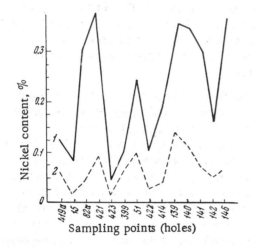

Fig. 37. Correlation of nickel in soils and plants (Linosyris villosa L.). 1) In soils; 2) in plant ash (in plotting on the graph the nickel in plants has been exaggerated by a factor of 2).

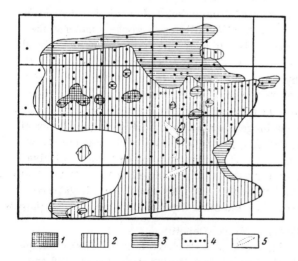

Fig. 38. Isoconcentrations of nickel in the soil (diagram). Nickel content: 1) 0.5%; 2) from 0.1 to 0.5%; 3) 0.1%; 4) sampling points; 5) dikes.

nickel, cobalt, and other elements in the entire biogeochemical profile, and this, together with an analysis of mine water, provided a rather clear pattern of their distribution. At the very beginning the analytical data revealed a rather good agreement between the content of nickel in soils and plants and the presence of nickel ores. The absence of nickel ore at any particular point always was accompanied by a sharp decrease of the nickel content in the soil, although this was expressed somewhat less clearly in plants.

The derived data were plotted on a map in the form of lines showing the isoconcentrations of nickel, cobalt, and copper and were compared with a geological map showing the boundaries of nickel ore concentrations. Soil and geobotanical maps were compiled in order to represent more fully the complex of geochemical and biogeochemical phenomena.

The collected soil and plant samples, after appropriate preparation, drying, grinding, burning, etc., were investigated by the polarographic method for their content of nickel, cobalt, and copper. The content of iron, manganese, and chromium in certain samples was determined, making it possible to find the ratio of the elements of the iron family for a particular case. The derived data (on the basis of hundreds of determinations) were broken down in the following manner with respect to the content of nickel, cobalt, and copper (Table 30).

The data in Table 30 show that in the absolute majority of cases (99 out of 150) the nickel content in soils was from 0.1 to 0.5% (mean $2.5 \cdot 10^{-1}$%); this applies to the central part of the first deposit. About 50 cases of a nickel content of less than 0.1% for the most part apply to the northern and northeastern boundaries of the area studied, where the deposit wedges out, approaching a zone of gabbros (profiles 1-3).

A nickel concentration in soils of less than 0.05% constitutes the clarke background characteristic of the Kimpersaiskii peridotite complex. The dispersion haloes of the ores of nickel deposits stand out rather clearly on this background. The cobalt content in the soils of the deposit correlates with the nickel content, as is shown very clearly in Table 31. It follows from the data in this table that in samples especially rich in nickel the Ni : Co ratio increases somewhat, and vice versa, where there is less nickel the ratio decreases. On the average, the Ni : Co ratio, as already noted, is close to 15 : 1. In soils obtained beyond the boundaries of the deposit (profile 3, borehole 9), the Ni : Co ratio usually is less than 10 : 1. It is characteristic that this same regularity is noted for nickel and copper, but it is expressed less clearly.

Analyses of Linosyris villosa obtained at the same points where the soil samples were taken reveal a regularity in the distribution of nickel, cobalt, and copper in plants as a function of the content of these elements in soils and ores.

The mean nickel content in the plant Linosyris villosa, collected over a nickel deposit, is approximately $3 \cdot 10^{-2}$%,

TABLE 31. Content and Relation of Nickel, Cobalt, and Copper
in Soils of Chugaevskii Area

Soil	Sampling site		Content in dry soil, %			Ratio		Abundance ratio		
	profile	hole	Co	Ni	Cu	Ni:Co	Ni:Cu	Co	Ni	Cu
Chestnut, clayey loam, solonetzic	1	237	$7 \cdot 10^{-3}$	$9.5 \cdot 10^{-2}$	$6.4 \cdot 10^{-2}$	14	15	7	24	3
Chestnut, ocherized	2	428	$1 \cdot 10^{-2}$	$1.4 \cdot 10^{-1}$	$9.5 \cdot 10^{-3}$	14	15	10	37	5
Same	2	415	$1.7 \cdot 10^{-2}$	$4.1 \cdot 10^{-1}$	$1.9 \cdot 10^{-2}$	24	22	17	100	10
Same	3	431	$1.6 \cdot 10^{-2}$	$2.6 \cdot 10^{-1}$	$9 \cdot 10^{-3}$	16	29	16	65	5
Same	3	7	$2.6 \cdot 10^{-2}$	$4.2 \cdot 10^{-1}$	$1.5 \cdot 10^{-2}$	25	28	26	105	8
Same	3	9	$3.7 \cdot 10^{-3}$	$3.1 \cdot 10^{-2}$	$5 \cdot 10^{-3}$	8	62	3.7	8	3
Same	4	50	$2 \cdot 10^{-2}$	$5.8 \cdot 10^{-1}$	$1.7 \cdot 10^{-2}$	21	35	20	145	9
Same	4	12	$1.3 \cdot 10^{-2}$	$1.1 \cdot 10^{-1}$	$1.5 \cdot 10^{-2}$	9	7	13	27	8
Same	5	55	$4.3 \cdot 10^{-2}$	$6.2 \cdot 10^{-1}$	$3.2 \cdot 10^{-2}$	15	20	43	155	16
Same	5	57	$2.2 \cdot 10^{-2}$	$3.6 \cdot 10^{-1}$	$1.7 \cdot 10^{-2}$	16	21	22	90	9
Chestnut, solonetizic	6	29	$7.6 \cdot 10^{-3}$	$6.7 \cdot 10^{-2}$	$8.4 \cdot 10^{-2}$	9	8	9.6	17	4
Highly ocherized	6	29	$1.2 \cdot 10^{-2}$	$2 \cdot 10^{-1}$	$1 \cdot 10^{-2}$	16	20	12	50	5
Dark chestnut	7	34	$8.5 \cdot 10^{-3}$	$1.2 \cdot 10^{-1}$	$1.2 \cdot 10^{-2}$	14	10	8.5	30	6
Chestnut, ocherized	8	70	$2.1 \cdot 10^{-2}$	$4.7 \cdot 10^{-1}$	$1.8 \cdot 10^{-2}$	22	26	21	102	9
Dark chestnut	8	64	$9 \cdot 10^{-3}$	$1.2 \cdot 10^{-1}$	$7.2 \cdot 10^{-3}$	13	16	9	30	4
Chestnut, clayey loam	8	71	$1.5 \cdot 10^{-2}$	$4 \cdot 10^{-1}$	$1.8 \cdot 10^{-2}$	26	22	15	100	9
Dark chestnut	10	140	$1.5 \cdot 10^{-2}$	$2.3 \cdot 10^{-1}$	$1 \cdot 10^{-2}$	15	22	15	57	5
Highly ocherized	15	141	$1.7 \cdot 10^{-2}$	$3 \cdot 10^{-1}$	$1.8 \cdot 10^{-2}$	16	17	18	75	5

cobalt $- 2.5 \cdot 10^{-3}\%$, and copper $- 1.5 \cdot 10^{-2}\%$, which corresponds to a Ni : Co ratio of 12 : 1 and a Ni : Cu ratio of 2 : 1. These values agree quite well with those which were obtained in an analysis of Linosyris villosa from another deposit, and this indicates a certain regularity and constancy in the distribution of nickel, cobalt, and copper in plants. A characteristic of the derived data is an almost total agreement in the content of copper in soils and plants, which is not observed with respect to nickel and cobalt. In most cases the content of nickel and cobalt in the ash of Linosyris villosa is 10 to 15 times lower than in the soil from which the plant was taken.

Despite this fact, there is a rather clear correlation in the distribution of nickel and cobalt between soils and plants, and this is reflected quite clearly in the corresponding diagrams in Fig. 37. Consequently, plants, to the same degree as soils (for given conditions), can be used in exploration for nickel and cobalt deposits. It also is possible to use abundance ratios for this purpose. The abundance ratio of copper in the ash of Linosyris villosa averages 10, that is, exactly the same as in soils, which, as we will see below, can be attributed to the great mobility of copper in soils and therefore its easy assimilability by plants.

The example of copper reveals that there also are chemical elements which enter into the biogeochemical cycle very vigorously; this increases the sensitivity of the exploration method based on an analysis of plant ash. In addition to copper, chromium, molybdenum, zinc, and other elements behave in a similar manner. Nickel, cobalt, iron, and manganese are stably fixed by the soil absorbing complex of steppe chernozem, chestnut, and other soils. They are less mobile and are intercepted by plants to a lesser degree. As a result of the lesser mobility of nickel and cobalt in the soil cover there is a gradual accumulation of these elements in the upper humus layer which, as will be demonstrated by use of a number of examples, correlates with the content of these elements in nickel silicate ores. The considerable accumulation of nickel and cobalt in soils makes it possible to use the latter more effectively than plants in exploration work. Because of this, we will now devote our principal attention to the results obtained in a study of the soils of the nickel deposits of the Southern Urals.

The considerable number of soil samples from the Chugaevskii deposit, investigated for their content of nickel, cobalt, and copper, have made it possible to obtain quite a clear pattern of their surface distribution, that is, to determine their topography and plot them on the map in the form of lines showing isoconcentrations. On the accompanying map of the deposit the points where the samples were taken, situated at distances of 50 and 25 m from one another, were connected by isolines showing the concentration of nickel, cobalt, and copper. It was necessary to prepare three sketch maps for this purpose, one for each of the elements.

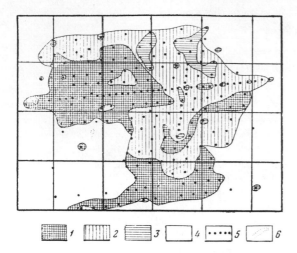

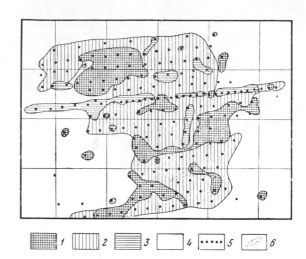

Fig. 39. Map if the isoconcentrations of cobalt in the soils of the Chugaevskii deposit. Cobalt content: 1) from 0.01 to 0.05%; 2) from 0.005 to 0.01%; 3) less than 0.005%; 4) geochemical background; 5) sampling points; 6) dikes.

Fig. 40. Map if the isoconcentrations of copper in the soils of the Chugaevskii deposit. Copper content: 1) from 0.01 to 0.05%; 2) from 0.005 to 0.01%; 3) less than 0.005%; 4) geochemical background; 5) sampling points; 6) dikes.

The first map (Fig. 38) shows the distribution of nickel. The maximum content of nickel in the soils, from 0.1 to 0.5% and above, falls rather well into the area bounded by the outline of the ore field, as determined by both deep and shallow drilling. The central part of the deposit stands out on the map as having the highest nickel content — from 0.5% and above (profile). These areas on the map are shown by heavy cross-hatching. The northern boundary of the deposit is shown on the map by an isoline (from 0.05 to 0.1%) with a low nickel content; it is shown on the map by horizontal ruling. This zone corresponds to poor nickel ores, with a transition to slightly nontronitized leached serpentinites.

The northeastern and eastern parts of the deposit are less clearly shown by isolines with a maximum nickel content in the soil. The isolines very often go beyond the boundary of the deposit. This can be attributed to the fact that until now the boundary of the deposit had not been determined precisely. With further exploration the boundary obviously will be shifted beyond its present position and will assume a more tortuous appearance, such as is characteristic of this type of deposit.

In a number of places, due to a lack of data, the isoline for a high nickel content comes into contact with a region of the lowest nickel content — less than 0.05%, representing the dispersion background (white on the maps). The southern part of the area, bounded by the isoline for 0.1-0.5% nickel, agrees quite well with the boundary of the deposit.

The represented areas with a high or low nickel content in the soil rather precisely reflect objective conditions, that is, the presence or absence of rich ores.

By comparing the distribution of nickel in soils and ores, and taking into account the geology of the underlying ore deposit, it is possible to discover a number of regularities which influence the accumulation of nickel in soils.

The nickel content in the ore, and the thickness of the ore layer, have a particularly important influence on the nickel accumulation in the soil. It can also be noted that in cases of an identical nickel content in ore, its content in the soil is somewhat less if the depth of the ore body differs from its depth at another point by more than 10 m. From all the data for the deposit we could not determine the influence of the character of the overburden. Possibly this can be attributed to its small thickness and quite good permeability (loams, unconsolidated ochers, nontronitized serpentinites).

The influence of hydrogeological conditions was not apparent in these two examples, since, in both cases, the ground water was situated below the ore, the migration of nickel in the soil therefore occurs under approximately similar conditions. Likewise, no changes were noted in the nickel content as a function of the character of the soils (chestnut, dark chestnut, salinized), as could be established easily by a simple superposing of the soil map of the deposit, compiled by A. I. Makarova, on the above-mentioned map of the isoconcentrations of nickel in soils. It becomes obvious that the principal factor involved in the accumulation of nickel in soils is the presence of nickel ores.

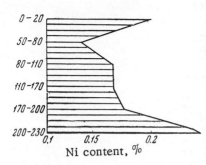

Fig. 41. Nickel distribution in the soil-geological profile of the Chugaevskii deposit (depth of the horizon in centimeters is plotted along the x axis).

Thus, the topography and quality of these ores can be predicted on the basis of quantitative determinations of the nickel in soils. Consequently, in a complex study of any region the soil-plant method can facilitate or partially replace rather tedious geological exploration work for nickel.

As already mentioned, the distribution of cobalt in the soils of nickel deposits often correlates with the distribution of nickel. Nevertheless, in a study of the map of isoconcentrations of cobalt (Fig. 39), it can be noted that cobalt does not rigorously correlate with nickel, especially in the case of moderate or low contents of these elements. There is a more irregular pattern in the distribution of cobalt. High and medium concentrations of cobalt often alternate. It is noted that maximum contents of cobalt are observed in ocherized chestnut soils associated with surface outcrops of ochers, and minimum and moderate contents are associated with the chestnut soil complex. All this becomes more understandable when the map of isoconcentrations of cobalt in soils is compared with the soil map of the deposit.

There is one very interesting peculiarity in the distribution of copper. The maximum copper content in soils corresponds to a minimum content of nickel, and vice versa. Profile 6 is illustrative of this relationship. By a comparison of the map of isoconcentrations of copper (Fig. 40) and nickel along profile 6, it can be noted that points exceptionally rich in nickel are characterized by a minimum content of copper. In most cases the copper (and cobalt) is accumulated in ocherous soils, although there are a number of exceptions. The copper content in ravines is particularly low, and this, to a certain degree, characterizes the relief of the deposit.

Briefly summarizing the data on the distribution of nickel, cobalt, and copper in the soils of the deposit, it can be noted that: 1) the nickel content correlates quite well with the content in nickel ores; 2) the similar correlation in the content of cobalt sometimes is disrupted in ocherous soils, where the content is considerably greater; 3) the behavior of copper in the zone of the deposit is independent of the location of rich nickel ores and is determined by the character of the overburden and relief conditions.

Several soil profiles were obtained for a determination of the conditions for migration of nickel in the vertical profile of soils and subsoils and used in a study of the nickel distribution in individual horizons. Table 32 gives certain data for one of these profiles to illustrate the results.

A very important peculiarity of this profile, and other similar profiles for nickel silicate deposits is the sharp increase in the content of nickel, cobalt, and copper in the uppermost soil horizon, from the surface to a depth of 20 cm. Downward in the profile the nickel concentration decreases appreciably and at a certain horizon, depending on the depth of the ore body, again begins to increase. In order to represent graphically the changes of the nickel content in the vertical profile, it has been shown as a curve in Fig. 41.

The decrease in the nickel content in the intermediate soil horizon and its increase at the two opposite poles very graphically illustrates the concentration of nickel in the soil as a result of the capillary rise of solutions containing nickel. The migration of cobalt duplicates the curve for nickel, although less clearly. Copper has the peculiarity of more even distribution in the profile.

In order to clarify the problem of the forms of compounds of nickel, cobalt, and copper and their relative mobility, we used the method of fractional mineralogical analysis of soils and made a study of the mobile components migrating into various solvents, such as 2% HCl, 5% N H_4Cl. A study of the soil mineralogical fractions – sandy-clayey and heavy – has revealed that all the nickel, cobalt, and copper is associated with the sandy-clayey complex and almost entirely pass into solution when treated with hot concentrated HCl in the presence of HNO_3. More interesting data were obtained when soils were treated with neutral weakly acidic solutions.

The results of these investigations are given in Table 33. These data fully confirm the earlier stated conclusion that there is a gradual increase in the content of nickel, cobalt, and copper as the upper soil horizon A is approached. However, the regularity of this pattern of distribution of the elements is noticeably disrupted in the corresponding soluble fractions of mobile forms of the elements. The insignificant quantities of nickel carried along by the water, approximately 0.01% of the total content in the soil, is surprising. This indicates that nickel is held rather stably in the soil and little is washed out by meteoric water; this facilitates its concentration in soils, despite its extremely slow

TABLE 32. Distribution of Nickel, Cobalt, and Copper
in Soil-Geological Profile (in %)

Depth of horizon, cm	Co	Ni	Cu	Ratio	
				Ni:Co	Ni:Cu
0—20	$1.2 \cdot 10^{-2}$	$2 \cdot 10^{-1}$	$2 \cdot 10^{-2}$	17	10
50—80	$8 \cdot 10^{-3}$	$1.4 \cdot 10^{-1}$	$1 \cdot 10^{-2}$	18	14
80—110	$7 \cdot 10^{-3}$	$1.7 \cdot 10^{-1}$	$1.4 \cdot 10^{-2}$	24	12
110—170	$5 \cdot 10^{-3}$	$1.7 \cdot 10^{-1}$	$1.4 \cdot 10^{-2}$	34	10
170—200	$5.3 \cdot 10^{-3}$	$1.8 \cdot 10^{-1}$	$1.5 \cdot 10^{-2}$	34	12
200—230	$5 \cdot 10^{-3}$	$2.5 \cdot 10^{-1}$	$1.8 \cdot 10^{-2}$	50	14

TABLE 33. Distribution of Soluble Nickel, Cobalt, and Copper by Soil Horizons

Character of material	Soil horizon and depth, cm	Content, %			Ratio	
		Co	Ni	Cu	Ni:Co	Ni:Cu
Soil, dark chestnut, clayey loam, profile 14	A 0—17	$2.3 \cdot 10^{-2}$	$3.5 \cdot 10^{-1}$	$1.1 \cdot 10^{-2}$	15.2	32
Same	B 17—34	$1.2 \cdot 10^{-2}$	$1.6 \cdot 10^{-1}$	$7.0 \cdot 10^{-3}$	12.5	22
Same	C 34—50	$5.8 \cdot 10^{-3}$	$1.2 \cdot 10^{-1}$	$5.4 \cdot 10^{-3}$	20	22
Water extract	A 0—17	$1.3 \cdot 10^{-4}$	$4.5 \cdot 10^{-5}$	$1.4 \cdot 10^{-4}$	0.35	0.32
Same	B 17—34	$1 \cdot 10^{-4}$	$1.2 \cdot 10^{-5}$	$1.1 \cdot 10^{-4}$	0.12	0.11
Same	C 34—50	$1 \cdot 10^{-4}$	$1.2 \cdot 10^{-5}$	$1 \cdot 10^{-4}$	0.12	0.12
Extract 2% HCl	A 0—17	$3.6 \cdot 10^{-3}$	$6.2 \cdot 10^{-2}$	$2.5 \cdot 10^{-3}$	17	25
Same	B 17—34	$3.5 \cdot 10^{-3}$	$9.6 \cdot 10^{-2}$	$2.6 \cdot 10^{-3}$	27.5	37

downward movement. The soluble part of copper and cobalt is considerably greater and exceeds nickel by a factor of almost 10, evidence of the greater mobility of these elements under soil conditions, a factor which explains a certain leveling out of their content and the nickel content in soil solutions and in plant ash.

Water-soluble compounds of nickel, cobalt, and copper in soils include chlorides, sulfates, and bicarbonates. The content of these components in the aqueous fraction is small and approximately equal. A more significant part of the nickel, cobalt, and copper (20% in horizon A and about 50% in horizon B) is removed by weak acid.

The presence of carbonates in the B horizon (the horizon of effervescence, with a depth of 30 cm) fully explains the passage of heavy metals into an acidic solution. With respect to the A horizon, not containing carbonates, the only possible sources of mobile compounds there are the ions Ni^{2+}, Co^{2+}, Cu^{2+}, and ions of other elements, sorbed on the surface of colloids and set free by exchange reactions with strong electrolytes.

Compounds with organic substances (humates) are the principal form in which nickel, cobalt, and copper are found in the upper humus horizon A, which we used as the principal indicator of the dispersion haloes of ore deposits. In the case of nickel it possibly can enter into the lattices of silicates of variable composition (montmorillonites, halloysites), in which it replaces the ions Mg^{2+} and Fe^{2+}.

Oktyabr'skii Nickel Silicate Deposit

The Oktyabr'skii deposit, to the south of the Novo-Taiketkenskii deposit, was selected for a study of the possibilities of applying the biogeochemical method of exploration when the ore body is covered by a thick layer of recent loams, Tertiary clays, or the products of the weathering of parent rocks. The Oktyabr'skii nickel silicate deposit is associated with the ancient weathered crust of a serpentinite apophysis, situated beyond the western contact of the Kimpersaiskii ultrabasic complex. The ultrabasites are represented by dunite serpentinites, and less frequently by peridotite and pyroxenite serpentinites.

The deposit is situated on a soddy highland, between 430 and 450 m above sea level, which drops off slightly in a southward direction. The modified serpentinites of the ore deposit are covered by a mantle of Quaternary loams from

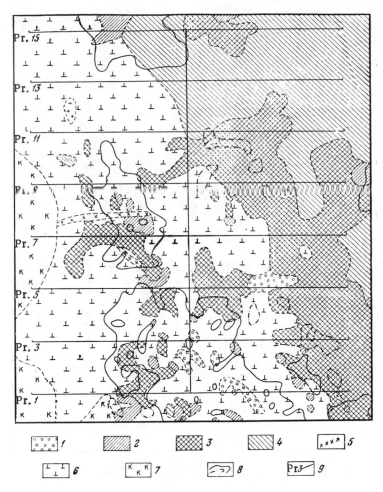

Fig. 42. Schematic geological map of the Oktyabr'skii nickel deposit. 1) Ochers; 2) silicified serpentinites; 3) nontronites; 4) leached serpentinites; 5) gabbro-diabases; 6) kaolinized gabbro-amphibolites; 7) chloritic quartz-granite shales; 8) outlines of ore bodies of different categories; 9) profiles of biogeochemical survey.

10 to 12 m deep, and also by the products of weathering of gabbroic rocks of variable thickness — from 1 to 10 m. The products of weathering of gabbro-amphibolites (gabbro-diabases) consist of a clayey material of light green and whitish color to reddish-brown and dark brown. The complete profile of the crust (from top to bottom) includes: ochers, kaolinized products of weathering, gabbro-amphibolites, nontronitized serpentinites, and leached serpentinites (thickness of about 50 m).

The lower part of the profile of the Oktyabr'skii deposit is characterized by rocks of a banded complex (taxites). The deposit includes bright yellow, brownish-yellow, and red ochers which outcrop at the surface in the form of spots (Rodionov and Sulin [1957]).

In addition to the loams, the covering deposits of the Oktyabr'skii deposit include varicolored clays whose thickness is as great as 20 m. The average thickness of the covering rocks of this deposit varies from 15 to 20 m. The depth of the water table varies from 12 to 22 m, that is, for the most part it is equal to the thickness of the covering rocks.

Drilling work has been completed in the Oktyabr'skii deposit and the ore bodies have been defined clearly in the horizontal plane and by depth; complete geological profiles also have been prepared. This work has made it possible to make a precise comparison of the results of the biogeochemical survey and specific geological data (Fig. 42). The first step in this comparison was a preliminary sampling for nickel and cobalt using a relatively open grid measuring 200 × 200 m.

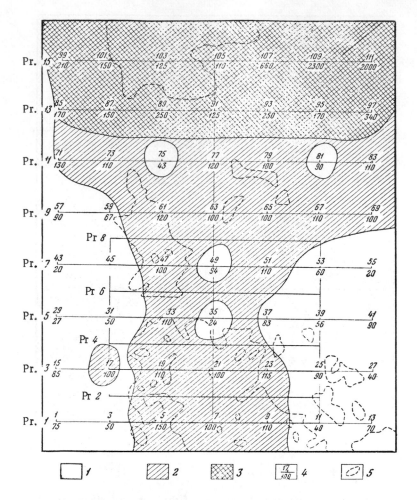

Fig. 43. Map if isoconcentrations of nickel in the soils of the Oktyabr'skii deposit. Nickel content: 1) more than 100 ten-thousandths (in %); 2) from 100 to 150 ten-thousandths (in %); 3) more than 150 ten-thousandths (in %); 4) numerator = number of sample, denominator = nickel content; 5) outlines of ore bodies.

The collected soils and plants were studied in a field laboratory and the data plotted on a map of the studied northern part of the deposit. It was thereby possible to obtain maps showing the isoconcentrations of nickel and cobalt in soils and plants. The clearest results were obtained for the nickel in soils. These data were expressed in the form of lines showing the isoconcentrations (Fig. 43). This figure also shows the area of the ore field, which in considerable part falls within the isoline representing a high nickel content in the soil – from 100 to 200 ten-thousandths of 1%.

The northern part of the surveyed area, represented on the map by heavy cross hatching, corresponds to the highest nickel content – greater than 200 units. Its origin can be attributed to the artificial contamination of the soil by the adjacent soil banks of the presently active Oktyabr'skii mine. The area adjacent to the mine also is contaminated by dust formed during the transporting of the ore. On the basis of our computations, and the data on the accompanying map (see Fig. 42), it has been established that the contaminated surface extends from the boundary of the mine to a distance of 500-600 m to the south.

When interpreting the results we excluded the nickel-contaminated surface from the total area covered by the survey. With respect to the remaining part of the area, beginning with profile 9, the natural distribution of nickel in soils is represented properly. The nickel concentration in the soil varies from 0.002 to 0.015%. A nickel content from 0.002 to 0.005% apparently should be regarded as the normal geochemical background surrounding the Oktyabr'skii deposit. A higher nickel content in the soil can be attributed to the influence of ore situated at a depth of 15 to 20 m or more. A comparison of the boundaries of the anomaly and the boundaries of the ore field reveals a correlation. Of

TABLE 34. Nickel and Cobalt Content in Soils and Plants (Ash), Oktyabr'skii Deposit

Profile No.	Sample No.	Soil and plant, site of sampling	Content.%		Ratio Ni : Co
			Ni	Co	
7	47	Chestnut, clayey loam,−200 m..........	0.0100	0.0008	12.2
7	48	White wormwood, −200 m	0.0100	0.0015	7
7	49	Dark chestnut, along control line.........	0.0094	0.0012	7.8
7	50	Common yarrow, along control line........	0.0075	0.0008	9.3
7	51	Chestnut, +200 m.....................	0.0110	0.0010	11
7	52	Common yarrow, +200 m..............	0.0080	0.0007	11.4
7	53	Chestnut, +400 m.....................	0.0060	0.0012	5
7	54	Common yarrow, +400 m..............	0.0075	0.0002	20
7	55	Chestnut, +600 m.....................	0.0020	0.0006	3.3
7	56-a	Common yarrow, +600 m	0.0075	0.0006	12.5
7	56-b	White wormwood, +600 m	0.0060	0.0005	12
7	57	Chestnut, −600 m	0.0090	0.0010	9
7	58	Steppe sage, −600 m	0.0065	0.0004	16
9	59	Chestnut, −400 m	0.0067	0.0004	17
9	60	White wormwood, −400 m..............	0.0071	0.0005	14
9	61	Chestnut, −200 m....................	0.0120	0.0004	30
9	62	White wormwood, −200 m.............	0.0075	0.0003	25
9	63	Dark chestnut, along control line.........	0.0100	0.0008	12.5
9	64	White wormwood, along control line	0.0088	0.0006	14.6
9	65	Chestnut, +200 m.....................	0.0100	0.0013	8
9	66	White wormwood, +200 m	0.0075	0.0005	15
9	67	Chestnut, +400 m....................	0.0110	0.0012	9
9	69	Chestnut, +600 m....................	0.0100	0.0010	10

course, the data from the preliminary sampling cannot provide more precise results because of the wide spacing of sampling points in the grid. However, a general tendency for the anomaly to be associated with the ore body is manifested quite well.

We made a more detailed survey in the southern part of the quadrangle, using grid "squares" measuring 50 × 100 m; this area is uncontaminated by the mine. The purpose of this study was to check the precise correlation between the ore and soil, and also to explain the conditions under which nickel and cobalt migrate to the surface, depending on the character of the covering rocks. The availability of detailed geological profiles, coinciding with certain of our profiles, will make it possible in the future to draw interesting conclusions concerning the influence of the thickness and character of the covering rocks on the conditions for the migration of nickel, and in general on the sensitivity of the method.

The data on cobalt do not provide sufficiently clear results on correlation between its content in the soil and the occurrence of ore. This can be attributed to the association of cobalt with ochers, which quite often are found in deposits.

The derived data from a survey of the humus layer of the soil revealed a relatively low nickel content in the soil over the Oktyabr'skii nickel deposit, almost 10 times lower than in the other deposits of the Kimpersaiskii group — Shcherbakovskii, Chugaevskii, and others. The reason for this is the great thickness of the covering rocks, screening the principal dispersion halo existing in the immediate vicinity of the ore.

In making a preliminary sampling of the soils, we at the same time selected samples of plants; the latter were reduced to ash and studied for their nickel and cobalt content. Table 34 gives data on the colorimetric determination of nickel with dimethylglyoxide (in the presence of persulfate) and cobalt with 1-nitroso-2-naphthol-3,6-sodium disulfonate after preliminary enrichment with rubeanic acid.

The data in Table 34 show relatively low nickel and cobalt contents in soils: the first in hundredths and thousandths, and the second in thousandths and ten-thousandths of 1%. The Ni : Co ratio is close to 12 : 1. The content of these elements in the ash of plants differs little from their content in the soils from which the plants were collected. The Ni : Co ratio in plants is somewhat higher than in soils.

By a comparison of zones with a high nickel content in soils and plants, it can be noted that the nickel content in soils correlates better with the zone of mineralization than the content in plants.

We selected several points at which soil samples Nos. 47, 61, and 65 were taken in order to check the influence of the thickness and character of the overburden on the nickel content of the soil. At the point at which soil sample No. 47 was taken, the ore was covered by 12 m of loam, 5 m of Tertiary clays, and 2 m of the kaolinized products of weathering of gabbro. The overburden was 19 m thick. The nickel content in the soil was 0.01%, which is anomalous, but not very high. At the point where sample No. 61 was taken, the ore was covered by 10 m of loam, 4 m of clay, and 2 m of the products of weathering of gabbro. The overburden was 16 m thick. The nickel content in the latter case was higher — 0.012%. The last case was sample No. 65, taken where the ore was covered by 12.5 m of loam and 9 m of clay. The total overburden was 21.5 m thick. The nickel content in the soil is lower than in the preceding sample — 0.01%.

Thus, a thickness of overburden up to 20 m is no obstacle to some increase in the nickel content in soil sampled from above ore. A decrease in the thickness of the overburden is reflected in an intensification of the anomaly, such as in sample No. 61, where the thickness of the overburden was 16 m, and the nickel content was 0.012%, and in sample No. 65, where the thickness of the overburden was 21.5 m and the nickel content was 0.01%.

Shcherbakovskii Nickel Deposit

A comparative study of the biogeochemical and the metallometric survey methods was made in the Shcherbakovskii nickel silicate deposit; this deposit is the only one where a metallometric survey has been made.

Investigations in the Shcherbakovskii nickel silicate deposit were made to clarify the reasons for the low effectiveness of the metallometric survey method in comparison with a biogeochemical survey.

The Shcherbakovskii deposit is situated on the gentle southwestern slope of the drainage divide between the Tygatsai and Shandysh Rivers and has a slightly dissected relief with elevations not exceeding 440-450 m (Abaturov, Nsanov, 1960). Nonuniformity of relief is related to outcrops of the bedrock — leached serpentinites and veins of gabbros, amphibolites, pyroxenites, and hornblendites — along whose contact the deposit was formed. The line of contact is tortuous; in the western part there are gabbro-amphibolites, while in the east there are serpentinites and taxites.

The principal ore-bearing rocks are the products of weathering of ultrabasic rocks: ochers, nontronitized and silicified leached serpentinites. They have developed to the greatest extent in the contact zone between the serpentinites (taxites) and gabbro dikes. The profile of the weathered crust and its composition are not unusual. There are ochers at top, followed by kaolinized products of weathering, gabbros, then nontronitized serpentinites and taxites, and at the base — weakly nontronitized or leached serpentinites, frequently carbonatized and opalized.

The ore deposit has a stratum-like position and a thickness of 10-15 m; it is covered by ochers and loams with a total thickness of 1 to 25 m. The covering deposits, in addition to loams and ochers, include varicolored and oolitic clays and glauconitic sands with a thickness of 8 to 10 m. The thickness of the quaternary loams rarely exceeds 8-10 m.

The deposit has a supergene origin; it was formed in the process of development of the weathered crust. The composition of the rocks making up the deposit — leached and concentrated serpentinites — differs sharply with respect to its content of ore and nonore minerals. The leached serpentinites contain up to 80% chrysotile and the nontronitized serpentinites consist of chlorite, montmorillonite, nontronite, oxides, and hydroxides of iron, manganese, opal, and quartz, with a varying content of ore elements — nickel and cobalt. For this reason the concept "ore" for a deposit of nickel silicate has an extremely conventional character, and the boundaries of ore bodies are determined exclusively by data from chemical analysis, applicable to conditions established by production (Abaturov, Nsanov, 1960).

The ferronickel ores of the Shcherbakovskii deposit are nontronites of a banded type and nontronitized serpentinites with a mean nickel content of about 1% and a mean cobalt content of about 0.05%. The nickel : cobalt ratio in the ore is 12 : 1-15 : 1.

It has been established that the content of thin clayey fractions in the ore smaller than 1 mm increases sharply toward the surface, for example, the content of fine fractions in weakly nontronitized serpentinites is about 50%, in nontronitized serpentinites about 60%, and in ochers 70-75%.

The content of ore elements of the weathered crust — nickel and iron — almost always is higher in the clayey fractions. The manganese and cobalt content often is greater in the medium fractions (1-2 mm).

TABLE 35. Content of SiO_2 and Ore Elements in Ferrous Minerals in %
(According to Abaturov and Nsanov, 1960)

	Manganese minerals from nontronitized serpentinites		In yellow ochers	In red ochers
	Fraction + 5mm	Fraction + 1 mm	Fraction + 1 mm	
SiO_2	–	7.33	8	6.25
Mn	35.53	31.79	29.55	10.98
Fe	6.34	–	–	–
Cr_2O_3	–	0.06	0.04	0.05
Ni	3.88	7.20	6.10	3.20
Co	1.70	4.57	1.50	0.71

The nonuniform distribution of nickel and cobalt in the different fractions of the ore substrate can be attributed to the different mineralogical composition of the fractions. For example, the fraction +1 mm contains: quartz, 27%; serpentine, 36%; amphibole, about 15%; nontronite, 14%; chlorite and jefferisite, 6%; and black ore minerals, primarily manganese oxides, 1%.

The +0.05 mm fraction consists for the most part of montmorillonite – beidellite with nontronite (75%) and chlorite (19%), about 1% of amphibole, pyroxene, and serpentine, and traces of quartz and black minerals.

The principal nickel-bearing minerals of the Shcherbakovskii deposit are the so-called stage minerals of the montmorillonite – beidellite group with nontronite and chlorite. The principal cobalt-bearing minerals in the weathered crust are black minerals, for the most part manganese and iron oxides and hydroxides. The nickel content in olive-green nontronites is up to 2%, the cobalt content 0.025%, and the Ni:Co ratio about 80:1. In black ore minerals the Ni:Co ratio is sharply displaced in the favor of cobalt and approaches unity.

It is entirely obvious that the behavior of cobalt in the weathered crust differs sharply from the behavior of nickel. Nevertheless, in tracing the Ni:Co ratio in the products of weathering and in the ore, there are no sharp deviations, apparently because we always are dealing with mixtures, not with pure minerals. The most perfect separation of nickel from cobalt occurs in nickel silicate minerals: garnierite $Ni_4(Si_4O_{10})(OH)_4$, revdinskite $(Ni, Mg)_6 \cdot (Si_4O_{10})(OH)_8$, garnierite-halloysite, and others, where the Ni:Co ratio attains 500:1 or more. On the other hand, the cobalt content often is greater than the nickel content in oxidized manganese minerals – manganese wad (asbolan wad).

With respect to the mineralogy of nontronitized and weakly nontronitized serpentinites, we note minerals of the montomorillonite – beidellite group, nontronite, saponite, and the halloysite group – ferrihalloysite, garnierite, and garnierite-halloysite – these being the principal carriers of nickel and oxidized siliceous ores.

The black minerals, as already mentioned, are manganese minerals, partly with magnetite, and chrome-spinel-lids with iron oxides and hydroxides. The greater part of the manganese, cobalt, and chromium is found in these minerals. The content of ore elements and SiO_2 in black minerals is shown in Table 35.

Among the nonmetalliferous minerals the most characteristic are calcium and magnesium carbonates, which are accumulated in the zone of leached carbonatized serpentinites, that is, in the lowermost horizon of the weathered crust. Dolomite and magnesite are the most common of the carbonates.

A second widespread nonmetalliferous component is silicon in the form of quartz, chalcedony, and opal. The migration of silicon coincides in a number of cases with the migration of calcium and magnesium during their movement from the upper part of the profile into the lower horizons. In contrast to magnesium, silica is accumulated in nontronitized and weakly nontronitized serpentinites in the form of talcs, but most commonly as opal-chalcedony-quartz vcins.

The mineralogical composition of the ore-bearing weathered crust and the distribution of individual chemical minerals is of help in analyzing the mechanism of formation of a siliceous nickel deposit. I. I. Ginzburg believes that the accumulation of nickel occurred as a result of the sorption of nickel by hydrous silicates. In this process ions of magnesium and calcium (and K, Na, etc.) are set free and migrate into the lower horizons of the profile. The minerals absorbing nickel are: ferrimontmorillonites and beidellites, ferrihalloysites, and vermiculites.

TABLE 36. Nickel Content in Natural Waters of the Kimpersaiskii Region

Sampling site	Date of sampling	Content, %
Well in alluvial deposits. Kimpersai village along banks of Ku-Agach River	July 20, 1960	$1.2 \cdot 10^{-6}$
Spring from alluvial deposits. Kimpersai village	July 20, 1960	$1.1 \cdot 10^{-6}$
Spring from alluvial deposits over serpentinites. Southwestern part of Kimpersai village	July 20, 1960	$1.2 \cdot 10^{-6}$
Ku-Agach River at Kimpersai village	July 20, 1960	$2.2 \cdot 10^{-6}$
Lake in basin of Eastern Kimpersaiskii nickel mine	Aug. 14, 1960	$2.4 \cdot 10^{-6}$
Lake in basin of "Gigant" chromium mine, Donskoi deposit	Aug. 3, 1960	$1.4 \cdot 10^{-6}$

The processes of weathering of serpentinites are accompanied by the reactions of oxidation, hydration, hydrolysis, and interion exchange, facilitated by the oxygen of the air and carbon dioxide.

On the basis of empirical data, it has been established that the relative mobility of individual chemical elements is dissimilar and can be expressed in the following series (according to Ginzburg):

$$Mg > Ca > Si > Ni > Fe^{2+} > Cr^{3+} > Al^{3+} > Ti^{4+} > Mn^{3+} > Co^{3+}.$$

The mobility of ore and other chemical elements is determined by the chemical and physicochemical properties of the ions, their susceptibility to step-by-step oxidation, hydrolysis, sorption on clayey and oxidized minerals (Mn, Co, Ni), and leaching.

A study of the residual products of the weathered crust — ochers — reveals that in some cases there is a total separation of individual elements — Ca, Mg, Mn, K, and Ni, and the accumulation of others — Fe^{3+}, Mn^{4+}, Co^{3+}, and others.

Nickel is noticeably carried downward from ochers, and there sorbed by nontronites and other clayey minerals. An important indicator of the mobility of ore elements is their presence in natural ground water, as well as their accumulation in the humus of soil plants.

Table 36 is given to show the distribution of nickel in the natural waters of the region. The data in Table 36 show appreciable quantities of nickel in the waters of the Kimpersaiskii region, which suggests that they have a possible influence on an increase of nickel in soils and plants.

Before proceeding to a discussion of our investigations for a comparative evaluation of the effectiveness of the biogeochemical exploration method and a metallometric survey, we first will briefly discuss the soil-geological and geobotanical peculiarities of the Shcherbakovskii deposit in which these investigations were made.

The topography of the deposit consists of alternating highlands with gentle slopes and valleys and reflects non-uniformity in the geological structure in individual parts of the deposit. In the northern part, in the Beskudukkii sector, there are nontronites and nontronitized serpentinites; in the central part leached and carbonatized serpentinites are predominant. The higher sector consists of ore-bearing nontronitized serpentinites and kaolinized gabbro-amphibolites. In the southern part there are rocks of a banded complex — weathered and dense, ore-bearing and without ore.

The soil and vegetation cover of the deposit is distributed in accordance with the relief and the geological structure. In ore-bearing sectors there are clayey and ocherous chestnut soils. Light-colored chestnut loamy soils of a light composition predominate in the lowest northwestern part. Very stony chestnut soils are found in the southern part.

The vegetation background in the deposit consists of a varied grass–sheep's fescue–feather grass grouping, occupying low areas and sloping parts of the deposit area. On the elevated part of the area there is a dominant association of wormwood–sheep's fescue–feather grass, while in the southern part of the quadrangle there is a scattering of other associations — goldilocks–feather grass and Agnus castus–black wormwood–ground pine.

The correlation of the vegetation associations can be seen clearly from the geological and geobotanical maps of the central part of the Shcherbakovskii deposit.

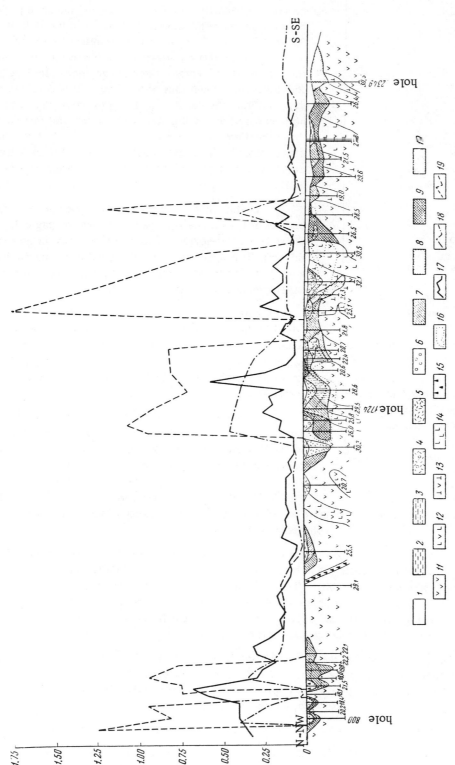

Fig. 44. Comparison of the results of biogeochemical and lithochemical surveys in the Shcherbakovskii nickel silicate deposit. 1) Clayey loams; 2) clays; 3) sandstones; 4) ochers from rocks of a banded complex; 5) kaolinized gabbro-amphibolites; 6) ochers from serpentinites; 7) nontronitized serpentinites; 8) nontronites from rocks of a banded complex; 9) slightly nontronitized serpentinites; 10) silicified serpentinites; 11) leached and dense serpentinites; 12) rocks of a banded complex (serpentinites + gabbroids); 13) rocks of a banded complex (serpentinites + pyroxenites); 14) dense gabbro-amphibolites; 15) weathered and dense gabbro-diabases; 16) outline of ore body; 17) curve showing nickel content, according to biogeochemical data; 18) curve showing nickel content, according to metallometric data; 19) curve showing nickel content, according to data from exploratory drilling.

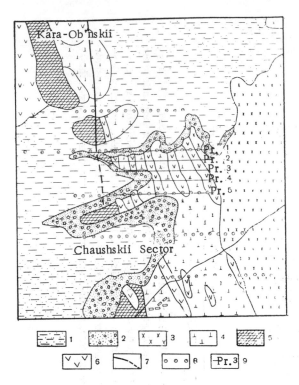

Fig. 45. Geological map of the Chaushskii sector.
1) Sands, gravel (Maastricht); 2) gravels, sands
(Campanian); 3) tuffs, extrusives (Chaushskii stage);
4) shales, extrusives, pyroclastic rocks (Lushnikovskii stage); 5) shales, quartzites (Ebetinskii stage);
6) serpentinites; 7) line of tectonic dislocations; 8)
planned boreholes of the Kimpersaiskii Geological
Exploration Party; 9) biogeochemical survey profile
lines.

With respect to the problem of the migration of chemical elements under the conditions prevailing in the Kimpersaiskii peridotite complex, we applied the example of
the distribution of the carbonate horizon in the soils of the
Shcherbakovskii deposit. It was established that the appearance of the carbonate horizon at the surface or closer to the
surface and its thickness reflect the geomorphological and
soil-geological conditions of the deposit to a considerable
degree. From the geochemical point of view the carbonate
horizon constitutes a singular shield which prevents the loss
of ore-bearing and ore-free chemical elements from the
upper humus horizon (downward in the profile), as is indicated by their appreciable accumulation in the upper soil
horizon.

A characteristic indicator of the appearance of carbonates at the surface is a specific brownish-gray color of
the soil; the salt-loving plants mentioned earlier grow on
this soil. It is apparent that relief conditions and the character of the underlying rocks are of great importance in the
development of carbonate salinization.

Figure 44 shows a schematic soil profile along the line
III-III in the Shcherbakovskii nickel deposit. The soils are
loamy, developed on the alkaline products of weathering of
serpentinites and the country rock: leached serpentinites,
kaolinized gabbro-amphibolites, nontronitized and silicified
serpentinites, etc.

The saline horizon of effervescence outcrops at the
surface or is displaced 25-30 cm downward. The thickness
of the horizon varies from 20 to 150 cm. Tongues of carbonaceous loam penetrate along cracks to a depth of 200-
250 cm. On the other hand, calcareous loam often is permeated by a dark humus substrate, washed into cracks formed
by desiccation of the soil by the rain. In both cases there is a disruption of the uniformity of the sometimes dense
covering rocks and dense clays become easily permeable for solutions and plant roots.

Applying the geological data obtained during a detailed drilling of the deposit, and data from the metallometric
survey, we attempted to compare the effectiveness of the biogeochemical exploration and metallometric survey methods. For this purpose we employed the data on profile III-III, shown in Fig. 44, which were available from the Kimpersaiskii Geological Exploration Party. The profile intersects the deposit from northwest to southeast over a distance
of 3600 m. Figure 44 shows the geological profile and data on the nickel content in rocks (ores), metallometric
samples, and in the humus layer of the soil. We obtained the soil data in the field.

The diagram shown as Fig. 44 indicates that the curve corresponding to the nickel content in ore correlates well
with the data obtained in the biogeochemical survey. The curve obtained on the basis of metallometric data, however,
does not always reflect the presence of ore at depth; for example, between boreholes Nos. 1800 and 2282 there was a
major zone, situated relatively close to the earth's surface, which was missed.

The data obtained in the biogeochemical survey very clearly reveal the position of this zone, and all the others.

On the diagram, to the north of borehole No. 815, the data from the biogeochemical survey reveal the presence
of a small ore-bearing zone. The absence of boreholes in this area does not make it possible to judge whether the
zone exists.

The data on the Oktyabr'skii and Shcherbakovskii deposits which we made available shook the unwarranted
skepticism of the geologists of the Kimpersaiskii Joint Party toward geochemical methods. However, as a final demon-
stration of the method and its application as an exploration technique under the conditions prevailing in northwestern

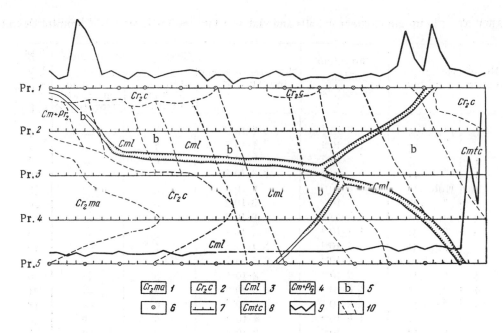

Fig. 46. Results of a biogeochemical survey for nickel in the Chaushskii sector. 1) Upper Cretaceous (Maastricht stage); 2) Upper Cretaceous (Campanian stage); 3) Cambrian system (Lushnikovskii stage); 4) Ebetinskii stage; 5) serpentinites; 6) planned boreholes of the Kimpersaiskii Geological Exploration Party; 7) biogeochemical survey profiles and sampling points; 8) Chaushskii stage; 9) anomalous contents of nickel in soil on 1st and 5th profiles; 10) boundaries of stages.

Kazakhstan it was necessary to prove the effectiveness of the biogeochemical method in specific exploration work. With this objective in mind, we undertook exploration for nickel and cobalt in areas where drilling work was planned. We now will discuss this work briefly.

Biogeochemical Exploration for Nickel and Cobalt in the Chaushskii Sector

The Chaushskii exploration sector is situated 15 km to the east of the rayon center Kherson in Aktyubinskii Oblast. The geological structure of the region is shown on the schematic map (Fig. 45). The region is part of the northern Kherson continuation of the Kimpersaiskii ultrabasite complex. In this sector there are a number of contacts between ultrabasic rocks (serpentinites) and metamorphosed extrusives and tuffs. There is a major fault line in the western part of the sector. These factors suggested the possible presence of mineralization in the sector. The work program of the Kimpersaiskii Geological Exploration Party called for the drilling of this entire area of about 20 km² during the two or three years to follow.

In order to decrease the amount of work involved, we proposed our assistance to the Kimpersaiskii Geological Exploration Party in the form of a biogeochemical survey of a part of the area planned for geological exploration work.

The area covered by the biogeochemical survey (soils) is shown on the map (Fig. 45) as a rectangle; it was covered by a geological survey using a grid in which the grid "squares" measured 50 × 250 m (the grid for drilling purposes has grid "squares" measuring 250 × 1000 m).

The results of the biogeochemical survey have been represented on a schematic map of the sector on which diagrams have been plotted showing the nickel content in soil samples along profiles 1 and 5 (Fig. 46).

The survey data revealed the presence of major anomalies on profiles 1 and 5. Despite the fact that a large part of the surveyed area was cultivated, the work of collecting data was completed in two days, during which 250 samples were collected over an area of 2.5 km².

The derived results were conveyed immediately to the Kimpersaiskii Geological Exploration Party for a practical check. It is to be hoped that this work will show local geological organizations that it is necessary to apply the biogeochemical exploration method, which, in conjunction with other geochemical and geological methods, will most effectively solve problems involved in the exploration of ore deposits.

TABLE 37. Chromium Content in Soils and Plants of the Geofizicheskoe IV Chromite Deposit

No. of profile	No. of pit or hole	Chromium content in soil, %	Chromium content in plants, %	Character and thickness of cover, m		Thickness of ore-bearing layer, m
				Mesozoic sediment. formations	Leached dunites and serpentinites	
0	Pit 26	$1.2 \cdot 10^{-1}$	$6.6 \cdot 10^{-2}$	7	—	1
0	" 93	$1.3 \cdot 10^{-1}$	$7.1 \cdot 10^{-2}$	7	—	1
1	" 25	$5 \cdot 10^{-2}$	$9 \cdot 10^{-2}$	6	—	3
1	" 11	$5 \cdot 10^{-2}$	$7.2 \cdot 10^{-2}$	6	—	10
2	Hole 31	$5.5 \cdot 10^{-2}$	$6 \cdot 10^{-2}$	6	6	25
2	" 29	$7 \cdot 10^{-2}$	$3 \cdot 10^{-2}$	8	12	20
2	Pit 6	$5 \cdot 10^{-2}$	$9 \cdot 10^{-2}$	10	—	14
3	" 31	$1.1 \cdot 10^{-1}$	$1.2 \cdot 10^{-2}$	5	—	6
3	Hole 16	$1 \cdot 10^{-1}$	$8.5 \cdot 10^{-2}$	7	—	29
3	" 22	$1 \cdot 10^{-1}$	$2.5 \cdot 10^{-2}$	7	—	19
4	" 11	$2 \cdot 10^{-2}$	$2 \cdot 10^{-2}$	5	18	6
4	" 4	$4.5 \cdot 10^{-2}$	$8.5 \cdot 10^{-2}$	8	—	21
5	" 79	$6.2 \cdot 10^{-2}$	$2.3 \cdot 10^{-2}$	6	—	18
5	" 1	$1.5 \cdot 10^{-1}$	$4 \cdot 10^{-2}$	5	9	24
6	" 12	$4.5 \cdot 10^{-2}$	$9 \cdot 10^{-2}$	3	19	18
6	" 20	$1.1 \cdot 10^{-1}$	$2 \cdot 10^{-2}$	6	3	12
7	Pit 16	$2.4 \cdot 10^{-2}$	$9 \cdot 10^{-2}$	5	28	15
7	Hole 30	$1.2 \cdot 10^{-1}$	Slight traces	5	20	28
8	" 46	$1.2 \cdot 10^{-1}$	$3 \cdot 10^{-2}$	4	14	7
9	" 45	$1.0 \cdot 10^{-1}$	$3.3 \cdot 10^{-2}$	2	47	12
10	" 52(Pit 3)	$1.2 \cdot 10^{-1}$	$3.5 \cdot 10^{-2}$	3	35	12
12	" 82	$8.2 \cdot 10^{-2}$	$7.4 \cdot 10^{-2}$	1	56	46

Chromite Deposit (Geofizicheskoe IV)

Ultrabasic rocks — dunites, and serpentinites, the products of metamorphosis of dunites — are the source of chromium in the Yuzhno-Kimpersaiskii ore region where the investigations were made. In the deposit studied the principal ore minerals of chromium are chromites or chrome-spinellids, which are represented by the formula

$$(Mg, Fe)(Cr, Al, Fe)_2O_4 \cdot \quad (Sokolov\ [1948]).$$

In the weathered crust, the bivalent iron of the chromite is oxidized, and as a result the crystal lattice of the mineral is destroyed. In dry and hot regions with high oxidation conditions the chromium (Cr^{3+}) in the soil-geological profile is oxidized to a pentavalent state in the anion CrO_4^{2-}, as a result of which it acquires a high mobility in the form of chromate-alkaline metals. In this form, the chromium obviously migrates with the soil and ground water, and as a result it can be found in mine water and fissure water in quantities from 0.001 to 0.01% in the dry residue.

Chromium in appreciable quantities is carried beyond the boundaries of the deposit in the process of weathering of ore-bearing serpentinites. A certain quantity enters the soil and is intercepted by surface plants.

The Geofizicheskoe IV deposit is part of the Dzhangiz-Agachinskii group of Yuzhno-Kimpersaiskii chromium ore deposits, situated on the eastern slope of the Or'-Ilekskii drainage divide. The region is a semidesert plain, slightly dissected by a system of shallow valleys. The chromite deposit consists of dunites and dunite-serpentinites of the southeastern part of the Kimpersaiskii ultrabasic complex. The dunite-serpentinite country rock, as a result of weathering, has been transformed into an unconsolidated mass, chloritized and talcized. The ore bodies consist of chrome-spinellid in dunite-serpentinite. In the surface zones there are remnants of the ancient weathered crust, sometimes covered by Tertiary and other sedimentary deposits. The ore bodies constitute a series of blocks and lenses, gently or steeply sloping from the surface to a depth of 200-300 m. The chromium ore consists of chrome-spinellid, serpentine, and olivine. The ore contains chlorite, calcite, magnesite, as well as magnetite and iron sulfides (pyrite).

The leached serpentinites have a high moisture content because of their considerable jointing. The water table varies between 18 and 20 m in depth, depending on the relief. The deposit has a completely smooth surface. The continuous cover of chestnut soils is held stably by a feather grass—sheep's fescue vegetation. Because of the high level

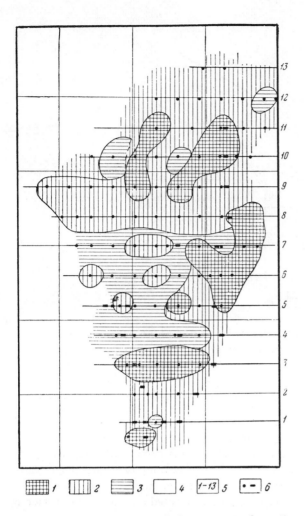

1 ⊞ 2 ⊟ 3 ▤ 4 ☐ 5 [1-13] 6 •−

Fig. 47. Isoconcentrations of chromium in the soils of the Chetvertoe Geofizicheskoe deposit. 1) Chromium content from 0.1 to 0.15%; 2) chromium content from 0.05 to 0.1%; 3) chromium content from 0.01 to 0.05%; 4) geochemical background; 5) geological profiles; 6) biogeochemical sampling points.

of the water table (averaging about 20 m from the surface), a large part of the commercial ore deposit falls in the zone of ground water circulation. In many places there are blocks of chromite which rise above the ground water level in the form of islands and often come close to the surface. A study of the depth of an ore body as a function of the ground water level makes it possible to explain the known leveling out of the chromium content in the ash of plants from those sectors of the deposit in which the ores lie below the ground water level.

The study of the chromite deposit was made by the soil-plant method in exactly the same way as in the nickel deposits. The soil and plant samples were taken using the existing rectangular grid at the sites of boreholes and prospect holes present in the deposit. At each borehole (or prospect hole) we selected soil samples in the A horizon, from the surface to a depth of 10 cm, and a sample of the vegetation, in most cases feather grass Stipa sp. In addition, some of the samples were taken on extensions of the geological profiles beyond the boundaries of the ore field in order to compare the chromium content over the deposit and beyond its boundaries. More than 200 samples of soils and plants were investigated for their chromium content. Two methods were used: colorimetric and spectral (Belyaev and Pavlenko [1954]). In order not to burden this book with a great mass of numerical data, we will illustrate the results in a single small table (Table 37), characterizing all the numerical data rather well.

The data in Table 37 show that the chromium content in soils and in the ash of plants from the chromite deposit is approximately identical and fluctuates near the mean value — about $1 \cdot 10^{-1}\%$. In attempting to characterize the peculiarities of the distribution of chromium in the soil as a function of the thickness of the overlying rocks or the "volume" of the ore stratum, we concluded that the chromium content of soils has no direct dependence on these factors. The only possible exception is when the ore is situated in the immediate vicinity of the surface. For example, there is a good correlation between the points at boreholes 35 and 37 (profile 7), 18 and 20 (profile 6), and the whole of profile 3 (Fig. 47). In these cases the chromium content in the soil increases appreciably. With respect to the other profiles, correlation is either totally absent, or is very frequently disrupted; the boundaries of the ore body therefore cannot be drawn using the lines showing isoconcentrations of chromium.

We drew a geological profile containing not only geological data, but also data, in the form of a curve, showing the chromium concentration in the soil. It was found that the chromium maxima do not fall in the ore-bearing sectors, but instead appear to be displaced, while soils with a low or moderate chromium content often lie closer to the ore blocks (Fig. 48). In attempting to explain the reason for this noncorrespondence in the distribution of chromium in soils over the ore deposit, we made a microscopic study of individual mineralogical components of the soil. It was established that the principal mass of chromium entering into the makeup of the soil is found in the form of unmodified chromite; however, the mobile part, which can be carried off by 2% HCl, is only about 10%, and the part which can be carried off by water is still less. The displacement of the chromium maxima can be attributed only to the mechanical movement of stable grains of chromite in the upper soil layer.

The insignificant percentage of chromium in a mobile state nevertheless is expressed in the accumulation of chromium by plants. In their life functions the plants utilize only that part of the chromium which is in an easily assimilable form, that is, in the form of soluble or dissolved chromates. These solutions migrate easily from the lower

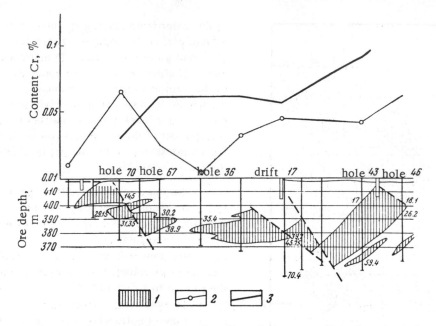

Fig. 48. Distribution of chromium in soils and plants as a function of ore depth (profile 8). 1) Chromium ore; 2) chromium content in plant ash (exaggerated by a factor of 2); 3) chromium content in soil.

ore horizons. Mine waters contain about $1 \cdot 10^{-6}\%$ chromium. These quantities also, for the most part, apply to the mobile chromium in the soil used by plants.

We compiled a sketch map showing the isoconcentrations of chromium in plants (Fig. 49), much like the soil map. When comparing the topography of the distribution of chromium in plants and the geological data, it is possible to note a rather clearly defined correlation of the chromium maxima in plants. It is characteristic that plants show a high reaction to chromium even at those points where the ore is situated below the ground water level. This is evidence that in a zone of the chromite deposit there are stagnant waters which are connected directly to the surface by capillary action.

The entire southern and southeastern part of the deposit with the first through the fifth profiles, where the ore approaches close to the surface (to a depth of 10-15 m), is characterized by a clearly defined high chromium content in plants, averaging from 0.08 to 0.2%, which considerably exceeds even the nickel and cobalt concentration in plants over nickel deposits. Almost all the samples taken near the margin, and in general outside the ore field, usually show small chromium concentrations in the plant ash, of the order of 0.01%. These concentrations obviously constitute the background chromium dispersion for the entire region over which the peridotite complex is found. Similar quantities of chromium were found in the ash of plants collected over nickel deposits. On the basis of the above facts, the conclusion can be drawn that soils over chromite deposits are enriched for the most part with unmodified chromite, and on this basis, a mineralogical and chemical analysis of the soil unquestionably can indicate the presence of a chromite deposit without its topography being relatively precise. An analysis of plant ash and the plotting of chromium data on a map showing isolines of concentrations cannot only indicate the presence of a deposit, but also can define its boundaries rather well.

The extensive areas of nickel and chromium deposits and their closeness to the surface has made it possible to trace the conditions under which chemical elements migrate in the biogeochemical profile: ore—ground water—soil—plants. The existence of a correlation has been established between the content of metals in ores, soils, and plants. On this basis it has been possible to outline the dispersion haloes of ore deposits and define the preliminary boundaries of the deposit by the plotting of the isolines of concentrations of nickel and chromium in soils (and plants) on a map.

It has been demonstrated on the basis of numerous examples that an Ni:Co ratio in soils and plants over nickel deposits of 10:1-20:1, in contrast to the usual ratio (4:1), is an important exploration indicator of nickel ores.

The influence of physical geography and geological and geomorphological conditions on the accumulation and distribution of nickel, cobalt, and other elements of the family in soils and plants over ore deposits has been clarified.

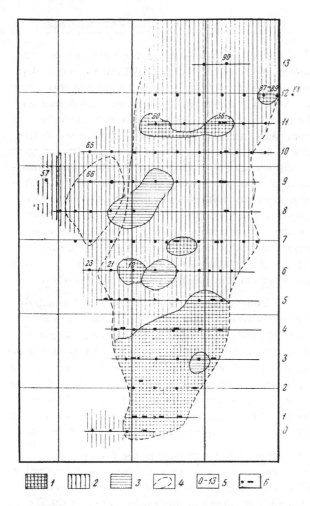

Fig. 49. Isoconcentration of chromium in plants of the Chetvertoe Geofizicheskoe deposit. Chromium content in ash: 1) from 0.05 to 0.1%; 2) from 0.01 to 0.05%; 3) less than 0.01%; 4) outlines of deposit; 5) geological profiles; 6) sampling points.

In particular, the importance of the climatic factor has been established. In chernozem and chestnut steppe soils the accumulation of nickel and cobalt occurs in the uppermost part of horizon A, while in the podzols of the forest zone it is closer to the ore body. Therefore, in the first case the principal exploration indicator is soils, and in the second— woody vegetation and the high humus content of the upper layer of the soil. This can be attributed to the disruption of the mobility of elements due to soil-forming processes, etc.

A study has been made of the various geological conditions influencing the sensitivity of the exploration method. It has been found that the accumulation of nickel in soils and plants is greater the higher the percentage content of nickel in the ore. The thickness of the overburden, if it does not exceed 20-30 m, is no hindrance to the use of the method. The character of the rocks covering the ore, soil varieties (in the same climatic zone), and the hydrological conditions in the nickel deposits of the Southern Urals do not significantly affect the use of the method. The geomorphological conditions of the deposits are not reflected in the distribution of nickel and cobalt in the soils, but there is an accumulation of copper only in the higher part of the quadrangle, clearly reflecting the hypsometric conditions of the deposit.

The mobile compounds of nickel, cobalt, and copper in the biogeochemical profile are forms of bivalent metals— chlorides, sulfates, and bicarbonates. In the case of chromium, the higher degrees of oxidation (chromates) are more characteristic. None are present in soils in significant quantities, as was established precisely by a study of water fractions.

Carbonates and organic compounds (in horizon A) constitute the principal reserve of nickel, copper, and cobalt in soils. In the case of nickel it is not impossible that there are isomorphic replacements in complex ferromagnesian silicates of the montmorillonite type and the formation of hydrosilicates, leading to a decrease of the soluble fraction of nickel under specific pH conditions.

The characteristic environmental-geochemical peculiarities of the studied Trans-Ural province are: 1) a dry continental climate; 2) alkaline conditions in the recent process of weathering and migration of ore elements in the soil-geological profile; 3) dark-chestnut and steppe soils on an ancient weathered crust of ultrabasites or ancient and recent covering sedimentary formations; 4) a xerophytic feather grass—sheep's fescue and wormwood—grass vegetation, forming a stable hummocky sod in the upper soil layer; 5) the presence of a carbonate horizon at the surface or at a depth of 20-30 cm, with a thickness of 1-1.5 m.

All these peculiarities of the studied zone favor the accumulation and retention of ore elements in the soil humus layer. For example, the deep root system of the xerophytic vegetation facilitates the subtraction of chemical elements from the lower horizons of the soil profile and their retention by the humus. The alkaline reaction and the shielding effect of the carbonate horizon hinder the loss of the nickel and cobalt ions into the lower-lying layers of the profile. This apparently explains why the biogeochemical method is more effective under specific conditions than the lithochemical method. At the same time, it should be noted that the greater effect of the concentration of nickel and cobalt in the humus layer of the soil in comparison with the ash of plants indicates the superiority of a soil survey over a plant survey. The great effective depth of the method (20-25 m), together with other good qualities, makes it suitable for use in the exploration of nickel and other ores under the conditions prevailing in the Southern Urals and elsewhere.

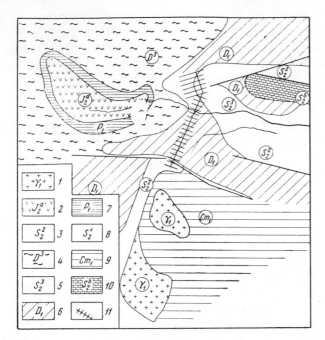

Fig. 50. Schematic geological map of the On-Kazhaa region. 1) Acidic granites, granite-porphyries; 2) sandstones, aleurolites, coaly shales; 3) limestones, shales; 4) varicolored sandstones, intercalations of fine-gravel conglomerates and limestones; 5) reddish sandstones; 6) extrusives and tuffs, primarily basic, sandstones, aleurolites; 7) sandstones, fine-gravel conglomerates; 8) conglomerates, sandstones with intercalations of limestones; 9) porphyrites and tuffs; 10) limestones with intercalations of aleurolites, marls, and sandstones; 11) soil sampling grid.

2. Tuvinskii Copper–Nickel–Cobalt Deposit

The experience with biogeochemical investigations in the Southern and Central Urals has shown that the distribution of heavy metals in soils and plants over ore deposits is dependent to a considerable degree on the geological, climatic, and soil conditions in the region. As a further check on the method, it was desirable to carry out investigations in the eastern and southeastern regions of the USSR, characterized by an abundance of mineral resources and a great variety of natural conditions. With this in mind, the carrying out of biogeochemical investigations in the Tuvinian ASSR was the most desirable, since it made it possible to judge the applicability of the method in other immense areas of the Asiatic part of the USSR — Eastern and Central Siberia, the Altai, Kazakhstan, and elsewhere.

A biogeochemical party of the V. I. Vernadskii Institute of Geochemistry and Analytical Chemistry of the USSR, under the direction of the author, began to operate in Tuva in 1952. It was attached to the Tuvinskii Complex Expedition of the Council for the Study of Productive Resources of the Academy of Sciences of the USSR. We will now discuss the experience obtained in the investigations made in accordance with the program for solution of the problems formulated in the work.

Geology and Geomorphology of the Region

The part of the Tuvinian ASSR which we studied adjoins the Ulug-Khemskii basin on the south and is situated in the basin of the middle course of the Elegesta River. The region belongs to the northern part of the foothills formed by tectonic scarps of the Western and Eastern Tannu-Ola Ranges (Vostochno-Tuvinskii anticlinorium), and is the meeting point of the most important orographic elements of Tuva (Lebedeva [1938], Kuznetsov [1946], (1948), Teodorovich [1949]).

The investigated sector (about 20 km in length) extends between two mountainous highlands, attaining an elevation of 1400 m; the first separates it from the Tannu-Ola, and the second from the Tuvinskii depression. In geomorphological respects the region can be characterized as moderately high mountain, within which there are a great many pointed peaks and crests, separated by valleys and ravines. The region is well covered by residual material and alluvial deposits, and its geological study is difficult.

The geological structure of the region includes ancient strata characteristic of the Eastern Tannu-Ola — Cambrian extrusives and extrusive-sedimentary rocks of the Upper Silurian and Lower Devonian. Within the region the core of the anticlinorium is made up of Lower Cambrian extrusives, with granitic intrusions emerging at the surface; it represents a complex of rocks of the Lower Caledonian folding (Krutov, 1955). Two horizons stand out in the Lower Cambrian rocks: at the bottom — one with a basic composition (diabasic porphyrites and tuffs), and at the top — one with an acidic composition (porphyrites, felsite-porphyries, their tuffs and breccia).

Marine sedimentary rocks of the Upper Silurian are laid down in nonconformity on the Lower Cambrian extrusives. In the lower part of the profile there is a predominance of sandstones with intercalations of siltstones and calcareous rocks, transformed into skarns, and in the upper part — reddish sandstones and conglomerates. In a number of cases the sedimentary complex is covered by a sedimentary-extrusive suite (D_1) of tuffs, welded tuffs, tuff conglomerates, and breccias, with intercalations of sandstones. Among the intrusive rocks the most widespread are granites and granosyenites, with a secondary development of diorites, granodiorites, and porphyries. Devonian sandstones, limestones, and conglomerates predominate in the northwestern part of the region, locally covered by recent alluvial deposits of no great thickness (Fig. 50).

The intrusions of the Caldeonian folding are associated with the formation of a number of deposits in Tuva (Vasil'ev, 1947), especially sulfide and sulfide-arsenide deposits, where the biogeochemical investigations were made. The region between these deposits (the On-Kazhaa River area) was promising for cobalt, nickel, and copper. The discovery of fault lines and other dislocation processes in this sector made it possible to postulate the presence of ore concentrations here, and biogeochemical exploration work accordingly was carried out.

The nonuniformity of the rocks making up the region and the influence of later tectonic activity are the reasons for the great surface dissection. In this region, over an area of 200 km², there are dozens of scattered steep-sloped hills which rise up to 300 m above the general surface. Despite this, the bedrock (with the exception of several outcrops) is well covered by a soil mantle with rather abundant vegetation, consisting of alternating forest groves and thickets of mountain steppe brush.

The hydrography of the studied region is for the most part characterized by the existence of numerous dry ravines which carry melt water and the rainfall from showers into the On-Kazhaa River and through it into the Elegest River, the principal drainage artery. Spring and summer water penetrates into the unconsolidated talus deposits and then along fissures into the crystalline rocks. It is found in mine drifts, sometimes at considerable depths. This water is the vehicle for the vertical and horizontal migration of the ions of heavy metals, which results in the appearance of dispersion haloes in soils and residual material. In the permafrost zone there is superpermafrost water which often appears at the surface in the form of insignificant springs. Its influence on the migration of the chemical elements is extremely limited because its zone of penetration extends only tens, or sometimes hundreds of centimeters from the surface.

In dry seasons of the year the region is without water. The ground water, associated with the extremely low channel of the Elegest River, extends to a considerable depth, to the level of the absolute elevation of the water in the river, that is, to a depth of 200-300 m. Its influence on the exchange of elements in the soil-geological profile therefore is extremely limited.

Climate

The deposit is situated in the zone of mountain-steppe and mountain-forest landscapes with steppe chestnut and gray forest soils. The climatic conditions of Tuva change considerably from north to south, from the Sayan to the Tannu-Ola foothills. In the central part of Tuva there is a relatively small region (350 km in length and 120 km wide) of semidesert, surrounded by rather moist mountain ranges. On the south the central Tuvinskii basin is bounded by the dry Mongolian steppe of the Eastern and Western Tannu-Ola, while on the north it is bounded by the Sayan. Despite the excess of moisture in the mountains and the taiga character of the northern slopes, the prevalent climate in Tuva is well-expressed continental, with extremely low temperatures in winter and extremely high temperatures in the middle of summer. The nearness of the deserts of Central and Soviet Central Asia contributes to this continentality, as does the general great distance of the country from the world oceans.

The amount of precipitation in the central part of Tuva (Kyzyl) does not exceed 200-230 mm. The mean annual temperatures of the Tuvinskaya Oblast are negative (-3.5 to $-5°C$), and the absolute temperature range is 96°, from $+39$ to $-57°C$.

As pointed out by B. F. Petrov [1952], the precipitation regime does not sufficiently moisten the soils of Tuva, especially in the central steppe part. Snow water is not utilized by the soil because it evaporates before the soil is thawed. In contrast to the arid spring, shower precipitation in the summer is not infrequent and is the principal source of soil moisture. The general moisture deficit, the short summer, and the considerable freezing of the soil are the factors responsible for the poor development of soil profiles and their salinization. The shortage of moisture results in the formation of carbonates in the chestnut soils, sometimes within several centimeters of the soil surface.

Vertical zonality in Tuva is of greater significance than north-south or east-west zonality. In Tuva there is an arid climate, which includes steppe and semidesert, a humid climate in the mountain-forest part of Tuva, and a polar climate in the high-mountain part. In all areas the exposure of the mountain slopes to the sun is of great importance. With respect to its climate, the studied region occupies an intermediate position between arid and humid. The influence of slope exposure is expressed in an alternation of larch taiga and steppe, and therefore in a change of soil varieties.

Soils

The soil cover of Tuva still has not been studied in many regions, particularly in the region of the On-Kazhaa River, where the biogeochemical investigations were made. According to the data supplied by Petrov [1952] and others,

Sample No.	Sampling site	Horizon and soil depth, m		pH
106	Profile 1. Northern sector, trench 561, gray mountain-forest soil	A₁	0-10	6.30
107	Dark brown clayey loam	B	30-36	6.78
108	Light gray calcareous clayey loam.	C	50-55	7.70
109	" " " " "	C	100-105	8.12
110	" " " " "	C	195-200	7.90
115	Profile 2. Northern sector, trench 561, gray mountain-forest soil	A₁	0-10	6.00
116	Dark brown clayey loam	B	35-40	6.38
117	Light gray calcareous clayey loam.	C	60-65	7.75
118	" " " " "	C	160-165	8.00

the soils of Tuva are characterized by a great variety — from peaty mountain-tundra to light chestnut steppe soils. The reasons for the areal nonuniformity of the soils of Tuva are the continental climate and the relief. The influence of relief is expressed in the formation of vertical zonality of the soils and reversed zonality due to the southern and northern exposure of slopes. There are steppe soils (chestnut, chernozem) on the southern slopes to great elevations, but on the northern slopes there are gray mountain-forest and podzol soils.

A distinguishing characteristic of the soils of Tuva is the poor development of soil-forming processes; this is associated with erosion and climatic peculiarities. The soil cover in the region of the On-Kazhaa River includes few varieties. This can be attributed to the moderate elevation of the mountains, since the individual peaks rise only 200 to 300 m above the valley floors. Gray mountain-forest, chestnut, and chernozem soils are the most common.

The gray forest soils are found in the lower zone of pure larch and birch forests with a rich grass cover consisting of typical meadow-forest forms. These are soils in large part heavy in mechanical composition and have a peaty upper layer. The thickness of the A horizon on slopes with a southern exposure is considerably greater than on slopes with a northern exposure.

The following is the description of a soil profile in an area of mixed forest, obtained on the northern slope of a high hill (northern sector, profile 22, according to Makarova): A_0, 0.5-10 cm, very peaty litter, consisting of mosses and residue of litter-fall. A_1, 0-10 cm, dark gray, high humus and moisture content. A_2, 10-15 cm, loamy, peaty, weakly podzolized. B, 15-40 cm, yellow-brown, clayey, unconsolidated, structureless, with traces of carbonate inclusions, effervesces with application of HCl. C, 55-65 cm, light-gray loam, very effervescent with application of HCl; at a depth of 1.5 m it undergoes a transition to rocky residual material.

A characteristic feature of this profile and others is the small thickness of the humus horizon and the closeness to the surface of the carbonate illuvial horizon. According to the data supplied by Petrov, such soils are characterized by a high humus content in the upper A_1 horizon, often exceeding 10-12%. At a depth of 10-15 cm in the A_2 horizon there is a decrease in the humus content to 2-3% and it continues to decrease at greater depths.

The distribution of humus and carbonates in the soil horizons is in good agreement with the pH value. Table 38 gives the pH of water extracts of gray mountain-forest soils of the northern part of the deposit. These data show the acid reaction of the soil in the A_1 horizon and the neutral reaction in the B horizon. Lower, in the C horizon (light-gray loam), it is clearly an alkaline reaction, and the pH for the most part averages about 8.

Beneath the humus layer of the gray mountain-forest soil there is a podzolized A_2 horizon (15-30 cm) of brownish-gray color with siliceous fragments; the underlying B horizon is of a brownish color with traces of inwash (does not effervesce), and finally, the C horizon is carbonate in character, in the form of a whitish zone, clearly separating the soil layer from the rock. Each of these horizons differs in structure, pH, and content of ore elements.

There are chernozem and chestnut soils in the steppe areas. Chestnut soils cover all the steep southern and southeastern slopes. For the most part the chernozems develop under steppes with various kinds of grasses or mixed feather grass and wormwood, on the boundary between the forest and steppe and in the intermontane valleys of the ranges. All chernozems in Tuva are thin. The thickness of the A horizon averages 20 cm.

A characteristic of the chernozems is the shallow depth of the carbonate horizon, for the most part at a depth of 30 cm.

Among the peculiarities of the local chernozems is an absence of a lumpy or granular structure. They usually are all structureless. There usually is a rapid transition from the humus horizon to the nonhumus horizon. For the most part the carbonates appear in a floury powder of a whitish-yellow color. The humus content in the upper soil horizons varies from 4 to 15%.

The soil profile in the sixth profile in the On-Kazhaa River region (a gentle slope with a southerly exposure) has the following characteristics: A_0, steppe litter, consisting of semidecomposed grasses, of a brownish color. A, 0-18 cm, black loam, slightly moist, with poorly expressed structure, an abundance of plant roots. Does not effervesce with application of HCl. B, 18-35 cm, dark brown, structureless loam, effervesces strongly with application of acid. C, reddish brown clay, carbonate, dense, on gentle slopes is replaced by rocky residual material. With respect to the structure of the humus horizon the chernozems resemble dark-chestnut soils, to which they are related genetically. The mountain chestnut soils are related to the characteristic relief conditions: 1) to the alluvial deposits of ancient and recent terraces; 2) to gentle slopes and intermontane basins; and, 3) to broad plains composed of sorted downwashed material at the foot of mountain ranges. Dark and light chestnut soils have developed in the area investigated.

By evaluating the steppe chernozem and chestnut soils which we studied with respect to their concentration of hydrogen ions, it can be concluded that they have a neutral reaction in the upper horizon and an alkaline reaction in the lower horizons. This can be attributed to the zonal character of the soils, with the accumulation of calcium carbonates being a typical phenomenon.

Carbonic acid is the principal source of hydrogen ions in the soils; the acid dissociates in soil solutions in accordance with the following reaction:

$$H_2CO_3 = H^+ + HCO_3^-$$
$$HCO_3^+ = H^+ + CO_3^{2-}$$

Considering the solubility of CO_2 in water under normal conditions to be 10^{-4} g equiv. per liter, it can be expected that the pH of the solution will be close to 4. For practical purposes such a pH value is observed only in highly acidic podzols. The hydrogen ions forming in the solution partially enter into the soil absorbing complex. The constant presence of calcium carbonates in steppe soils leads to a decrease of the free hydrogen ions by means of formation of bicarbonates:

$$H_2CO_3 + CaCO_3 = Ca(HCO_3)_2.$$

Calcium ions enter into exchange reactions with the hydrogen ions of the soil absorbing complex and thereby lower the exchange acidity of the soil in accordance with the equation:

$$2H^+ + CaCO_3 = Ca^{2+} + H_2O + CO_2.$$

In addition to the Ca, Mg, K, Na, Fe, Al, and a whole series of other ions participate in the exchange reactions. This explains the well-known constancy of hydrogen ions in steppe soils, corresponding to a neutral reaction.

The concentration of hydrogen ions is of the greatest importance for many biochemical reactions in soils — the life of bacteria (pH 7) and fungi (pH 5), as well as for the normal growth of higher cultivated and wild plants. The pH is of the greatest importance in redox reactions in the soil. Free oxygen is the principal oxidizer in soil solutions. There is a more active oxidation of carbon compounds (hydrocarbons, etc.) in alkaline media. Because of this it is entirely natural that chestnut soils form in Tuva in the case of relatively high redox potentials — Eh = 500-600 mV. It is known that in the case of such potentials (when pH $\sim$ 7) it is possible for hydrates to become oxidized — $Fe(OH)_2$, $Co(OH)_2$, and $Mn(OH)_2$. This explains the brownish-cinnamon and reddish hue of the chestnut and light-chestnut soils, which often are colored by iron oxides. In forest podzols and in soddy-podzols, where the potentials drop to 200-300 mV, there is a reverse process of reduction of oxidized soil minerals to the formation of the easily mobile forms Fe^{2+}, Mn^{2+}, and Co^{2+}.

By comparing these two processes — the oxidation of metals in chestnut soils and partial oxidation of chernozem soils — with the reduction of metals in gray mountain-forest and podzolized soils, it is possible to explain the nonuniform distribution of metals in the soil horizons; this is of basic importance in a comparative evaluation of the soil-plant (biogeochemical) method and a metallometric survey.

Vegetation

The distribution of vegetation in Tuva has both vertical and horizontal zonality. In contrast to regions farther to the north, in this region the influence of reverse zonality is of importance. Grass-Caragana steppes on the southern slopes and larch forests on the northern slopes constantly replace one another, creating a singular landscape. The vegetation on the southern slopes is appreciably more impoverished than on the northern slopes, but there is a rather great variety of species (Sobolevskaya [1950], Shreter [1954]).

As has been mentioned already, the On-Kazhaa River region is an area with local relief not exceeding 1400 m. The distribution of vegetation here, therefore, is subject more to the influence of slope exposure than to absolute elevation above sea level. This explains the alternation of the grass-Caragana steppe and small forests and groves on the northern and northeastern slopes of the steep hills. On the south and north the region is bounded by mountains with more significant elevations, as great as 1700 m. A mountain range to the south extends in a north-south direction, and contains a sulfide-arsenide deposit. There are highlands to the north which separate the region from the dry central Tuvinskii basin. The southern slope of the range is covered by steppe vegetation (the southern sector of the deposit), whereas the northern slope is a typical larch taiga with an admixture of birch (the northern sector of the deposit). A large part of the On-Kazhaa River region, where the exploration work was done, is covered by steppe.

The steppe vegetation of the On-Kazhaa River region is quite varied in botanical respects. However, it consists primarily of grasses and yellow acacia (Caragana arborescens). Depending on the relief, character of the soils, and geological conditions, the composition of the vegetation changes appreciably. Along the slopes of low steep hills in the central part of the region ordinary steppe vegetation predominates, including Avenastrum mongolicum, Caragana spinosa, Caragana pygmaea, Stipa capillata, Thymus asiaticus, Allium austrosibiricum, Pulsatilla Turzianinovii, Cotoneaster nigra, and others.

In the middle of summer the general background of the steppe is yellowish-gray. The average height of Caragana spinosa is 60-70 cm and the average height of Caragana pigmaea is 40-50 cm. Grasses are much lower than Caragana.

In the lowest parts of the area there are Thalictrum minus, Phlomis tuberosa, and others. The grasses often form a continuous cover, but the species of Caragana form the most typical associations (irrespective of relief). Caragana pygmaea occupies all the high and more or less elevated places on light-chestnut soils; Caragana spinosa occupies low spots and gentle slopes, where dark-chestnut soils predominate. Even on steep and rocky slopes, where the vegetation changes somewhat, Caragana pygmaea is a constant member of the association. Taking into account the widespread occurrence and well-developed root system of Caragana, we used it in the biogeochemical survey of promising areas for ash content of nickel, cobalt, and copper.

The flora of stony denuded surfaces differs sharply from the surrounding steppe and forest vegetation. They are covered almost entirely by lichens (several species) and mosses. Houseleek Orostachys spinosa L. grows between the rocks in small sectors covered by soil; it forms dense hillocks of a reddish-gray color. Caragana pygmaea also is found here among the rocks.

The vegetation of ancient mine workings (copper and other deposits) is of great interest. The principal plants on ancient spoil banks (with malachite and azurite) are Gypsophila Patrinii, Silene jeniseensis, Diplachne squarrosa, and others. The number of Caragana on ancient mine workings is much smaller than in steppe areas. In most cases the spoil banks of ancient mine workings are covered lushly with lichens.

The ancient mine workings stand out as bright green spots on the yellowish-gray background of the steppe, making them readily noticeable during the exploration for ore. Ancient mine workings always are situated in small depressions and always are surrounded by a reddish fringe, created by the color of the fringe vegetation — lichens, Gypsophila Patrinii, and others.

The finding of Gypsophila Patrinii and other plants at ancient copper workings can be attributed to their high tolerance to the high copper content of the soil, attaining 1%. This also is indicated by the high copper content in the ash of Gypsophila Patrinii growing over ore (up to 0.1%).

The plants associated with copper mineralization (Gypsophila Patrinii, and others) were used for exploration work in the On-Kazhaa River region, especially for the orientation of the profiles along which the soil and plant samples were taken. The profiles along which Gypsophila Patrinii was most common (profiles 5 and 6) revealed the presence of ore.

The area over which biogeochemical investigations were made can be divided into three parts: 1) the region of the sulfide-arsenide deposit (southern and northern sectors), where a zonal check was made of the effectiveness of the biogeochemical exploration method; 2) the region of the copper deposit, 10 km north of the first; 3) the sector between the first and second, which appeared promising with respect to mineralization (On-Kazhaa River region), where biogeochemical exploration for cobalt, nickel, and copper was carried on.

Great attention was given to the study of secondary dispersion haloes of ore elements. A considerable part of the data relating to the geochemistry and mineralogy of the copper-nickel-cobalt deposit was discussed in Chapter IV, dealing with the theory of formation of secondary dispersion haloes (The Zone of Oxidation of the Sulfide-Arsenide Deposit in Tuva).

Secondary Dispersion Haloes

As already mentioned, the deposit was formed in the process of contact-skarn metamorphism, accompanied by hypogene mineralization of sulfides and arsenides of iron, nickel, cobalt, copper, and other heavy metals. Among the primary minerals of nickel and cobalt in the deposit are smaltine $CoAs_{3-2}$, chloanthite $NiAs_{3-2}$, niccolite $NiAs$, rammelsbergite $NiAs_2$, safflorite $CoAs_2$, skutterudite $CoAs_3$, gersdorffite $NiAsS$, and others. Among the iron minerals there are pyrite and arsenopyrite $FeAsS$. The most widespread copper minerals are chalcopyrite $CuFeS_2$, bornite Cu_5FeS_4, chalcosite Cu_2S, and covellite CuS.

The minerals of cobalt, nickel, and copper included in the ore body form veins in the form of more or less solid masses or are dispersed in the country rock. The ore veins below the zone of oxidation are in quartz or skarn rocks, making up the deposit: limestones and shales of the Lower Silurian, extrusives and tuffs of the Lower Cambrian and Devonian (Fig.51). The ore veins in virtually the entire deposit are close to the surface. The upper part, the most accessible for exploration, is therefore greatly weathered. The primary sulfide-arsenide minerals are oxidized, acquiring a new form of compound which is stable in the zone of oxidation: cobalt arsenides form erythrite $Co_3(AsO_4)_2$ $\cdot$ $8H_2O$, nickel arsenides form annabergite $Ni_3(AsO_4)_2$ $\cdot$ $8H_2O$. Despite the constant presence among the primary minerals of arsenopyrite $FeAsS$ and enargite Cu_3AsS_4, the products of oxidation are virtually free of copper arsenate [trichalcite $Cu_3(AsO_4)_2$ $\cdot$ $5H_2O$] and iron arsenate [scorodite $Fe^{3+}(AsO_4)$ $\cdot$ $2H_2O$] because of the poor stability of these minerals. The differences between nickel, cobalt, copper, and iron cause a dissimilar direction in the processes of secondary mineral formation in the zone of oxidation. The secondary minerals of copper in the deposit are malachite and azurite; those of cobalt erythrite and asbolan; and those of nickel annabergite, and apparently bunsenite. The latter, simultaneously with cobalt, is included in asbolans and psilomelane-wads.

We have noted that the stability of cobalt and nickel arsenates is highly dependent on weathering conditions. Cobalt arsenate — erythrite — can be preserved stably over a long period under conditions of low moisture content when the soil and ground water has a neutral or alkaline reaction. Under these conditions, erythrite, lying close to the earth's surface, closer to the soil layer (as was observed in the southern sector of the deposit), is covered on top by a yellowish-orange crust of mineral, forming in the process of secondary change of erythrite. Structural x-ray observations made in the laboratory by E. S. Makarov (at the Institute of Geochemistry and Analytical Chemistry of the Academy of Sciences of the USSR) revealed no irregularities of the crystal structures of erythrite in the new mineral, indicating a high resistance of the mineral under these particular conditions. The new formations in erythrite have an extremely low solubility in water in comparison with erythrite and safeguard the mineral against the chemical effect of surface water. In contrast to the southern sector, the erythrite from the northern sector of this same deposit contains no conspicuous new formations in the mineral, it has a bright rose color, and is quite soluble in water. This can be attributed to the different weathering conditions prevailing in the northern sector of the deposit, where gray mountain-forest, weakly podzolized soils are widespread.

It has been noted that nickel arsenate — annabergite — does not give rise to new formations under the conditions which have been described for cobalt in the southern sector. This apparently can be attributed to the absence of the mineral in the upper horizons of the weathered crust in the southern sector of the deposit.

The problem of hypergene mineral formation over ore deposits is of appreciable significance in the interpretation of conditions for the genesis and preservation of secondary dispersion haloes. The dispersion haloes of the vein deposit which we studied constitute a typical example of an anomaly in residual skeletal soils and other residual

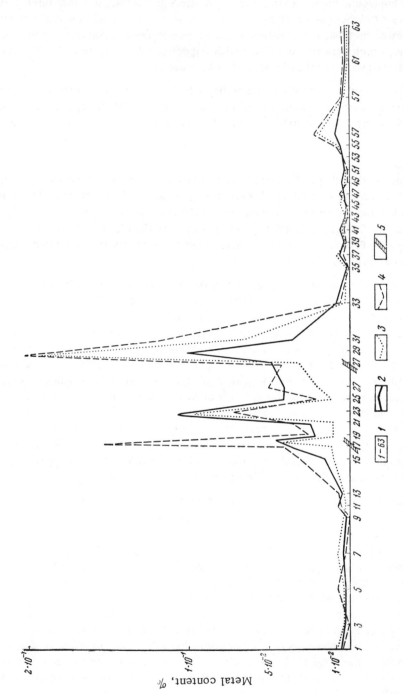

Fig. 51. Distribution of cobalt, nickel, and copper in soils of the sulfide-arsenide deposit (Southern sector, profile 2). 1) Number of sample; 2) cobalt content; 3) nickel content; 4) copper content; 5) ore veins.

TABLE 39. Cobalt, Nickel, and Copper Distribution in Chestnut Soils
of Profile 2 (Southern Sector)

Sample	Content			Ratio	
	Co	Ni	Cu	Ni : Co	Cu : Co
1	$5 \cdot 10^{-3}$	$6 \cdot 10^{-3}$	$5 \cdot 10^{-3}$	1.2	1
3	$3 \cdot 10^{-3}$	$3 \cdot 10^{-3}$	$2 \cdot 10^{-3}$	1	0.7
5	$3 \cdot 10^{-3}$	$3 \cdot 10^{-3}$	$8 \cdot 10^{-3}$	1	2.7
7	$4.3 \cdot 10^{-3}$	$8 \cdot 10^{-3}$	$3.4 \cdot 10^{-3}$	2	0.8
9	$2.4 \cdot 10^{-3}$	$4 \cdot 10^{-3}$	$1 \cdot 10^{-3}$	1.7	0.4
11	$7 \cdot 10^{-3}$	$3 \cdot 10^{-3}$	$6 \cdot 10^{-3}$	0.4	0.9
13	$5 \cdot 10^{-3}$	$4 \cdot 10^{-3}$	$7 \cdot 10^{-3}$	0.8	1.4
15	$1.5 \cdot 10^{-2}$	$1 \cdot 10^{-2}$	$3 \cdot 10^{-2}$	0.7	2
17	$3.5 \cdot 10^{-2}$	$1 \cdot 10^{-2}$	$4 \cdot 10^{-2}$	0.3	1
18	$4.6 \cdot 10^{-2}$	$4 \cdot 10^{-2}$	$1.5 \cdot 10^{-1}$	0.9	3
19	$2.2 \cdot 10^{-2}$	$1 \cdot 10^{-2}$	$2.5 \cdot 10^{-2}$	0.5	1.1
21	$2.3 \cdot 10^{-2}$	$1 \cdot 10^{-2}$	$3.8 \cdot 10^{-2}$	0.5	1.7
23	$1 \cdot 10^{-1}$	$9 \cdot 10^{-2}$	$7 \cdot 10^{-2}$	0.9	0.7
25	$4 \cdot 10^{-2}$	$1 \cdot 10^{-2}$	$2 \cdot 10^{-2}$	0.25	0.5
27a	$4 \cdot 10^{-2}$	$2 \cdot 10^{-2}$	$5 \cdot 10^{-2}$	0.5	1.2
27b	$4.7 \cdot 10^{-2}$	$3 \cdot 10^{-2}$	$4 \cdot 10^{-2}$	0.6	0.8
29	$1 \cdot 10^{-1}$	$1.9 \cdot 10^{-1}$	$2 \cdot 10^{-1}$	2	2
31	$3.5 \cdot 10^{-2}$	$6.5 \cdot 10^{-2}$	$1.2 \cdot 10^{-1}$	2	3
33	$7 \cdot 10^{-3}$	$3.4 \cdot 10^{-3}$	$4 \cdot 10^{-3}$	0.5	0.6
35	$1 \cdot 10^{-3}$	$1 \cdot 10^{-3}$	$1 \cdot 10^{-3}$	1	1
37	$6 \cdot 10^{-3}$	$6 \cdot 10^{-3}$	$3 \cdot 10^{-3}$	1	0.5
39	$3 \cdot 10^{-3}$	$2 \cdot 10^{-3}$	$3 \cdot 10^{-3}$	0.6	1
41	$5 \cdot 10^{-3}$	$5 \cdot 10^{-3}$	$3.5 \cdot 10^{-3}$	1	0.7
43	$2 \cdot 10^{-3}$	$1.5 \cdot 10^{-3}$	$1.5 \cdot 10^{-3}$	0.7	0.7
45	$1 \cdot 10^{-3}$	$4 \cdot 10^{-4}$	$1 \cdot 10^{-3}$	0.4	1
47	$2.4 \cdot 10^{-3}$	$3 \cdot 10^{-3}$	$2 \cdot 10^{-3}$	1	0.8
49	$3 \cdot 10^{-3}$	$3 \cdot 10^{-3}$	$1 \cdot 10^{-3}$	1	0.3
51	$2 \cdot 10^{-3}$	$1 \cdot 10^{-3}$	$1 \cdot 10^{-3}$	0.5	0.5
53	$3 \cdot 10^{-3}$	$3 \cdot 10^{-3}$	$3 \cdot 10^{-3}$	1	1
55	$3.8 \cdot 10^{-3}$	$5 \cdot 10^{-3}$	$6.5 \cdot 10^{-3}$	1.2	1.5
57	$7 \cdot 10^{-3}$	$1.7 \cdot 10^{-2}$	$2 \cdot 10^{-2}$	2	3
59	$3 \cdot 10^{-3}$	$2.8 \cdot 10^{-3}$	$3 \cdot 10^{-3}$	0.9	1
61	$2 \cdot 10^{-3}$	$2 \cdot 10^{-3}$	$2 \cdot 10^{-3}$	1	1
63	$2 \cdot 10^{-3}$	$3 \cdot 10^{-3}$	$4 \cdot 10^{-3}$	1.5	2
65	$1.6 \cdot 10^{-3}$	$3 \cdot 10^{-3}$	$1.6 \cdot 10^{-3}$	2	1

material. Dispersion haloes are formed in alluvium and residual material forming trains and alluvial fans. They also are formed by soluble salts migrating in soils and rocks. The deposits in Tuva, lying at a depth of 5 to 15 m, are detected by the biogeochemical method from the dispersion haloes.

Data obtained by the chemical and spectral analysis of soils and plants can be used for the biogeochemical outlining of the dispersion haloes in the plane of the field sheet. The study of a halo at depth is accomplished by an analysis of soils and rocks taken from vertical profiles, usually at right angles to the strike of the ore vein.

We will cite two examples. The first is for a case when the veins cut the steep southern slope of a mountain (southern sector of the deposit); in the second case the veins pass along the margin of the heavily forested northeastern slope of this same mountain (northern sector of the deposit). In the southern sector the dispersion halo of a sulfide-arsenide deposit over a rather extensive area (profiles 2, 6, 7, and 10) is outlined by plotting a number of intersections at right angles to the strike of the ore veins. In this area it also was possible to trace the influence of relief, steepness of slope, depth of the ore body, character of the soils, and vegetation.

In the northern sector similar horizontal intersections were observed along profiles 561, 583, and 593, two of which were studied in depth (profiles 561 and 583). We will consider the results obtained in the study of the southern sector of the deposit, especially data from analysis of soils and plants along profile 2.

Sample	Profile	Content, %			Ratio	
		Co	Ni	Cu	Ni : Co	Cu : Co
1	6	$1.4 \cdot 10^{-3}$	$1.2 \cdot 10^{-3}$	$7.8 \cdot 10^{-3}$	1	5.5
2	6	$1 \cdot 10^{-3}$	$1.6 \cdot 10^{-3}$	$5.8 \cdot 10^{-3}$	1.6	5.8
3	6	$1 \cdot 10^{-3}$	$2.0 \cdot 10^{-3}$	$7 \cdot 10^{-3}$	2	7
4	6	$1 \cdot 10^{-3}$	$1.1 \cdot 10^{-3}$	$3.5 \cdot 10^{-3}$	1	3.5
5	6	$1.2 \cdot 10^{-3}$	$2.3 \cdot 10^{-3}$	$5.8 \cdot 10^{-3}$	2	5
6	6	$1.1 \cdot 10^{-3}$	$3.4 \cdot 10^{-3}$	$8.6 \cdot 10^{-3}$	3	8
7	6	$3.2 \cdot 10^{-3}$	$6.5 \cdot 10^{-4}$	$3.3 \cdot 10^{-3}$	0.2	1
8	6	$5.5 \cdot 10^{-3}$	$3.3 \cdot 10^{-3}$	$2.2 \cdot 10^{-2}$	0.6	4
9	6	$4.5 \cdot 10^{-3}$	$4.6 \cdot 10^{-3}$	$1.6 \cdot 10^{-2}$	1	4
10	6	$4.8 \cdot 10^{-2}$	$2.7 \cdot 10^{-2}$	$8.8 \cdot 10^{-2}$	0.5	2
11	6	$7.5 \cdot 10^{-2}$	$3.3 \cdot 10^{-1}$	$5 \cdot 10^{-1}$	0.4	0.7
12	6	$6.7 \cdot 10^{-2}$	$2.9 \cdot 10^{-2}$	$2.4 \cdot 10^{-1}$	0.4	3
13	6	$4.3 \cdot 10^{-2}$	$2.5 \cdot 10^{-2}$	$1 \cdot 10^{-1}$	0.6	2.5
14	6	$1.5 \cdot 10^{-2}$	$1.2 \cdot 10^{-2}$	$3.1 \cdot 10^{-2}$	0.7	2
15	6	$4.6 \cdot 10^{-3}$	$1 \cdot 10^{-2}$	$3 \cdot 10^{-2}$	2	6
16	7	$1.4 \cdot 10^{-2}$	$8.6 \cdot 10^{-3}$	$1.8 \cdot 10^{-2}$	0.6	1.3
18	7	$3 \cdot 10^{-2}$	$1.8 \cdot 10^{-2}$	$1 \cdot 10^{-1}$	0.6	3.3
19	7	$4.7 \cdot 10^{-2}$	$6.2 \cdot 10^{-2}$	$1.5 \cdot 10^{-1}$	1.5	3
20	7	$9.5 \cdot 10^{-2}$	$6.2 \cdot 10^{-2}$	$1.5 \cdot 10^{-1}$	0.6	1.5
21	7	$3 \cdot 10^{-2}$	$1.8 \cdot 10^{-2}$	$8.5 \cdot 10^{-2}$	0.6	3
22	7	$2 \cdot 10^{-2}$	$1.3 \cdot 10^{-2}$	$8.6 \cdot 10^{-2}$	0.7	4.3
23	7	$7 \cdot 10^{-3}$	$1.4 \cdot 10^{-2}$	$4 \cdot 10^{-2}$	2	6
24	7	$3.8 \cdot 10^{-3}$	$5.2 \cdot 10^{-3}$	$1.3 \cdot 10^{-2}$	1.4	3
25	7	$1 \cdot 10^{-2}$	$2.5 \cdot 10^{-3}$	$8.6 \cdot 10^{-3}$	0.3	0.8
26	7	$2.4 \cdot 10^{-3}$	$3 \cdot 10^{-3}$	$9.5 \cdot 10^{-3}$	1	4

The polarographic method was used for the study of soils and plants. The soil and plant samples were obtained along profile 2 at intervals of 10, 20, and 30 m. An analysis of the soil samples (horizon A_1, 0-7 cm) revealed extremely nonuniform quantities of cobalt, nickel, and copper (Table 39).

The data in Table 39 show the variation of cobalt in soils from $1 \cdot 10^{-3}$ to $1 \cdot 10^{-1}\%$, of nickel from $4 \cdot 10^{-4}$ to $1.9 \cdot 10^{-1}\%$, and of copper from $1 \cdot 10^{-3}$ to $2 \cdot 10^{-1}\%$. Such a phenomenon usually indicates the presence of a very large ore anomaly. In addition, extremely unusual ratios Co : Ni : Cu, for the most part 1 : 0.7 : 1.25, indicate the presence in this region of cobalt mineralization, when cobalt not only reaches the level of its constant companions — nickel and copper — but often even exceeds their content in the uppermost soil layer. (The data shown in Table 39 are represented in diagrammatic form in Fig. 51 for greater clarity.)

In Fig. 51 the content of nickel, cobalt, and copper in different parts of the profile (in %) has been plotted along the y axis and the distance in meters to the east and west of test hole 53 (at the mouth of shaft 4) has been plotted along the x axis. The horizontal scale is 1 : 4000.

The relief of the deposit in the area of profile 2 is extremely irregular. The eastern margin of the profile first dips steeply westward into a small ravine running toward the mouth of shaft 4 and then gradually rises gently (5°) farther to the west. The highest elevations are found at the ore veins (samples 23 and 29). Still farther to the west there is a 7° drop toward the road.

The geological profile along profile 2 has the following structure: 1) a soil layer with a thickness of 50 to 100 cm; 2) residual material consisting of sharp-angled fragments of gray-green skarn with coatings of oxides and hydroxides of iron and manganese; the fragments lie in unconsolidated clayey-limestone material; thickness of the residual material is 0.5-4 m; 3) rock, consisting of interstratified aleurolites and limestones, strongly skarnified; in low-lying parts of the profile (samples 5, 57) there are alluvial deposits forming from the downwashing of products of weathering from the higher-lying parts of the deposit.

TABLE 41. Cobalt, Nickel, and Copper Content
in the Dark Gray Mountain-Forest Soils of Profile 10

Sample	Content, %			Ratio	
	Co	Ni	Cu	Ni:Co	Cu:Co
76	$2 \cdot 10^{-3}$	$2 \cdot 10^{-3}$	$2 \cdot 10^{-3}$	1	1
78	$3 \cdot 10^{-3}$	$1 \cdot 10^{-3}$	$6 \cdot 10^{-3}$	0.3	2
79	$2 \cdot 10^{-3}$	$2 \cdot 10^{-3}$	$2 \cdot 10^{-3}$	1	1
80	$3 \cdot 10^{-3}$	$1.5 \cdot 10^{-3}$	$3 \cdot 10^{-3}$	0.5	1
81	$2.5 \cdot 10^{-3}$	$2 \cdot 10^{-3}$	$2 \cdot 10^{-3}$	0.8	0.8
83	$7.2 \cdot 10^{-3}$	$5 \cdot 10^{-3}$	$7 \cdot 10^{-3}$	0.7	1
84	$4 \cdot 10^{-3}$	$3 \cdot 10^{-3}$	$2 \cdot 10^{-3}$	0.7	0.5
85	$8 \cdot 10^{-3}$	$7 \cdot 10^{-3}$	$1.3 \cdot 10^{-2}$	0.8	1.6
86	$5 \cdot 10^{-3}$	$4 \cdot 10^{-3}$	$5 \cdot 10^{-3}$	0.8	1
86_1	$4.6 \cdot 10^{-3}$	$3 \cdot 10^{-3}$	$6 \cdot 10^{-3}$	0.7	1.3
87	$1 \cdot 10^{-2}$	$5 \cdot 10^{-3}$	$5 \cdot 10^{-3}$	0.5	0.5
89	$4 \cdot 10^{-3}$	$2 \cdot 10^{-3}$	$1 \cdot 10^{-3}$	0.5	0.3
89_1	$3 \cdot 10^{-3}$	$1.7 \cdot 10^{-3}$	$1 \cdot 10^{-3}$	0.6	0.4
90	$2 \cdot 10^{-3}$	$2 \cdot 10^{-3}$	$2 \cdot 10^{-3}$	1	1
90_1	$2.7 \cdot 10^{-3}$	$2.5 \cdot 10^{-3}$	$1 \cdot 10^{-3}$	1	0.4
91	$2 \cdot 10^{-3}$	$1.5 \cdot 10^{-3}$	$2 \cdot 10^{-3}$	0.8	1
92	$2 \cdot 10^{-3}$	$2 \cdot 10^{-3}$	$2 \cdot 10^{-3}$	1	1
94	$1 \cdot 10^{-3}$	$1 \cdot 10^{-3}$	$1 \cdot 10^{-3}$	1	1

Within the limits of the profile the skarnified rocks are intersected by ore veins (samples 18, 23, and 29), which in this area consist of secondary minerals of cobalt, nickel, and copper (erythrite, malachite, and others). At the outcrop of the vein there is an extensive dispersion halo of ore elements in the soils. The halo extends 150 m along profile 2. The emergence of the halo in the soil layer is noted by several maxima on the curves of copper, nickel, and cobalt (see Fig. 51).

Figure 51 clearly shows the anomaly corresponding to the ore-bearing zone. The smooth variation of the curves from the first to the thirteenth and from the thirty-third to the sixty-third samples at the opposite ends of the profile indicates the absence of ore in these sectors. The copper, nickel, and cobalt content in these soil samples is equal to the geochemical background of the area around the zone of mineralization. It is characterized by the following mean values: cobalt, $3.5 \cdot 10^{-3}$%; nickel, $3.5 \cdot 10^{-3}$%; and copper, $3.3 \cdot 10^{-3}$%. The Co:Ni:Cu ratio is 1:1:1. Thus, the geochemical background of the deposit exceeds the mean content of cobalt and copper in the rocks; no increase of nickel is observed.

The most important geochemical characteristic of the soils over hydrothermal deposits of cobalt is a Co:Ni ratio attaining several units. Clearly defined maxima in the content of cobalt, nickel, and copper in the soils of the southern sector sometimes correspond to significant concentrations of these elements. The mean content of cobalt is $3.5 \cdot 10^{-2}$, that of nickel $2.5 \cdot 10^{-2}$, and that of copper $4.7 \cdot 10^{-2}$%, which corresponds to a Co:Ni:Cu ratio of 1:0.7:1.25. The Co:Ni:Cu ratio in the ores of the southern sector is somewhat different, namely, 1:1:0.4.

Thus, in the humus layer of chestnut soils the copper content is considerably higher than the content of cobalt and nickel; this apparently is related to a high fixation of copper by surface plants and its accumulation in the humus layer of the soil.

In order to check the possibility of outlining the dispersion halo of cobalt, nickel, and copper over the entire area of the deposit, a study was made of soil and vegetation samples obtained along several profiles running parallel to profile 2, in the following order: at distances of 400 m (profile 6), 500 m (profile 7), and 800 m (profile 10). Data obtained by polarigraphic determinations of cobalt, nickel, and copper in soils along all three profiles have been given in Tables 40 and 41.

The distribution of copper, nickel, and cobalt in soils along profiles 6, 7, and 10 is similar in many ways to the distribution in profile 2. Copper varies from $1 \cdot 10^{-3}$ to $5 \cdot 10^{-1}$%, cobalt from $1 \cdot 10^{-3}$ to $7.5 \cdot 10^{-2}$%, and nickel from $6.5 \cdot 10^{-4}$ to $3.3 \cdot 10^{-1}$%. In this area, as well, the amplitude of variation in metal content is typical for ore deposits. The resulting data also are presented in the form of curves in Fig. 52, which have been shown on a plan of the deposit at a scale of 1:4000.

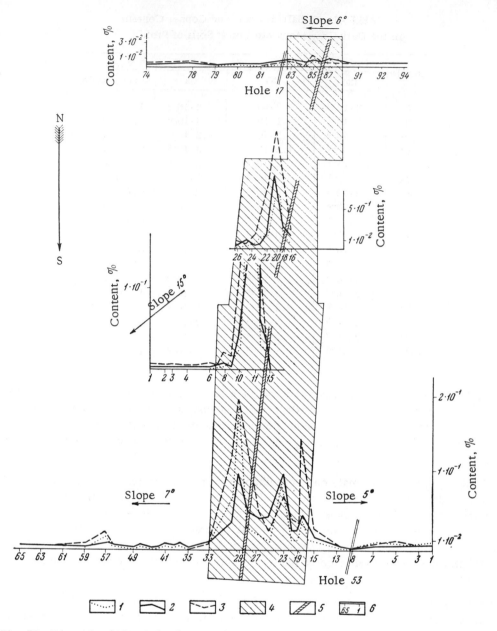

Fig. 52. Dispersion haloes of cobalt, nickel, and copper in the soils of a sulfide-arsenide deposit (Southern sector). 1) Nickel content in soils; 2) cobalt content in soils; 3) copper content in soils; 4) dispersion halo of nickel, cobalt, and copper; 5) ore veins; 6) biogeochemical sampling points and profiles.

The profiles were laid out in the diagram without conforming to horizontal scale. The diagram therefore should be considered schematic. Nevertheless, the positions of the maxima clearly indicate the direction and approximate topography of the ore zone, which has a virtually meridional direction. The certain deviation of the maxima from the true orientation of the ore veins can be attributed to peculiarities of the relief. Displacement of an anomaly is always downslope; the reverse is never observed.

A comparison of the diagrams for copper, nickel, and cobalt for all four profiles shows a general tendency to an increase in the concentrations over the ore zone. However, if we take adjacent points along the profile, there is no total parallelism in the content of copper, nickel, and cobalt. For example, in the thirteenth sample (profile 6) the content of cobalt is $4.3 \cdot 10^{-2}\%$, that of nickel $2.5 \cdot 10^{-2}\%$, and that of copper $1 \cdot 10^{-1}\%$, while in the twelfth sample the values are $6.7 \cdot 10^{-2}\%$ for cobalt, $2.9 \cdot 10^{-2}\%$ for nickel, and $2.4 \cdot 10^{-1}\%$ for copper, that is, although the nickel content is almost equal in both samples, in sample 12 there is 1.5 times more cobalt and 2.5 times more copper than in sample 13. The same can be said of sample 11, etc.

118

TABLE 42. Cobalt, Nickel, and Copper Content
in the Dark Gray Mountain-Forest Soils of the Northern Sector

Sample	Pro-file	Content, %			Ratio	
		Co	Ni	Cu	Cu : Co	Cu : Co
96	561	$3 \cdot 10^{-3}$	$4 \cdot 10^{-3}$	$3 \cdot 10^{-3}$	1.3	1
98	561	$5 \cdot 10^{-3}$	$7 \cdot 10^{-3}$	$4 \cdot 10^{-3}$	1.4	0.8
99	561	$2 \cdot 10^{-3}$	$3 \cdot 10^{-3}$	$3 \cdot 10^{-3}$	1.5	1.5
100	561	$1.8 \cdot 10^{-3}$	$3.4 \cdot 10^{-3}$	$4.7 \cdot 10^{-3}$	2	3
101	561	$1.5 \cdot 10^{-2}$	$2 \cdot 10^{-2}$	$6 \cdot 10^{-3}$	1.3	0.4
102	561	$1.2 \cdot 10^{-2}$	$1.2 \cdot 10^{-2}$	$1 \cdot 10^{-2}$	1	0.8
103	561	$5 \cdot 10^{-3}$	$3 \cdot 10^{0}$	$1 \cdot 10^{0}$	0.6	2
104	561	$1.8 \cdot 10^{-2}$	$8.2 \cdot 10^{-2}$	$7.1 \cdot 10^{-2}$	4.5	3.5
111	561	$4.1 \cdot 10^{-3}$	$7 \cdot 10^{-3}$	$1.2 \cdot 10^{-2}$	1.7	3
112	561	$7.5 \cdot 10^{-3}$	$6 \cdot 10^{-3}$	$5.7 \cdot 10^{-3}$	0.8	0.7
113	561	$5 \cdot 10^{-3}$	$5 \cdot 10^{-3}$	$1 \cdot 10^{-2}$	1	2
114	561	$2 \cdot 10^{-3}$	$2 \cdot 10^{-3}$	$3 \cdot 10^{-3}$	1	1.5
120	561	$3 \cdot 10^{-3}$	$3 \cdot 10^{-3}$	$4 \cdot 10^{-3}$	1	1.3
121	561	$4 \cdot 10^{-3}$	$2 \cdot 10^{-3}$	$4 \cdot 10^{-3}$	0.5	1
122	561	$5 \cdot 10^{-3}$	$4 \cdot 10^{-3}$	$5 \cdot 10^{-3}$	0.8	1
124	561	$2 \cdot 10^{-3}$	$1 \cdot 10^{-3}$	$2 \cdot 10^{-3}$	0.5	1
126	561	$1 \cdot 10^{-3}$	$1 \cdot 10^{-3}$	$2 \cdot 10^{-3}$	1	2
127	561	$1 \cdot 10^{-3}$	$1 \cdot 10^{-3}$	$1 \cdot 10^{-3}$	1	1
128	561	$6 \cdot 10^{-3}$	$9 \cdot 10^{-3}$	$7 \cdot 10^{-3}$	1.5	1
130	526	$8 \cdot 10^{-3}$	$6.1 \cdot 10^{-3}$	$1.8 \cdot 10^{-2}$	0.7	2.3
131	526	$7.6 \cdot 10^{-3}$	$5 \cdot 10^{-3}$	$4.2 \cdot 10^{-2}$	0.7	6
132	526	$1.4 \cdot 10^{-1}$	$2.1 \cdot 10^{-1}$	$2.5 \cdot 10^{-1}$	1.5	1.9
133	526	$5.5 \cdot 10^{-2}$	$7.1 \cdot 10^{-2}$	$1.7 \cdot 10^{-1}$	1.3	3
134	526	$3.3 \cdot 10^{-2}$	$1.5 \cdot 10^{-2}$	$3.5 \cdot 10^{-2}$	0.5	1
135	526	$6.6 \cdot 10^{-3}$	$6 \cdot 10^{-3}$	$1 \cdot 10^{-2}$	1	1.6
136	526	$6 \cdot 10^{-3}$	$6 \cdot 10^{-3}$	$1.6 \cdot 10^{-2}$	1	2.5
137	526	$7 \cdot 10^{-3}$	$1 \cdot 10^{-2}$	$5 \cdot 10^{-3}$	1.2	0.6
138	526	$2.5 \cdot 10^{-3}$	$4 \cdot 10^{-3}$	$2.2 \cdot 10^{-3}$	1.6	0.8
1	583	$6 \cdot 10^{-4}$	$1.9 \cdot 10^{-3}$	$2.5 \cdot 10^{-3}$	3	4
2	583	$8.3 \cdot 10^{-4}$	$2.2 \cdot 10^{-3}$	$3.6 \cdot 10^{-3}$	2.5	4
3	583	$3.4 \cdot 10^{-3}$	$1.3 \cdot 10^{-2}$	$1 \cdot 10^{-2}$	3.5	3
4	583	$6.6 \cdot 10^{-3}$	$1.1 \cdot 10^{-2}$	$1 \cdot 10^{-2}$	1.8	1.5
5	583	$4.1 \cdot 10^{-3}$	$2 \cdot 10^{-2}$	$1.1 \cdot 10^{-2}$	5	2.4
6	583	$4.4 \cdot 10^{-3}$	$9.2 \cdot 10^{-3}$	$7.7 \cdot 10^{-3}$	2	1.7
7	583	$3.2 \cdot 10^{-3}$	$3.1 \cdot 10^{-3}$	$7 \cdot 10^{-3}$	1	2
8	593	$4 \cdot 10^{-3}$	$4.5 \cdot 10^{-3}$	$5.2 \cdot 10^{-3}$	1	1.3
9	593	$1 \cdot 10^{-3}$	$3 \cdot 10^{-3}$	$6.6 \cdot 10^{-3}$	3	6.5
10	593	$4 \cdot 10^{-3}$	$2 \cdot 10^{-3}$	$3.6 \cdot 10^{-3}$	0.5	0.9
11	593	$1 \cdot 10^{-3}$	$6 \cdot 10^{-4}$	$2.3 \cdot 10^{-3}$	0.6	2.3
12	593	$2.2 \cdot 10^{-3}$	$1.2 \cdot 10^{-3}$	$3.3 \cdot 10^{-3}$	0.5	1.5

The reason for such a change in the ratio of cobalt, nickel, and copper in different soil samples is the different mineral composition of the ore-bearing horizons which are exposed at the surface. In exactly the same way, a change in the ratios of metals with depth has been noted in profiles run on slopes.

The dying out of sharp variations in the content of cobalt, nickel, and copper at the ends of profiles indicates that in these places there are no dispersion haloes of ore bodies. The appreciable narrowing of the haloes upslope from profile 2 to profile 10 can be attributed to a considerable plunging of the ore veins beneath the alluvial deposits. Thus, whereas in profile 2 the ore is close to the surface, in profile 7 it sinks to a depth of 2.5 m, and in profile 10 to 11 m. Together with the narrowing of the haloes, with the increasing depth of the ore veins there is some attenuation of the anomalies, that is, a drop in the concentrations of copper, nickel, and cobalt in the soils. For example, whereas in profiles 2 and 6, where the ore approaches the soil layer, there sometimes were tenths of a percent of nickel and cobalt, in profiles 7 and 10 there were only hundredths or thousandths of a percent.

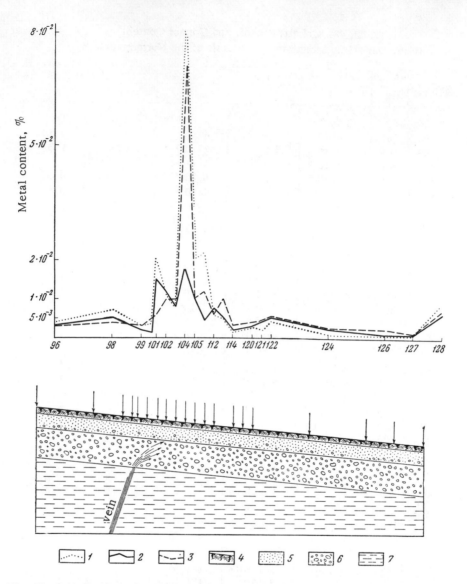

Fig. 53. Distribution of cobalt, nickel, and copper as a function of the width of the dispersion halo (Northern sector, profile 561). 1) Nickel content in soil; 2) cobalt content in soil; 3) copper content in soil; 4) soil layer; 5) clayey loam; 6) residual material; 7) igneous rock.

Similar investigations were made in the northern sector of the deposit. A comparison of these two sectors was of considerable interest because the mineralogical composition of the ore veins of the northern sector differs appreciably from that in the southern sector. In the norther sector primary and secondary copper sulfides are represented to a greater extent than in the southern sector, and this is associated with an increase in the mean content of copper in the ore. In addition, the sectors differ in their soils and vegetation. Whereas the southern sector is covered by steppe vegetation (with the exception of profile 10) and for the most part has chestnut soils, the northern sector is covered by a larch forest. The soils of the northern sector are the dark gray mountain-forest type, in certain cases underlain by permafrost.

Here, as in the southern sector, a study has been made of several soil profiles along trenches (561, 562, and 583), but at some distance from them in order to avoid contamination by metals from spoil banks along the trenches. All three profiles intersect rich ore concentrations in sulfide-arsenide veins, whose upper parts are completely oxidized. The principal minerals of cobalt, nickel, and copper in the zone of oxidation in the northern sector of the deposit are malachite, azurite, annabergite, erythrite, and oxides. In almost all trenches ore is noted at a depth of 1.5-2 m. In trench 526 it is most enriched with erythrite and approaches close to the soil layer. Samples from the upper horizon

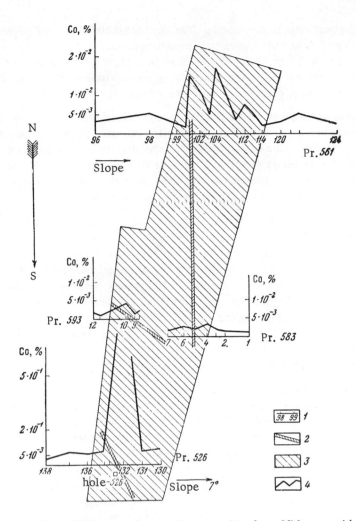

Fig. 54. Dispersion halo of cobalt in soils of a sulfide-arsenide
deposit (Northern sector). 1) Number of sample; 2) ore veins;
3) dispersion haloes; 4) cobalt content in soil.

A_1, 0-7 cm, were obtained for polarographic analysis. The collected data have been given in Table 42.

The cobalt content in dark gray mountain-forest soils varies from $6 \cdot 10^{-4}$ to $1.4 \cdot 10^{-1}\%$, nickel content from $6 \cdot 10^{-4}$ to $2.1 \cdot 10^{-1}\%$, and copper content from $1 \cdot 10^{-3}$ to $2.5 \cdot 10^{-1}\%$. Consequently, the same appreciable variations in the content of these elements in soils were noted in the northern sector as in the southern sector; these variations are extremely characteristic of ore deposits. Evidence of the presence of mineralization in these areas are Co:Ni:Cu ratios close to 1:1:1, well known for such cases. The northern sector is a continuation of the southern sector. It also is well explored, and therefore, in this area, it also was possible to make a similar investigation of the copper, nickel, and cobalt in soils and plants associated with ore enrichment.

The distribution of ore elements in dependence on the nearness of the zone of mineralization is reflected quite well in the diagrams in Fig. 53 which show that the increase in the concentration of cobalt, nickel, and copper in soil samples 101, 102, and 103 in profile 561 is related to an ore vein lying close beneath the soil layer.

Soil samples 103 to 111 inclusive were obtained in the downslope dispersion halo where the increase in the metal content in the soil is related to the migration of soil solutions enriched with ore elements. As confirmation it should be noted that the Silurian shales and limestones containing the ore possess low concentrations of cobalt, nickel, and copper not exceeding the mean value of the background — $2 \cdot 10^{-3}\%$ of metal.

Similar graphs of the distribution of copper, nickel, and cobalt also were prepared for other profiles in the northern sector — 526 and 583. Figure 54 shows the general layout of the sector, with clearly defined anomalies in the distribution of cobalt in soils sampled over the deposit. The dark crosshatching in this figure shows the dispersion haloes along the ore veins. The haloes have a clearly expressed tendency to be displaced to the right of the veins, that is, downslope, by an average width of 50 m. However, in general, if the thickness of the vein is from 50 to 100 cm, the dispersion haloes can be considerably larger, depending on the strike of the vein. There are many veins which extend for 150 to 200 m; in most cases they do not exceed several tens of meters.

The extent of the dispersion haloes of copper, nickel, and cobalt in the upper humus horizon of the soil is of basic importance, because this governs the layout of the sampling grid used in the search for and exploration of ore deposits. On the basis of experimental data it was established specifically for this region that the required distance between profiles is 100 m and the necessary sampling interval is 20 m. However, experience shows that when a highly sensitive method is used for determining cobalt, nickel, and copper the distance between profiles can be increased by a factor of 1.5-2, that is, grid "squares" measuring 20 × 200 m can be used.

In addition to a study of the horizontal extent of dispersion haloes, a study of their extent in depth also is of interest. In this case as well, it was noted that the soil layer to a depth of 1 m does not contain appreciable quantities of rock-forming and ore minerals. It can be concluded on this basis that the soils over the studied deposit are preserved for a rather long time, sufficient for complete weathering of the primary minerals. The stability of soils can be facilitated by the presence of forest and steppe vegetation completely covering the deposit. Consequently, in this area we can speak only of chemical or biogeochemical dispersion haloes of ore elements, since with relatively small slopes there will be no mechanical movement of ore minerals. Such profiles are 2, 7, and 10 in the southern sector and almost all the profiles in the northern sector. The soils in these areas are well developed and held quite firmly in place by grassy and woody vegetation. Under these conditions the migration of chemical elements usually takes place by circulation of solutions in vertical and horizontal directions.

The best method for the study of dispersion haloes in depth is a system of vertical profiles run along lines cutting the vein at a right angle. A study was made of several such profiles, of which two are characteristic. One of these profiles was in the northern sector of the sulfide-arsenide deposit, and the other in the copper deposit at Uzunoi. The first sector differs from the second not only in the difference in types of mineralization, but also by the presence of permafrost and the character of the soils and vegetation. Both profiles were run on slopes with a steepness up to 10°. We first will discuss the profile run along trench 561 in the northern sector. As in the southern sector, the mineralization is associated with a system of fractures in earlier formations and skarnified sectors of the Upper Silurian carbonate stratum. There is less significant mineralization in the slightly modified aleurolites and sandstones of the Silurian and in the granites and sedimentary-extrusive rocks of the Lower Devonian (Krutov, 1955).

The rocks making up the sector consist of limestones, sandstones, and shales of Silurian age. The rocks have been modified greatly by weathering processes. There is a layer of coarse debris above the rock. The thickness of this material is several meters, but in most cases not more than 1-2 m. Directly above this debris there is a horizon of gray clayey loam, up to 1 m thick. Along almost the entire profile the soil is developed on clayey loam and lies directly on the debris only in the steeper parts of the profile. Depending on the character of the rock, the thickness of the soil layer varies from 0.5 to 1.2 m. The thickness of the A horizon, as already noted for similar cases, varies from 8 to 15 cm, and the B horizon varies from 20 to 30 cm. Effervescence with HCl is noted beginning at a depth of 50-60 cm. At the surface there is a larch forest with an admixture of birch. The soil is densely covered by grassy plants, in places by foxberry and mosses. The soils and the clayey loams underlying them are very moist and only at a depth of 1.5-2 m are free of ice in summer. Over the vein the clayey loams are mixed with unconsolidated material of the ore minerals erythrite and malachite, often changing the color of the rock itself. Four vertical profiles were obtained in this area: over the vein, 10 m to the west, upslope, and 10 and 20 m to the east of the vein (downslope). In each profile samples were taken from the corresponding soil and residual material horizons. The ore samples were packeted separately to avoid contamination by others. The samples first were ground coarsely, quartered, and the selected part of the sample carefully pulverized in an agate mortar. After fusion with soda the sample was investigated for its content of cobalt, nickel, and copper by the polarigraphic method. Table 43 gives the results of the analysis. This table shows the patterns of distribution of cobalt, nickel, and copper in the soil-geological profile over the ore deposit. There is an accumulation of ore elements in the residual material and in the upper humus horizon A. In these horizons there also is a migration of the chemical elements in dependence on slope, that is, a displacement of the concentration of cobalt, nickel, and copper in the soil and residual material in a downslope direction; this is very clearly illustrated in the schematic Fig. 52.

TABLE 43. Cobalt, Nickel, and Copper Content in the Soil and Residual Material
(Profile 561)

Soil profile	Horizon and soil depth, cm	Content,%			Ratio	
		Co	Ni	Cu	Ni : Co	Cu : Co
1 - 10 m to west of vein	A 0—10	$2.8 \cdot 10^{-3}$	$2.6 \cdot 10^{-3}$	$1 \cdot 10^{-2}$	0.9	3.5
	B 25—35	$2.5 \cdot 10^{-3}$	$3.5 \cdot 10^{-3}$	$1.6 \cdot 10^{-2}$	1.4	6
	C 90—100	$9 \cdot 10^{-3}$	$1.1 \cdot 10^{-2}$	$1.3 \cdot 10^{-2}$	1.2	1.4
	C+D 150—160	$9 \cdot 10^{-3}$	$1.1 \cdot 10^{-2}$	$3 \cdot 10^{-2}$	1.2	3.3
2 - Over vein	A 0—15	$8.5 \cdot 10^{-3}$	$3 \cdot 10^{-3}$	$1.3 \cdot 10^{-2}$	0.36	1.5
	B_1 20—30	$5 \cdot 10^{-3}$	$1.5 \cdot 10^{-3}$	$6.2 \cdot 10^{-3}$	0.3	1.2
	B_2 50—60	$2.8 \cdot 10^{-2}$	$5 \cdot 10^{-3}$	$3.4 \cdot 10^{-3}$	0.2	0.2
	C+D 160—170	2.66	1.4	$4.3 \cdot 10^{-1}$	0.53	0.2
3 - 10 m east of vein	A 0—10	$1.2 \cdot 10^{-2}$	$1.2 \cdot 10^{-2}$	$1.1 \cdot 10^{-2}$	1	1
	B 25—30	$6 \cdot 10^{-3}$	$1 \cdot 10^{-2}$	$1 \cdot 10^{-2}$	1.6	1.6
	C 90—160	$1.1 \cdot 10^{-2}$	$7 \cdot 10^{-3}$	$7.3 \cdot 10^{-2}$	0.6	0.6
	C+D 150—160	$4 \cdot 10^{-2}$	$3.7 \cdot 10^{-2}$	$2.3 \cdot 10^{-1}$	1	5.7
4 - 20 m to east of vein	A 0—10	$2.6 \cdot 10^{-3}$	$5 \cdot 10^{-3}$	$1.4 \cdot 10^{-2}$	2	5.4
	B 25—30	$2.7 \cdot 10^{-3}$	$6.2 \cdot 10^{-3}$	$1 \cdot 10^{-2}$	2.3	4
	C 90—100	$4.3 \cdot 10^{-3}$	$6 \cdot 10^{-3}$	$2 \cdot 10^{-2}$	1.5	5
	C+D 150—160	$4 \cdot 10^{-3}$	$5.4 \cdot 10^{-3}$	$5 \cdot 10^{-2}$	1.4	1.2

The figure shows the distribution of cobalt in profile 561 (based on the data in Table 43), reflecting the patterns of distribution of ore elements in the zone of oxidation of the sulfide-arsenide deposit. The movement of cobalt in the residual material in the direction of profiles 3 and 4 apparently should be attributed to the water present above the permafrost layer, which percolates downslope. It is shown at the same time that the migration of cobalt is quite difficult upslope, that is, to the west of the ore point (2).

Similar dispersion diagrams were prepared for nickel and copper. They revealed that copper possesses a greater mobility than cobalt and can be traced easily not only in the third profile, but in the fourth as well; the copper content in the latter reaches $5 \cdot 10^{-2}\%$. Judging from all data, nickel behaves much like cobalt.

As already noted, profile 52 is for the copper sulfide deposit at Uzunoi. The profile was run along the southeastern slope of a steep hill (from top to bottom), at the boundary between the forest and the steppe. The profile intersects the ore vein at a right angle (azimuth 295°). The slope of the area is 8-10°.

The profile consists of the soil layer, about 70 cm thick, and residual material constituting a gray clayey loam with occasional angular fragments of porphyrites, sandstones, and shales. In the interval 7-8 m (from west to east) there is an ore zone consisting of pulverized clayey material with fragments of dense rock measuring from 0.5 to 10 cm. Along the interfaces there are slight encrustations of malachite and chrysocolla. In the interval 8-30 m there are fine-grained, brown, platy sandstones, highly broken, with pulverized reddish-brown clayey material. The residual material is from 1.5 to 3 m thick. The soil layer and the upper part of the residual material is penetrated by plant roots. The soils are not adequately stable so that, as we will see later, the content of cobalt, nickel, and copper in the humus horizon is not too high.

Along this profile soil and rock samples were obtained at five sites: at the eastern side of trench 52 (beginning of the profile), 5 m to the east (at the vein), and 10, 15, and 25 m from the beginning of the trench. The data cited in Table 44 confirm the earlier detected patterns in the distribution of cobalt, nickel, and copper in the profile over the zone of mineralization. There is a sharp increase in the Cu:Co ratio, which is a specific characteristic of the copper deposit.

The variations in the content of cobalt, nickel, and copper in the vertical soil-geological profile are less significant than those observed in the samples studied earlier. This phenomenon can be attributed to the inadequate stability of the soil, as a result of which the lower soil horizons are differentiated poorly and are not always distinguishable from the residual material (horizon B_2).

TABLE 44. Cobalt, Nickel, and Copper in Soils and Residual Material (Profile 52)

Soil profile	Horizon and soil depth, cm	Content, %			Ratio	
		Co	Ni	Cu	Ni : Co	Cu : Co
Along western edge of	A 0—8	$2.5 \cdot 10^{-3}$	$3.5 \cdot 10^{-3}$	$5 \cdot 10^{-3}$	1.4	2
trench 52, 5 m from vein,	B_1 25—35	$2 \cdot 10^{-3}$	$3 \cdot 10^{-3}$	$3.4 \cdot 10^{-3}$	1.5	1.7
upslope	B_2 60—70	$1.6 \cdot 10^{-3}$	$3.7 \cdot 10^{-3}$	$4.4 \cdot 10^{-3}$	2.3	2.8
	C 140—150	$3.5 \cdot 10^{-3}$	$5.5 \cdot 10^{-3}$	$4.3 \cdot 10^{-3}$	1.6	1.2
Over vein	A_1 0—10	$2.5 \cdot 10^{-3}$	$5 \cdot 10^{-3}$	$1 \cdot 10^{-2}$	2	4
	A_2 20—25	$2.6 \cdot 10^{-3}$	$8 \cdot 10^{-3}$	$1 \cdot 10^{-2}$	3	4
	B_1 35—45	$2 \cdot 10^{-3}$	$2.8 \cdot 10^{-3}$	$1 \cdot 10^{-2}$	1.4	5
	B_2 60—70	$1.6 \cdot 10^{-3}$	$3 \cdot 10^{-3}$	$6 \cdot 10^{-2}$	2	37
	C 160—170	$3.3 \cdot 10^{-3}$	$3.6 \cdot 10^{-3}$	$7 \cdot 10^{-2}$	1.2	20
	C/D 200—210	$4 \cdot 10^{-3}$	$9.4 \cdot 10^{-3}$	$1 \cdot 10^{-1}$	2.3	25
10 m from vein, downslope	A 0—10	$2 \cdot 10^{-3}$	$3 \cdot 10^{-3}$	$1.1 \cdot 10^{-2}$	1.5	5.5
	B 35—40	$1 \cdot 10^{-3}$	$2.5 \cdot 10^{-3}$	$6 \cdot 10^{-3}$	2.5	6
	C 80—90	$3.5 \cdot 10^{-3}$	$5.6 \cdot 10^{-3}$	$2.1 \cdot 10^{-2}$	1.6	6
	C/D 140—160	$1 \cdot 10^{-2}$	$7 \cdot 10^{-3}$	$2.6 \cdot 10^{-2}$	0.7	2.6
15 m from vein, downslope	A 0—10	$2 \cdot 10^{-3}$	$5 \cdot 10^{-3}$	$1 \cdot 10^{-2}$	2.5	5
	B_1 25—35	$1.5 \cdot 10^{-3}$	$4.6 \cdot 10^{-3}$	$9 \cdot 10^{-3}$	3	6
	B_2 40—50	$7 \cdot 10^{-4}$	$7 \cdot 10^{-4}$	$3.3 \cdot 10^{-2}$	1	4.7
	C 140—150	$1.5 \cdot 10^{-3}$	$6 \cdot 10^{-3}$	$4.8 \cdot 10^{-2}$	4	32
25 m from vein, downslope	A 0—10	$2.8 \cdot 10^{-3}$	$4.5 \cdot 10^{-3}$	$1 \cdot 10^{-2}$	1.6	3.2
	B_1 20—30	$1.4 \cdot 10^{-3}$	$3 \cdot 10^{-3}$	$4 \cdot 10^{-3}$	2.1	3
	B_2 70—80	$1 \cdot 10^{-3}$		$9 \cdot 10^{-3}$	0.6	9
	C 120—130	$1.6 \cdot 10^{-3}$	$2.5 \cdot 10^{-3}$	$4.6 \cdot 10^{-3}$	1.5	3
	C/D 160—170	$8 \cdot 10^{-3}$	$9.4 \cdot 10^{-3}$	$1.5 \cdot 10^{-2}$	1.2	2

Cobalt, Nickel, and Copper in Plants Growing above Ore Deposits in Tuva

In order to obtain a full idea concerning the vertical migration of cobalt, nickel, and copper over the deposits in Tuva it was extremely important to determine the distribution of these elements in plants. In this area as well, clarification of the biogeochemical role of plants in the formation of dispersion haloes required determination of the abundance ratios of cobalt, nickel, and copper. In this way it was possible to show to what extent plants reflect the special properties of a particular type of deposit.

A study was made of the plants of the southern and northern sectors of the sulfide-arsenide deposit and other areas. The southern sector, as already mentioned, is covered for the most part by steppe vegetation (grasses, wormwood, etc.), while the northern sector is a typical example of a mountainous taiga underlain by permafrost. The plant samples were selected from a grid of soil profiles; therefore each vegetation sample corresponded to a particular soil.

The plants were burned in porcelain dishes and the ash, after solution in acids, was studied by the polarographic method. Table 45 gives data obtained during the investigation of the ash of plants sampled in the southern sector.

The cobalt content in the plants of the southern sector of the deposit varies from $1 \cdot 10^{-3}$ to $9 \cdot 10^{-2}\%$, nickel content from $6.5 \cdot 10^{-4}$ to $6.2 \cdot 10^{-2}\%$, and copper content from $1.5 \cdot 10^{-3}$ to $3 \cdot 10^{-1}\%$. Virtually identical results were obtained in a study of the plants of the northern sector of the deposit. In contrast to the grassy vegetation of the southern sector, the leaves and needles of the trees contain relatively higher quantities of copper (in comparison with cobalt and nickel), which was reflected in an increase of the Cu:Co ratio from 6 to 12. The results of the analyses have been given in Table 46 and in Fig. 55. The factor responsible for the change in the Cu:Co ratio in the plants of the northern sector is the greater mobility of copper in dark-gray mountain-forest soils, and also the somewhat different composition of the ore, to wit: whereas the mean Cu:Co ratio in the ores of the southern sector was 0.4, in the ores of the northern sector it approaches 1.

The accumulation of ore elements in plants is of basic importance for the biogeochemical exploration method. The role of plants is not only the extraction of metals from the deeper layers of the soil and subsoil, but also their fixation in place in the form of insoluble compounds with humus. In addition, plants create specific physicochemical

TABLE 45. Cobalt, Nickel, and Copper in Ash of Plants of the Southern Sector
(Profile 2)

Samp. No.	Plant	Content, in %			Ratio	
		Co	Ni	Cu	Ni : Co	Cu : Co
5	Pasqueflower (stem) Pulsatilla Turzaninovii. Kryl. et Serg	$6.2 \cdot 10^{-3}$	$1.2 \cdot 10^{-3}$	$6 \cdot 10^{-3}$	0.2	1
7	Larch (needles) Larix sibirica L..........	$2.1 \cdot 10^{-3}$	$2.0 \cdot 10^{-3}$	$1.5 \cdot 10^{-3}$	1	0.7
8	Iris (above ground) Iris flatrissimess L	$1 \cdot 10^{-2}$	$7 \cdot 10^{-3}$	$5.4 \cdot 10^{-2}$	0.7	5.4
18	Cotoneaster (stem) Cotoneaster uniflora, Bge ...	$1.5 \cdot 10^{-2}$	$6 \cdot 10^{-3}$	$2.1 \cdot 10^{-2}$	0.4	1.7
21	Pasqueflower (stem)....	$1.2 \cdot 10^{-2}$	$6 \cdot 10^{-3}$	$2 \cdot 10^{-2}$	0.4	1.7
25	Vetch (stem) Vicia cracca L	$2.5 \cdot 10^{-2}$	$1.1 \cdot 10^{-2}$	$3.4 \cdot 10^{-2}$	0.4	1.4
27	Cold wormwood (stem) Artemisia frigida Willd. .	$1.7 \cdot 10^{-2}$	$3 \cdot 10^{-2}$	$3 \cdot 10^{-1}$	1.8	18
29	Siberian flax (above grnd.) Linum sibiricum Dc. ...	$1.3 \cdot 10^{-2}$	$1 \cdot 10^{-2}$	$4 \cdot 10^{-2}$	1	3
31	Shepherd's purse (stem) Capsella bursa pastoris L.	$9 \cdot 10^{-2}$	$6.2 \cdot 10^{-2}$	$1.4 \cdot 10^{-1}$	0.7	1.6
33	Skullcap (stem) Scutellaria grandiflora Sims ..	$1.4 \cdot 10^{-3}$	$6.5 \cdot 10^{-4}$	$3 \cdot 10^{-3}$	0.5	2.1
35	Pasqueflower (stem)....	$1.9 \cdot 10^{-3}$	$1.6 \cdot 10^{-3}$	$1.3 \cdot 10^{-3}$	0.9	0.7
39	Skullcap (stem)	—	$1.4 \cdot 10^{-2}$	$1.9 \cdot 10^{-2}$	—	—
43	Pasqueflower (stem)....	$2.8 \cdot 10^{-3}$	$2.2 \cdot 10^{-3}$	$8 \cdot 10^{-3}$	0.8	2.8
48	" "	$3 \cdot 10^{-3}$	$4.4 \cdot 10^{-3}$	$1.4 \cdot 10^{-2}$	1.5	4.7
49	" "	$2.5 \cdot 10^{-3}$	$2.4 \cdot 10^{-3}$	$1.2 \cdot 10^{-2}$	1	4.8
54	" "	$3.6 \cdot 10^{-3}$	$3.1 \cdot 10^{-3}$	$8.7 \cdot 10^{-3}$	0.9	2.1
58	" "	$2.1 \cdot 10^{-3}$	$3 \cdot 10^{-3}$	$1 \cdot 10^{-2}$	1.4	5
62	" "	$2 \cdot 10^{-3}$	$2 \cdot 10^{-3}$	$8 \cdot 10^{-3}$	1	4
	Mean	$7.2 \cdot 10^{-3}$	$8.0 \cdot 10^{-3}$	$4.2 \cdot 10^{-2}$	1	6

conditions in soils which influence the migration of chemical elements over the zone of mineralization (pH, redox potential, etc.).

When there is an excess content of individual chemical elements in soils over ore deposits in many cases there are deviations from the normal development of these plants − in the chemical composition of the plants, the color of the leaves and flowers, in morphology, and, finally, the intensity of development of individual species. The majority of the plants in the biocenosis remain without apparent changes. For example, in the larch forest in the northern sector of the copper-nickel-cobalt deposit in Tuva there were no anomalous phenomena in the development of woody species, such as birch, larch, etc. In the southern sector, on the other hand, there was an obvious relationship between plants and the geological conditions in the deposit (Figs. 56 and 57). Thus, the plants are adapting to a definite level of cobalt, nickel, and copper in the soils.

Changes in the surface over the ore zone − denudation, ancient mine workings, recent exploration trenches − facilitate a sharp enrichment of the surface with ore minerals, which leads to changes in the appearance of the vegetation cover. On the spoil banks of the southern and northern sectors of the deposit enriched with cobalt, nickel, and copper, there is an abundance of dicotyledonous alyssum (Alyssum biovulatum N. Busch). In the ancient mine workings of the copper deposit the most common plants are those of the pink family: gypsophila (Gypsophila Patrinii Ser.), and others. The following plants are common on the copper–nickel–cobalt deposits: cinquefoil, dog rose, and others, in which chlorosis is developed. Whereas externally these phenomena can appear to be "random," chemical analysis shows appreciable changes in the composition of the plant ash, as clearly shown by the data in Table 47.

The data in Table 47 show a sharp increase of nickel in dicotyledonous alyssum collected in the southern and northern sectors of the deposit. The nickel content in the ash of Lena alyssum from Mount Khrustal'nii, where there

TABLE 46. Cobalt, Nickel, and Copper Content in Plants of the Northern Sector
(Profile 561)

Samp. No.	Plant	Content, in %			Ratio	
		Co	Ni	Cu	Ni : CO	Cu : Co
95	Birch (leaves) Betula verrucosa L..........	$1.2 \cdot 10^{-3}$	$4 \cdot 10^{-3}$	$1.2 \cdot 10^{-2}$	3.3	10
96	Larch (needles) Larix sibirica L.............	$1.6 \cdot 10^{-3}$	$2.7 \cdot 10^{-3}$	$1.8 \cdot 10^{-2}$	1.7	11
97	Birch (leaves) Betula verrucosa L..........	$1.0 \cdot 10^{-3}$	$3.3 \cdot 10^{-3}$	$1.3 \cdot 10^{-2}$	3.3	13
98	The same............	$1 \cdot 10^{-3}$	$8 \cdot 10^{-3}$	$1.7 \cdot 10^{-2}$	8	17
99	The same............	$1.1 \cdot 10^{-3}$	$4.8 \cdot 10^{-3}$	$8.1 \cdot 10^{-3}$	4.4	7.4
100	Larch (needles) Larix sibirica L.............	$2.5 \cdot 10^{-3}$	$1.6 \cdot 10^{-3}$	$1.1 \cdot 10^{-2}$	0.6	4
101	The same............	$4 \cdot 10^{-3}$	$6 \cdot 10^{-3}$	$1.2 \cdot 10^{-2}$	1.5	3
102	Birch (leaves) Betula verrucosa L..........	$3.2 \cdot 10^{-3}$	$3 \cdot 10^{-3}$	$3.8 \cdot 10^{-3}$	0.9	1
104	Larch (needles) Larix sibirica L.............	$9 \cdot 10^{-3}$	$1.1 \cdot 10^{-2}$	$1.6 \cdot 10^{-2}$	1.2	1.8
105	The same............	$6.3 \cdot 10^{-3}$	$1.4 \cdot 10^{-2}$	$1.8 \cdot 10^{-2}$	2.2	2.9
111	The same............	$2.5 \cdot 10^{-3}$	$5.5 \cdot 10^{-3}$	$3 \cdot 10^{-2}$	2.2	12
112	The same............	$1 \cdot 10^{-3}$	$3 \cdot 10^{-3}$	$1.6 \cdot 10^{-2}$	3	16
113	Birch (leaves) Betula verrucosa L..........	$1 \cdot 10^{-3}$	$3 \cdot 10^{-3}$	$2.2 \cdot 10^{-2}$	3	22
114	Larch (needles) Larix sibirica L.............	$1.4 \cdot 10^{-3}$	$8 \cdot 10^{-3}$	$1.3 \cdot 10^{-2}$	5.8	10
119	Birch (leaves) Betula verrucosa L..........	$1.2 \cdot 10^{-2}$	$7 \cdot 10^{-2}$	$6 \cdot 10^{-1}$	5.8	50
120	The same............	$1 \cdot 10^{-2}$	$6 \cdot 10^{-3}$	$3.6 \cdot 10^{-2}$	0.6	3.6
121	The same............	$9 \cdot 10^{-3}$	$7 \cdot 10^{-3}$	$2.5 \cdot 10^{-2}$	0.8	2.7
127	The same............	$4.2 \cdot 10^{-3}$	$2 \cdot 10^{-3}$	$1.6 \cdot 10^{-2}$	0.5	4
128	Larch (needles) Larix sibirica L.............	$2 \cdot 10^{-3}$	$2.3 \cdot 10^{-3}$	$1.8 \cdot 10^{-2}$	1.2	9
	Mean . . .	$3.8 \cdot 10^{-3}$	$8.2 \cdot 10^{-3}$	$4.7 \cdot 10^{-2}$	2.1	12.3

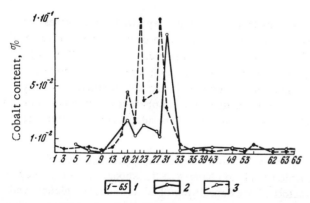

Fig. 55. Relative content of cobalt in soils and plants of a sulfide-arsenide deposit (Southern sector, profile 2). 1) Number of sample; 2) cobalt content in plant ash (%); 3) cobalt in soil.

is little nickel in the soil, does not exceed thousandths of a percent, whereas in the dicotyledonous alyssum from the spoil banks of the northern sector it attains 0.18%, that is, a hundred or more times greater. There also is some increase in the cobalt and copper content, but it is less significant than the increase of nickel.

Despite the high content of ore elements in the ash of dicotyledonous alyssum, especially nickel, the plant develops better than under ordinary conditions. Adaptation to a high nickel content apparently is a common characteristic of certain closely related species: dicotyledonous alyssum and Bertolonius alyssum (Minguzzi and Vergano [1948]).

Table 47 also gives two analyses of bilobular cinquefoil — normal and with chlorosis — sampled on the spoil banks of the copper-nickel-cobalt deposit. The data in Table 47 show a sharp increase in the content of nickel in the ash of cinquefoil with chlorosis, despite a relatively identical copper content. There also was an increase in cobalt content. It therefore can be postulated that chlorosis in cinquefoil is caused by the high nickel content, with an admixture of cobalt.

TABLE 47. Cobalt, Nickel, and Copper Content in Plants from Spoil Banks

Plants and sampling site	Sampling date	Content, %			Ratio	
		Co	Ni	Cu	Ni : Co	Cu : Co
Lena alyssum from basic extrusives of Mount Khrustal'naya, profile 4	May 23, 1959	0.0008	0.0014	0.020	1.8	25
Dicotyledonous alyssum, northern sector, from spoil banks over vein 3	July 13, 1959	0.018	0.180	0.033	10	1.8
Dicotyledonous alyssum, southern sector, from spoil banks, profile 3	July 10, 1959	0.018	0.030	0.050	1.7	3
Bilobate cinquefoil, normal, southern sector, from spoil bank	July 10, 1959	0.0028	0.005	0.051	2	18
Bilobate cinquefoil, with chlorosis, southern sector, near spoil bank	July 10, 1959	0.008	0.020	0.062	2.5	8

TABLE 48. pH Values of Ground and Surface Water in Vicinity of Deposit

Sample No.	Origin of water	Sampling date	pH	Comments
105	Elegest River, above Khovu-Aksy village	8/6/59	7.8	Clear water, slightly mineralized
106	Elegest River, below Khovu-Aksy village	8/12/59	7.8	The same
101	Drift No. 2, hole 50 m from exit (zone of mineralization). Southern sector	8/6/59	2.4	Clear water forming from the melting of blocks of ice in the mine drift
102	Hole 149, depth 107 m (horizon of drift No. 2). Southern sector, profile 6a	8/6/59	2.6	Water slightly turbid, highly mineralized
103	Drift 4b (ore-free), 150 m from exit. Southern sector	8/6/59	8.1	Clear water, slightly mineralized
57	Deep hole in drift 11b. Northern sector	7/13/59	8	Clear, very cold, slightly mineralized water

It is clear also that in addition to the high content of ore elements in soils, their accumulation in plants is influenced by other factors as well: the mobility of metal compounds in the soil-geological profile, assimilability of individual elements, water regime of soils, pH of the medium, etc. Determination of the concentration of hydrogen ions in the waters of the deposit revealed appreciable differences (Table 48). These data show that the surface waters of the studied region differ little in their pH from the most common river water. The water sampled in the mineralization zone (samples 101 and 102) show a very acidic reaction. Deep water (sample 57) and water sampled beyond the limits of the mineralization zone (sample 103) are alkaline.

Mobile Forms of Cobalt, Nickel, and Copper in Soils over Sulfide-Arsenide Deposits

As already noted, the most important minerals of cobalt, nickel, and copper in the zone of oxidation of sulfide-arsenide deposits are sulfates, arsenates, carbonates, oxides, etc. With the exception of sulfates, which are equally characteristic of cobalt, nickel, and copper, all other minerals possess specific properties for each element. For example, the most stable and least soluble copper minerals are the carbonates — azurite and malachite — whereas the most stable and least soluble cobalt minerals are arsenate erythrine and oxides. These minerals are the carriers of the greater part of these elements in the zone of oxidation, its least mobile part. Sulfates, chlorides, and bicarbonates are more mobile. However, their content is insignificant, if judged from the water-soluble fraction, being only about 1% of the total content.

The predominance of the carbon ion in the water fraction obtained with the various soil horizons indicates the relatively low importance of sulfates and chlorides, which at first glance does not appear entirely understandable, considering the specific character of the deposit.

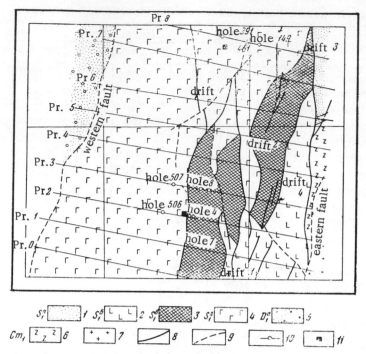

Fig. 56. Schematic geological map of the southern sector of the sulfide-arsenide deposit. 1) Sandstones; 2) polymetallic skarns; 3) granitic skarns; 4) aleurolites; 5) skarn conglomerates; 6) extrusives; 7) granites; 8) ore veins; 9) tectonic dislocations (faults, fractures); 10) geological profile with test holes; 11) prospect holes.

The absence of sulfates indicates a late stage in the oxidation of the ore-bearing zone, when carbonates appear in large quantities. They form a rather thick horizon (the horizon of effervescence). Experience shows that carbonates are the principal pH regulator of the soil and facilitate the accumulation of heavy metals, including cobalt, nickel, and copper. The carbonate horizon is enriched with heavy metals and apparently is a source from which plants extract the elements which they lack.

The light fraction constitutes more than 95 % of the soil, excluding coarse plastic material. The remainder can be related conditionally to the heavy fraction, consisting of stable minerals — zircon, magnetite, and others. It has been established by means of oxidizing a solution of soil in nitric acid that cobalt, nickel, and copper are fully bonded to the light fraction of the soil, consisting of sandy-clayey and humus particles.

A study of the mineralogical composition of the soils sampled over the ore deposit has shown that the upper A_1 and A_2 horizons, and in part the B horizon, are devoid of ore-bearing minerals of cobalt, nickel, and copper (arsenates, carbonates, oxides). Certain of them do not favor a low pH, such as carbonates, etc. But nevertheless in this deposit there are other forms of heavy metals which are stable at various pH values. These are organic compounds. Soil samples were processed with neutral and slightly acidic water solutions for a more detailed study of soluble and exchangeable forms of heavy metals.

On the basis of our investigations, the distribution of mobile and stable forms of cobalt, nickel, and copper in the soil-geological profile is characterized as follows: 1) the greatest quantities of metals correspond to the illuvial-residual material horizon in the immediate vicinity of the vein and downslope; 2) a second zone with a high content of ore elements corresponds to the upper humus horizon A_1; 3) the maximum concentration, occurring in the illuvial-residual material horizon, is displaced appreciably downslope a distance of 10-15 m from the vein. Anomalously high concentrations of elements in the humus horizon are situated closer to the epicenter of the outer margin of the vein, downslope and over the entire surface of the anomaly in the residual material.

Experience in Exploration Work in the On-Kazhaa River Region

The testing of the biogeochemical soil-plant method in the sulfide-arsenide deposit of Tuva has shown its suitability for the detection of shallow-lying ore veins. On the basis of a study of two sectors of the deposit, situated under

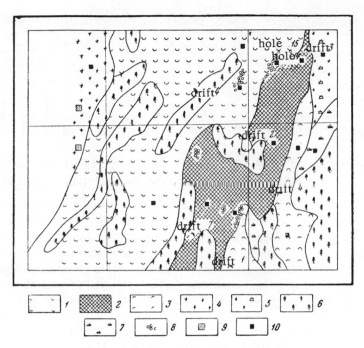

Fig. 57. Schematic geobotanic map of the southern sector of the sulfide-
arsenide deposit. 1) Caragana-wormwood-fescue association, including
Alyssum biosulatum and Potentilla acaulis; 2) Caragana-wormwood-
alyssum association Alyssum biovulatum and also Thymus Festuca, Potentilla Acaulis; 3) Caragana-fescue association, including Bupleurum and
cold wormwood; 4) sedge-false oat association, including Bupleurum; 5)
sedge-false oat association, including the leguminous grass Caragana pyg-
macea; 6) larch forest with admixture of birch; 7) shrubby thickets of cotoneaster, spirea, and Caragana; 8) site of chloritic forms of vegetation; 9)
geobotanical reference sectors; 10) reconnaissance mapping control points.

different physicogeographic and soil-plant conditions, we concluded that the method is suitable for the sampling of
regions which are promising from the metal-bearing point of view. This method can be used to exclude from exploration work plans dozens of square kilometers of unpromising areas which contain insignificant and scattered ore
occurrences. According to available computations, the cost of this work is 10 times less than exploration work conducted by the usual methods of drilling, digging of open trenches, etc.

As already pointed out, the testing method includes the preparation of appropriate maps, which show the geological and geomorphological peculiarities of the studied area and the grid used in the sampling work.

The most suitable map is a topographic base at a scale of 1:10,000. It is desirable to have two such maps.
Geological data is plotted on one; the strike of fissures in alluvial or residual materials fans and characteristic relief
features (steepness of slope, outcrops, etc.). The second map carries the selected profiles and the sampling grid. The
reference line is oriented along the postulated strike of the ore veins. The reference line is intersected by profiles (at
an angle of 90°), along which soil and plant samples are selected at defined intervals.

The soils were sampled from the uppermost humus horizon A at depths of 0 to 7 cm. The soil, in 200- to 300-g
samples, was placed in cotton sacks, dried in the sun, and pulverized by hand. Before analysis, the sample was passed
through a fine screen (100 meshes). The resulting fraction, greater than 0.1 mm, was used for chemical analysis. The
fine fraction (smaller than 0.1 mm) is richer in cobalt, nickel, and copper than the coarse fraction, as was established
by a special check (Table 49).

The sampling technique includes a determination of the corresponding chemical elements in the soils and plants.
Rapid methods are used for this purpose because they make it possible to cover a larger area in biogeochemical exploration or to outline the dispersion haloes using a denser grid. The soil and vegetation samples must be studied after making of tests, thereby making it possible to introduce corrections into the field work. The sensitivity of the method

TABLE 49. Relative Content of Cobalt, Nickel, and Copper in Different Soil Fractions

Sample No.	Soil	Fraction, mm	Content, %			Ratio	
			Co	Ni	Cu	Cu	Ni : Co
53	Dark chestnut	<0.1	$5 \cdot 10^{-3}$	$5 \cdot 10^{-3}$	$4.5 \cdot 10^{-3}$	1	0.9
53	The same	>0.1	$3 \cdot 10^{-3}$	$3 \cdot 10^{-3}$	$3 \cdot 10^{-3}$	1	1
85	Dark gray, mountain-forest	<0.1	$8 \cdot 10^{-3}$	$8 \cdot 10^{-3}$	$1.2 \cdot 10^{-2}$	1	1.5
85	The same	>0.1	$5 \cdot 10^{-3}$	$4.5 \cdot 10^{-3}$	$7 \cdot 10^{-3}$	0.9	1.4

should be adequate for determination of the cobalt, nickel, and copper in soils and plants, both over the ore zone and beyond it. Only under these conditions is it possible to distinguish clearly between the background and anomalies.

The spectral method and the method of total evaluation of the metal content using rubeanates, etc., were used for this purpose. The method of total evaluation of the content of cobalt, nickel, and copper from the blackening of the filters by rubeanates was particularly suitable under field conditions. In order to speed up the solution of the sample, a weighed portion of the soil was placed in a quartz glass test tube and the soil was fused with potassium bisulfate ($KHSO_4$) for 1 to 2 minutes. In this process the ore-bearing and other minerals (oxides, carbonates) are destroyed and the cobalt, nickel, and copper pass into solution in the form of sulfates. The most stable humates are burned and the clayey minerals are subjected to the effect of SO_3, forming during the heating of potassium bisulfate, in accordance with the equation:

$$2KHSO_4 = K_2SO_4 + SO_3 + H_2O.$$

The resulting melt is dissolved in hot diluted HCl and after dilution and alkalization the rubeanates of cobalt, nickel, and copper are precipitated, exactly as is recommended before polarographic analysis. In practical work the soils must be fused with $KHSO_4$ or dissolved in 20% HCl, to which has been added several drops of strong HNO_3. The choice of the method is dependent on circumstances — the availability of electric power, etc. The data from the check in general revealed satisfactory results for all three methods of reducing the sample to a solution. Each method therefore was used, depending on circumstances.

The exploration work was carried on along the line of tectonic faulting between the northern sector of the sulfide-arsenide deposit and the copper sulfide deposit, over an area of 15 km². The region is divided into two equal parts by the broad valley of the On-Kazhaa River and therefore it hereafter will be referred to by that name. The principal direction of the profile corresponds to the strike of the faults (northeast, azimuth 22°). At a distance of 7 km to the north of the cobalt deposit the direction changed to northwest (azimuth 340°) along the contact of Silurian and Devonian deposits. Figure 58 shows a general view of the region in the form of a schematic map with plotted profiles. As already mentioned, the profiles were spaced 400 m apart and the sampling points were 20 m apart.

The content of cobalt, nickel, and copper was established initially by the method of total evaluation using rubeanates. The derived indices were plotted on the map at the points where samples were taken. It was thereby possible to detect zones with a high metal content between profiles 5 and 8, 9 and 14, 17 and 22, and in profiles 1, 3, and 4. The soil samples from these zones also were studied by the polarigraphic method. Points with closely similar metal contents were connected by lines showing isoconcentrations. Maps were compiled to show the isoconcentrations of cobalt, nickel, and copper. As a result, the zones with a high metal content became clearly defined. The first and second enriched zones directly adjoin the deposits — a sulfide-arsenide deposit along the 22nd profile and a copper sulfide deposit along the first profile. In the interval between these profiles there also are several other zones, extending in an east-west direction, where the soil metal content is greater by a factor of 5-10 than the background. Figure 58 shows the isoconcentrations of copper. The zones denoted by heavy cross-hatching correspond to areas with a copper concentration greater than $1 \cdot 10^{-2}\%$. The copper content in the soils from $5 \cdot 10^{-2}\%$ has been denoted by lighter cross-hatching.

The zone directly adjoining the 22nd profile obviously corresponds to an alluvial fan of sandy-clayey material from the direction of the sulfide-arsenide deposit, extending toward the On-Kazhaa River. The origin of the second occurrence, situated closer to the stream, has not yet been explained. It is postulated that to the east of this occurrence there is a still undetected zone of mineralization, apparently in the vicinity of Khrustal'nyi Mountain (named by the author); solid products of weathering, and products in solution move downslope through ravines.

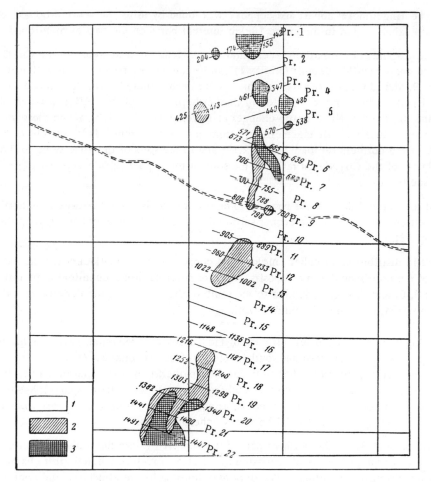

Fig. 58. Map of the isoconcentrations of copper in the On-Kazhaa sector. Copper content: 1) less than $2 \cdot 10^{-3}\%$; 2) from $2 \cdot 10^{-3}$ to $1 \cdot 10^{-2}$; 3) more than $1 \cdot 10^{-2}\%$.

The extensive area on the map without cross-hatching constitutes the background where the copper concentration in the soil approaches the mean content for rocks. The detection of other zones with a high metal content in the soil, greater than $1 \cdot 10^{-2}\%$, remote from known ore-bearing areas, indicated the presence of new centers of mineralization within the investigated region.

Judging from the distribution of the detected zones, certain of them apparently are genetically related to the sulfide-arsenide deposit, and others are related to the copper sulfide deposit. The solution of the problem of which metallogenetic zone the detected anomalies are related to was of scientific and practical interest. It was established that these two zones, despite their closeness, differ considerably with respect to the content and ratio of cobalt, nickel, and copper in the zone of oxidation of primary ores and in soils and plants.

On this basis it proved to be possible to trace the change in the ratio of cobalt, nickel, and copper in the soils of the On-Kazhaa region along the fault lines connecting these two deposits. The solution of this problem required more precise analyses of soil samples taken along the individual profiles intersecting the region. Polarographic analyses were made of the soils from enriched zones, on the one side adjacent to the copper sulfide deposit (profile 1), and on the other side adjacent to the northern sector of the sulfide-arsenide deposit (profile 22).

The data reveal that the content and ratio of the ore elements in the soils of profiles 1 and 22 differ appreciably from one another. This can be judged from the ratio of the mean values obtained for the two profiles. Thus, whereas in the soils of profile 22 (northern sector) the Co : Ni : Cu ratio is 1 : 1.8 : 2.1, in the soils of profile 1 the ratio is 1 : 1.8 : 12.3.

The divergence between cobalt and copper is particularly great. This phenomenon is associated with an appreciable increase of copper in the soils of the copper sulfide deposit, and a simultaneous decrease of cobalt. The contact between the two ore-bearing zones — cobalt and copper — was found by using the ratio of cobalt, copper, and nickel in the soils of the On-Kazhaa region in the entire 10-km interval between the earlier mentioned ore deposits.

Data from polarographic determinations reveal that the tendency to a decrease in the Cu:Co ratio in the soils collected closer to the copper sulfide deposit (profile 1) can be traced in a southward direction in a number of profiles (3, 4, 5, 6, 7, 8, 9, and 11), approximately to the middle of the studied area. The mean Co:Ni:Cu ratio for these profiles is 1:1.8:5.2. Then, in the direction of the northern sector of the sulfide-arsenide deposit, in profiles 12, 13, 16, 17, 19, and 21, the Co:Ni:Cu ratio changes and averages 1:1.4:1.7. When these values are compared with the earlier obtained values for soils taken directly from ore-bearing zones, it is possible to see a similarity of the ratios in the soils of the northern sector — 1:1.8:2.1 — and in the soils of the zone lying to the north — 1:1.4:1.7. There also is a similarity of the Co:Ni:Cu ratios in the soils of the copper sulfide deposit — 1:1.8:12.3 — and in the profiles lying to the south — 1:1.8:5.2.

On the basis of the derived data it was possible to determine the boundary between the northern sector of the sulfide-arsenide deposit and the zone of the copper sulfide deposit. The boundary passes along the ravine of the On-Kazhaa River (see Fig. 58).

The characteristic distribution of cobalt, nickel, and copper in the two adjacent sectors indicated the presence of dispersion haloes of the corresponding ore deposits. A more detailed biogeochemical exploration of the sector situated near profiles 5, 6, and 7, that is, 2.5 km to the south of the copper sulfide deposit, revealed the presence of copper ore veins in this area, confirmed by mining work.

* * *

The distinguishing characteristic of the climate of the Tuvinian Autonomous Region is the predominant influence of exposure to the sun on the northern and southern slopes of the mountains. Over the same deposit in Tuva it is possible to observe completely different conditions for the weathering of rocks and minerals, depending on the direction which the slopes face. For example, on the southern steppe slopes of the copper–nickel–cobalt deposit there is predominantly a sialic-carbonate weathering process, as can be judged from the character of the soil cover, with calcified products of weathering and an illuvial horizon of chestnut soils.

On the northern forested slope (the northern part of the deposit), where the moisture content is high and permafrost is common, there is a typical process of formation of a sialic-clayey weathered crust characterized by the minerals kaolin and montmorillonite, and others. The dark gray forest soils are elutriated and contain virtually no sesquioxides and carbonates. Due to the differing weathering conditions in the southern and northern sectors of the deposit the processes of secondary mineral formation have been different in the zone of oxidation of the sulfide-arsenide deposit.

Despite the same chemical composition of the ore in the southern and northern sectors, consisting of chalcopyrite $CuFeS_2$, smaltine $CoAs_3$, safflorite $CoAs_2$, niccolite $NiAs$, gersdorffite $NiAsS$, pyrite FeS, and arsenopyrite $FeAsS$, there are great differences in the mineralogical composition of new formations in the weathered crust — in the chemical composition of the soils, water, and plants. The most conspicuous characteristic in the southern sector is a predominance in the products of weathering of the copper minerals malachite $2CuCO_3 \cdot H_2O$ and azurite $3CuCO_3 \cdot H_2O$, forming in an alkaline or close to neutral medium. Moreover, in this region there is an almost complete absence of nickel and iron arsenates: annabergite $Ni_3(AsO_4)_2 \cdot 8H_2O$ and scorodite $Fe^{3+}(AsO_4) \cdot 2H_2O$, which most frequently are found in the northern sector.

Erythrite — $Co_3(AsO_4)_2 \cdot 8H_2O$, cobalt arsenate forming during the oxidation of cobalt arsenides — behaves differently under the conditions prevailing in the southern and northern sectors of the deposit. In the upper horizons of the soil-geological profile in the southern sector, the erythrite is covered by an orange-yellow mineral crust, apparently close to roselite, but completely dissimilar in color. This new formation is less soluble in water and safeguards the erythrite from the effects of external weathering agents. This phenomenon is not observed in the northern sector. The erythrite forming in the process of oxidation of primary ores therefore is dissolved easily by the descending surface waters.

Under the conditions prevailing in the sialic-carbonate weathered crust in the southern sector of the deposit, the copper, nickel, and cobalt are less mobile than in the northern sector. In the southern sector the content of ore elements in the soils therefore is higher than in the northern sector. Thus, the cobalt content in the chestnut soils of the southern sector of the deposit (profiles 2, 6, and 7) averaged $3 \cdot 10^{-2}\%$, while in the gray forest soil of the northern sector of this same deposit (profiles 561, 526, 583, and 693) it rarely exceeded $1 \cdot 10^{-2}\%$. On the other hand, an inverse dependence is observed in plants: the cobalt content in the ash of the grassy steppe plants of the southern sector is $1-2 \cdot 10^{-3}\%$, while in the plants of the forested northern sector it attains hundredths of a percent and averages $5 \cdot 10^{-3}\%$. This dependence is not expressed less clearly in the case of nickel and copper. It becomes obvious that in chestnut soils the migration of nickel, cobalt, and copper is difficult due to the presence of a sialic-carbonate process of weathering of ore-bearing rocks. The limited removal of ore elements by the descending surface waters, because of the high pH of the solution, causes a tendency for metals to accumulate in the humus layer of the soil.

In the northern sector of the deposit, where there are gray and dark gray mountain-forest soils under the larch taiga, there is a removal of metals downward in the profile, which can be attributed to the greater moisture content of the soil-geological profile, whose lower horizons lie above permafrost. Here the accumulation of metals in the soil layer is badly expressed due to the thinness of the humus horizon. The high mobility of nickel, cobalt, and copper in the profile of dark gray mountain-forest soils also explains their easy assimilability by plants, so that there is a certain accumulation of ore elements in the ash.

Proceeding on the basis of these findings, with respect to biogeochemical exploration for nickel, cobalt, and copper, it can be recommended that on the southern steppe slopes of the mountains the biogeochemical survey should be made using soils, while on the northern slopes plants should be used. The effective depth of the method does not exceed 10-15 m.

A certain pattern has been discovered in the distribution of plant associations as a function of the outcropping of ore-bearing rocks in the southern sector. Aleurolites are related to a Caragana-wormwood-fescue association, garnet skarns to a Caragana-wormwood-borage association, and polymetal skarns to a Caragana-wormwood-fescue association. The surrounding vegetation background is a sedge-trisetum association.

It is noted that there is a well-expressed high nickel content in Alyssum biovulatum N. Busch collected on the spoil banks of the copper-nickel-cobalt deposit. Like Alyssum Bertolonii Desv., Alyssum biovulatum N. Busch is a concentrator of nickel and can be used for the exploration of ore under the conditions prevailing in Tuva and in the krays and rayons bordering it.

Over the ore-bearing zone of the copper-nickel-cobalt, copper and copper-polymetal deposits of Tuva, there is a massive chlorosis of a number of plants: in resinous thyme, bilobed cinquefoil, dog rose, cotoneaster, Caragana, bedstraw, and even in larch. This phenomenon can be attributed to the high content of ore elements in the dispersion halo of the ore deposits and can be used in exploration work.

There is a specific flora on old mine workings and recent spoil banks of the copper-nickel-cobalt and copper deposits: dispermous alyssum Alyssum biovulatum N. B., gypsophila Gypsophila Patrinii Ser., and various other species of the pink family.

3. Kadzharanskii Copper-Molybdenum Deposit in the Armenian SSR

The Kadzharanskii ore-bearing region is in a zone of mountainous dry steppes, thinly forested (on the northern slopes), characteristic of the southeastern mountainous part of Armenia which is turned toward the Araks (Kafanskii and Megrinskii Rayons). Here, despite the great elevation (2000 m), the climate of the region lying to the south exerts an influence. This influence has made its impression on weathering processes and the character of the soils and vegetation. The region is of great exploration interest because many ore deposits already have been discovered here — copper, molybdenum, zinc, lead, etc. This part of the book discusses the results of biogeochemical investigations of copper and molybdenum.

Molybdenum was discovered in the ash of trees for the first time by Demarque in 1900. Later, Kornek (1919) and Konishi and Zuguer (1936) discovered molybdenum in many plants. According to data furnished by Kh. G. Vinogradova [1943, 1954], there are certain plants which are concentrators of molybdenum, e.g., plants of the bean and thistle families.

Under ordinary conditions, when the molybdenum content in soils is relatively low, these plants accumulate hundredths and thousandths of a percent of metal in the ash. A study of this problem in regions of ore deposits has revealed a somewhat different behavior of plants to high concentrations of molybdenum in soils. High contents of molybdenum in soils and plants were noted for the first time in the Somerset region in England; this caused an endemic illness of cattle called "teartness." In 1947, M. N. Senilova, while making a molybdenumometric survey using the soils and plants of the Shalginskii deposit, discovered high contents of molybdenum in the soils and plants over the zone of mineralization. The molybdenum content in the ash of certain species of wormwood exceeded 0.01%. We made

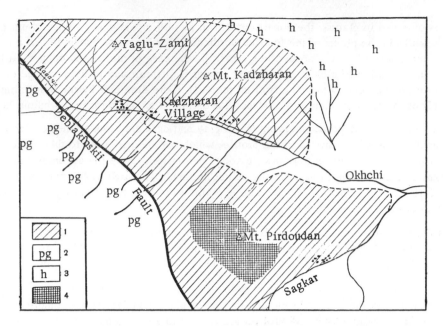

Fig. 59. Geological map of the Kadzharanskii ore region.
1) Monzonites; 2) porphyry granites; 3) hornfels; 4) zone of mineralization.

similar investigations in 1952-1954 in the molybdenum deposits at Kyzyk-Chadre (Tuva) and in the eastern Trans-baikal (Bugdaya), V. V. Baranova did such work in 1957 in the Tyrny-Auzskii deposit, and V. Marmo at Rautsio, Fin-land, in 1954. We will now proceed to a discussion of specific data obtained from the study of the effectiveness of the biogeochemical exploration method in the copper-molybdenum deposit at Kadzharan (Armenian SSR).

General Geological Information Concerning the Region

The area of the Kadzharanskii deposit is a high mountain country with elevations greater than 2000 m above sea level, dissected by large and small watercourses, by the Okhchi, Sagkar, and other rivers. The relief is typical for the geologically youthful high mountain southeastern part of Armenia. The structure of the region includes in-trusive rocks of Tertiary age: porphyrites, porphyritic granites, and monzonites. The copper-molybdenum mineraliza-tion on Mount Pirdoudan involves monzonites, which on the southwest are bounded along the Debaklinskii fault by porphyritic granites and on the north by contact hornfels (Fig. 59).

Recent deposits are expressed as alluvial and residual material. In the Kadzharan region they are not developed extensively due to the steepness of the slopes. The alluvial and residual material attains its maximum thickness on the northern slopes of Mount Pirdoudan, in the bend toward the steep bank of the Okhchi, closer to Kadzharan village, where the thickness of the recent sandy-clayey and rocky sediments attains 10-20 m. The greater part of the region (up to 80%) is covered by a relatively thin layer of soil and residual material from 1 to 5 m thick. However, through-out the entire deposit, the processes of the weathering of rocks containing ore can be traced to considerable depths. They are observed along the fissures in the country rock, especially close to tectonic dislocations. These zones are the most accessible to the action of natural solutions and therefore have the highest moisture content.

The monzonites, constituting the ore-bearing areas at Kadzharan, have been modified greatly by hydrothermal processes. In the main body they are represented by varieties from dark gray fresh monzonites with grains of inter-mediate size to slightly modified monzonites which have been kaolinized along the fissures. The ore-bearing mon-zonites are of a grayish-white and brown color, frequently ferruginated, sericitized, silicified, and kaolinized; quartz and sulfide veins penetrate the mineralization zone.

The residual material consists of clayey loam, in a lesser number of cases of sandy loam, grus, and large frag-ments of intrusive rocks. Closer to the rock the residual material is highly kaolinized. On the surface the residual material is covered by a rather stable soil layer.

Kadzharan is only a small part of the extensive metallogenetic province which extends from the northwestern part of Armenia toward the southeast. In this area there are several copper, copper-molybdenum and polymetal de-posits — Kafanskii, Agarakskii, Dzhindarinskii, Bugakarskii — although the region as a whole has not been studied ade-quately (Mkrtchyan [1948]). The use of complex geochemical investigations will facilitate a more rational conduct of mineral exploration work, especially in the new promising Kadzharan, Agarak, Dastakert, and other sectors.

TABLE 50. Distribution of Molybdenum in Earth's Crust

Contained in	Content, %	Author, year
Lithosphere	$2 \cdot 10^{-4}$	Vinogradov [1956]
Rocks		
ultrabasic	$4 \cdot 10^{-9}$	" "
basic	$1.4 \cdot 10^{-4}$	" "
intermediate	$9 \cdot 10^{-5}$	" "
acidic	$1.9 \cdot 10^{-4}$	" "
sedimentary	$2 \cdot 10^{-4}$	" "
Natural surface waters	$1 \cdot 10^{-7}$	Kuroda et al. [1954]
Soils		
soddy-podzol	$2 \cdot 10^{-4}$	Vinogradov [1956]
chernozem	$2 \cdot 10^{-4}$	" "
chestnut	$2.5 \cdot 10^{-4}$	" "
mean content	$2 \cdot 10^{-4}$	" "
Plants (in ash)	$1 \cdot 10^{-3}$	" "

TABLE 51. Distribution of Molybdenum in Rock-Forming Materials

Minerals	Content in rock, %	Content in mineral, γ/g	Molybdenum of rock suitable as mineral, %
Quartz	28.9	0.01	0.3
Feldspar	62.4	1.20	79
Biotite	8.1	2.30	19.6
Accessory	0.06	13.20	1.1

Geochemical Characteristics of Molybdenum in the Zone of Oxidation of the Sulfide Deposit

Molybdenum is a typical representative of the elements possessing variable valence. In the earth's crust molybdenum is known in a 4- and 6-valence state. The first of these valences is characteristic of deep processes, and the second is characteristic primarily of conditions at the earth's surface (Fersman [1939]).

The distinguishing properties of molybdenum in geochemistry are: 1) the capability of Mo^{4+} to give rise to the stable sulfide MoS_2 (molybdenite) at relatively high temperatures; 2) the formation by the Mo^{6+} ion of volatile halide compounds, especially MoF_6; 3) the high mobility of Mo^{6+} compounds in solution under conditions of hypergenesis; 4) the easy assimilability of molybdenum by surface plants.

The paragenetic relationships of molybdenum in primary sulfides are observed with rhenium. The behavior of rhenium in soils, unconsolidated underlying rocks, and ground water has not been studied. In the weathered crust, molybdenum is associated in oxygen compounds with vanadium, calcium, and lead, for example, in the minerals vanadinite $Pb_5(VO_4)_3Cl$, powellite $Ca(MoO_4)$, and wulfenite $Pb(MoO_4)$ (Yanishevskii [1936], Khitarov and Ivanov [1937], and Akopyan [1948]).

Molybdenum is widely dispersed in the earth's crust, as can be judged from the data given in Table 50. In contrast to many other chemical elements, it is not linked closely to a particular type of igneous rock. The distribution of molybdenum in rock-forming minerals, extracted from biotite granites (Table 51), reveals, however, that four-fifths of the molybdenum in granite is in feldspars. This confirms the relationship of molybdenum to a later rock series (Studenikova, Glinkina, and Pavlenko [1957]).

Among the mobile salts of molybdenum in natural surface waters are oxygen compounds in which the molybdenum is in the form of the anion MoO_4^{2-}. The most probable forms of mobile molybdenum in the weathered crust of crystalline ore-bearing rocks are the products of oxidation of molybdenite:

$$2MoS_2 + 9O_2 + 2H_2O = 2(MoO_2 \cdot SO_4) + 2H_2SO_4.$$

However, the existence of $MoO_2 \cdot SO_4$ is possible only in the immediate vicinity of the zone of oxidation of the sulfide deposit, where the acidic reaction of the solution is still maintained. Molybdates are relatively mobile compounds in the case of a higher pH, as is indicated by the constant presence of molybdenum in river and spring water in quantities close to 0.02 mg/liter (Malyuga [1958]). Ground and river waters are enriched appreciably with molybdenum, from 0.12 to 0.60 mg/liter.

Ground and soil waters are constant sources of molybdenum. It is extracted by surface plants growing over ore deposits. Later, in Chapter IX, the text will give several examples of the correlation of the molybdenum content in ore, soil, and plants and the method for using this correlation in exploration work.

The frequent correlation between rhenium and molybdenum in molybdenite (Noddack [1933], Basitova [1950]) is a reliable method of geochemical exploration for molybdenum using rhenium. In addition, the high stability and solubility of the compounds of alkaline and alkaline earth chemical elements of the $KReO_4$ type makes it possible to postulate the capture of rhenium by surface plants.

Mineralogy and the Chemical Aspects of Processes in the Zone of Oxidation of the Copper-Molybdenum Sulfide Deposit

The copper-molybdenum hydrothermal mineralization at Kadzharan is characterized by the following paragenesis of primary sulfide minerals: chalcopyrite $CuFeS_2$, molybdenite MoS_2, pyrite FeS_2, galena PbS, sphalerite ZnS, argentite AgS, and gray copper ores $Cu_{12}Sb_4S_{13}$ (tetrahedrite group). The ore minerals are associated with quartz veins and veinlets and dispersed in the country rock (stockwork-disseminated type of mineralization) (Magak'yan [1950], Akopyan [1948]).

Among the ore elements lacking in appreciable quantities are tungsten, vanadium, and rhenium, with which molybdenum often is associated. Geochemically these relationships are manifested in other specific cases, which will not be considered here. In primary sulfides molybdenum is associated more with rhenium, while in oxygen compounds in the weathered crust it is associated with vanadium, calcium, and lead.

The makeup of the primary minerals in the Kadzharan deposit to a considerable degree determines the list of secondary minerals forming in the zone of oxidation. The following are encountered: malachite, azurite, powellite $Ca(MoO)_4$, ferrimolybdite $Fe_2O_3 \cdot MoO_3 \cdot 8H_2O$, stilpnosiderite (limonite), lampadite (copper-manganese pitchblende), jarosite, cuprite, halloysite, chrysocolla, brochantite; among the minerals of secondary enrichment are: chalcosite, covellite, and bornite.

The oxygen compounds include mobile forms of molybdenum in a state of hypergenesis. In contrast to deep primary minerals, in which molybdenum is for the most part in a tetravalent state, at the surface it forms anions of the MoO_4^{2-} type, close to $(CrO_4)^{2-}$ and $(WO_4)^{2-}$. The soluble salts formed (excluding lead compounds) migrate easily in natural waters, penetrate into fissures in minerals and rocks, and facilitate the process of secondary mineral formation in the zone of oxidation.

The investigations of N. I. Khitarov and L. A. Ivanov [1936] and V. I. Smirnov [1955] have shown that the possible forms of molybdenum in the weathered crust are the products of oxidation of molybdenite:

$$2MoS_2 + 9O_2 + 2H_2O = 2(MoO_2 \cdot SO_4) + 2H_2SO_4.$$

The formation of the compound $MoO_2 \cdot SO_4$ is entirely possible in the immediate vicinity of the zone of oxidation of the sulfide deposit. The acid solutions, passing through skarn and other rocks, often consisting of limestones and dolomites, are neutralized rapidly, so that molybdenum compounds undergo substantial changes:

$$2CaCO_3 + MoO_2 \cdot SO_4 \rightleftarrows CaMoO_4 + CaSO_4 + 2CO_2.$$

Powellite and calcium sulfate form as a result of this reaction. In exactly the same way, with the prolonged action of water containing bicarbonates on oxidizing molybdenite it is possible to have a different but similar reaction:

$$Ca(HCO_3)_2 + MoO_2 \cdot SO_4 \rightleftarrows CaMoO_4 + H_2SO_4 + 2CO_2,$$

$$Ca(HCO_3)_2 + H_2SO_4 = CaSO_4 + 2H_2O.$$

A more stable mineral — wulfenite ($PbMoO_4$) — is formed with molybdenum in a natural way in the zone of oxidation of polymetallic deposits containing lead and molybdenum. The conditions for preservation of the secondary

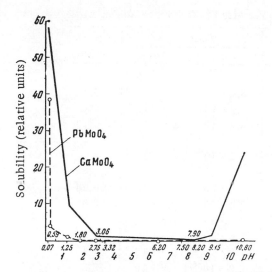

Fig. 60. Dependence of the solubility of CaMoO₄ and PbMoO₄ on pH at 20°.

molybdates, powellite, and wulfenite, in the zone of oxidation are described in the study by Khitarov and Ivanov. They established that the solubility of these minerals (powellite to a greater extent than wulfenite) increases sharply at two extreme values of the concentration of hydrogen ions, at pH 1.6 and 7.5 (Fig. 60). At a pH less than 3, the solubility of molybdates increases sharply. In the pH range from 3 to 9 the solubility of powellite and wulfenite is extremely low, whereas above 9 it again begins to increase.

Taking into account the mean pH values of the upper part of the soil-geological profile over the molybdenum deposit at Kadzharan, close to 7, it was possible to assume that under surface conditions molybdenum possesses extremely low mobility. However, the finding of perceptible quantities of molybdenum in river water (from 0.015 to 0.0291 mg/liter), in spring water (from 0.31 to 0.4 mg/liter), and rather high concentrations in mine waters (up to 1 mg/liter), as well as in soils and in the ash of plants (up to 0.1%), indicates that care should be taken with respect to the modeling of natural processes. For example, it is known that the capacity for metals to migrate is influenced to the greatest degree by the anions and cations accompanying them, especially organic compounds. From this point of view the following are of interest in the Kadzharanskii deposit: iron, copper, and soil acids.

In studying the conditions for the migration of molybdenum compounds in the zone of oxidation, we noted the behavior of calcium molybdenate, which often is found in molybdenum deposits. We established that during the heating of a neutral solution containing a molybdate and a solution of iron sulfate there is a chemical reaction resulting in the formation of a rather stable ferrimolybdite:

$$Fe_2(SO_4)_3 + 3H_2O \rightleftarrows Fe_2O_3 + 3H_2SO_4,$$
$$3CaMoO_4 + 3H_2SO_4 + Fe_2O_3 = Fe_2^{3+}(MoO_4)_3 + 3CaSO_4 + 3H_2O.$$

Paragenetic formations of ferrimolybdite often are associated with powellite (Yanishevskii [1936]). The above-cited reactions apparently occur widely in the zone of oxidation of the molybdenum deposits. However, they are possible only when there is a relatively low pH. The attempts of Khitarov and Ivanov [1937] to identify ferrimolybdite in the ore of the Langarskii molybdenum deposit (Uzbek SSR) have been unsuccessful, obviously because the conditions for secondary mineral formation in this deposit do not favor the above-cited reactions. As water extracts have shown, the factor responsible for this is the high pH of the medium (7.5) and the specific composition of the mobile components in water solutions.

Molybdenum in the Rocks, Waters, Soils, and Plants of the Kadzharan Region

Molybdenum in the porphyrites and porphyritic granites of the Kadzharan region constitutes $1 \cdot 10^{-3}\%$. Monzonites contain $2 \cdot 10^{-3}\%$ of molybdenum, while greatly modified monzonites average about $7 \cdot 10^{-3}\%$.

It has been established by investigations in the Kadzharan deposit that the copper-molybdenum sulfide ores are situated under the constant influence of meteoric water, so that the zone of oxidation of primary ores sometimes is situated at a considerable depth, from 30 to 80 m. Therefore, in a number of cases the upper part of the Kadzharan deposits — the Mount Pirdoudan, Karmir-Karskii, and Davachinskii sectors — consists of strata of unconsolidated leached products of weathering (eluvium, residual material), preserving the initial structure of the ore-bearing rocks — monzonites and porphyrites.

Due to the high content of molybdenum in the rocks making up the region, there is an increase in the general level of dispersed molybdenum in soils, natural waters, and plants. The molybdenum content in the soils of the Kadzharan deposit varies from $2 \cdot 10^{-3}$ to $3 \cdot 10^{-2}\%$, while in the ash of plants it varies from $2 \cdot 10^{-3}$ to $4 \cdot 10^{-2}\%$. The molybdenum content in ground and surface waters is shown in Table 52.

TABLE 52. Copper and Molybdenum Content in Waters in the Vicinity of the Kadzharan Deposits

Water and its origin	Content,%		Ratio
	Cu	Mo	Cu : Mo
Rivers and streams of Kadzharan region	—	$2 \cdot 10^{-6}$	—
Goluboe Lake, Mount Kaputdzhukh	$6.4 \cdot 10^{-7}$	$1.8 \cdot 10^{-6}$	0.35
Dzhermuk (hot spring)	$3 \cdot 10^{-6}$	$1.4 \cdot 10^{-6}$	2.1
Dzhermuk (cold spring)	$6.4 \cdot 10^{-7}$	$1.5 \cdot 10^{-6}$	0.43
Spring 500 m to north of drift 101, right bank of the Kyz-Koshty River (Dastakert)	$6.2 \cdot 10^{-6}$	$3.2 \cdot 10^{-6}$	2
Acidic spring, at confluence of Davachi and Okhchi Rivers	$2 \cdot 10^{-6}$	$1.25 \cdot 10^{-6}$	1.6
Drift 34, Mount Pirdoudan	$1.35 \cdot 10^{-5}$	$5.7 \cdot 10^{-6}$	0.24
Spring near drift 2, Mount Pirdoudan	$2.4 \cdot 10^{-5}$	$3.5 \cdot 10^{-6}$	6.8
Spring near bridge over Okhchi River, Mount Pirdoudan	$2.2 \cdot 10^{-6}$	$1.8 \cdot 10^{-6}$	1.2
Mineral spring along river, Mount Davachi	$2.6 \cdot 10^{-5}$	$2.3 \cdot 10^{-6}$	11.3
Spring on southern slope, Yaglu-Zami (profile 8)	$7 \cdot 10^{-6}$	$7 \cdot 10^{-6}$	1.1
Spring on southern slope, Mount Kadzharan (profile 16)	$9.2 \cdot 10^{-6}$	$1.2 \cdot 10^{-5}$	0.8
Spring at foot of Mount Ostroi (southeastern side)	$5.8 \cdot 10^{-6}$	$4.1 \cdot 10^{-6}$	1.4
Spring at foot of Mount Dvenadtsat' Orlov (northeastern foot)	—	Traces	—
Drift 2, Atkyz deposit	$7.6 \cdot 10^{-3}$	$5.4 \cdot 10^{-6}$	1400
Hole, Azatek deposit	$5.5 \cdot 10^{-6}$	$1.6 \cdot 10^{-6}$	3.4

The data in Table 52 show that the ground and mine waters near Kadzharan (Mounts Pirdoudan and Yaglu-Zami) are enriched appreciably with molybdenum in comparison with other oreless regions of Armenia. Similarly, the streams and rivers of the Kadzharan area contain high quantities of molybdenum in comparison, for example, with the molybdenum content in river and sea water, apparently not exceeding $1 \cdot 10^{-7}\%$ (Kuroda and Sandell [1954]). There is no doubt but that the composition of the waters of the region where exploration for molybdenum was carried out is one of the important ways in which to evaluate the potentialities of the region. Experience has shown, however, that the interpretation of the numerous anomalies revealed by the hydrogeologic method presents great difficulties with respect to a number of metals. In such cases it is extremely advantageous to consider the ratio of the elements characteristic for a particular paragenesis. Table 52 shows the ratio of copper to molybdenum in waters. It is clear that low ratios correspond to waters which are associated with copper-molybdenum ores. The ratio of copper to molybdenum in mine and other waters does not correspond to their ratio in ore, and always is lower by a factor of 10-15, which apparently indicates a greater mobility of molybdenum in the zone of oxidation in comparison with copper.

Biogeochemical Conditions in the Kadzharan Ore Region

The climate in the region of the Kadzharan copper-molybdenum deposit is typical for the high-mountain southeastern part of Armenia. The mean annual quantity of precipitation is about 600 mm, which is distributed very unevenly. The maximum quantity of precipitation occurs in May and June. The snow cover in winter attains 50 cm. The ranges in the Kadzharan region extend in a north-south direction, which creates a sharp difference in the temperatures on the northern and southern slopes and leads to a considerable moistening of the northern slopes (Figurovskii [1920]).

The relief is highly dissected. Mount Pirdoudan, with which the deposit is associated, has steep slopes (25-30°), descending northward to the Okhchi River, and dipping southward to its tributary, the Sagkar River.

The soil cover is determined by elevation above sea level and the orientation of the slopes. Brown soils are found most frequently up to an elevation of 1800 m; there are chestnut soils at greater elevations (1800-2400 m). The southern slopes of Mount Pirdoudan are covered by chestnut soils on shallow residual material. The northern slopes are covered by gray mountain forest skeletal soils. In the remaining sectors there are chestnut soils on residual material and proluvial-residual material (Klopotovskii, 1947).

The southern and southeastern slopes of Mount Pirdoudan and the left bank of the Okhchi River, where there is a promising sector, are covered by upland-xerophytic vegetation, which includes the following species: tragacanth milk vetch Astragalus aurens W. and Lagurus W., thyme Thymus Kotshyanus Boisset Hoh, Armenian everlasting Helichrysum armeniacum, stonecrop Sedum oppositifolium Sims, steppe timothy Phleum phleoides Sims, Transcaucasian thyme Thymus transcaucasicus Konn, and dew grass Dactylis glomerata L. On land which has not been used for many

TABLE 53. Molybdenum Content in Chestnut Soils of Main Sector of the Kadzharanskii Deposit (Profile 4, Horizon A, Depth 0-10 cm)

Samp No.	Sampling site	Content, %	Concentration coefficient
130	20 m to north, downslope	$8 \cdot 10^{-3}$	26.7
128	At exit of drift 34	$6 \cdot 10^{-3}$	20
126	20 m to south, upslope	$1 \cdot 10^{-2}$	33.3
124	40 " " " "	$1 \cdot 10^{-2}$	33.3
122	60 " " " "	$1 \cdot 10^{-2}$	33.3
120	80 " " " "	$1.25 \cdot 10^{-2}$	41.2
118	100 " " " "	$1.67 \cdot 10^{-2}$	56
116	120 " " " "	$1.67 \cdot 10^{-2}$	56
114	140 " " " "	$1.60 \cdot 10^{-2}$	53
112	160 " " " "	$1.10 \cdot 10^{-2}$	33.3
110	180 " " " "	$2.04 \cdot 10^{-2}$	68.7
108	200 " " " "	$1.5 \cdot 10^{-2}$	50
106	220 " " " "	$1.25 \cdot 10^{-2}$	41.2
104	240 " " " "	$8.3 \cdot 10^{-3}$	27.6
102	260 " " " "	$1.13 \cdot 10^{-2}$	37.6
100	280 " " " "	$1.02 \cdot 10^{-2}$	34

TABLE 54. Distribution of Copper and Molybdenum in Soil-Geological Profiles (Profile 2, Mount Pirdoudan)

Sample No.	Soil-geological profile	Depth of horizon, cm	Content, %		Ratio Cu : Mo
			Cu	Mo	
728	20 m to south of drift 34 (ore-free)	0—10	$1.1 \cdot 10^{-1}$	$1 \cdot 10^{-2}$	11
729	Same	25—35	$2.4 \cdot 10^{-1}$	$2.1 \cdot 10^{-2}$	11.4
730	"	50—60	$2.3 \cdot 10^{-1}$	$2.5 \cdot 10^{-2}$	9.2
731	"	100—110	$2.4 \cdot 10^{-1}$	$1.25 \cdot 10^{-2}$	20
732	"	135—145	$2.8 \cdot 10^{-1}$	$1.4 \cdot 10^{-2}$	20
734	70 m to south of drift 34 (over ore)	0—7	$1.2 \cdot 10^{-1}$	$1.6 \cdot 10^{-2}$	7.5
735	Same	25—35	$1.4 \cdot 10^{-1}$	$1.4 \cdot 10^{-2}$	10
736	"	50—60	$3.7 \cdot 10^{-1}$	$7.1 \cdot 10^{-2}$	5.2
737	"	100—110	$3.3 \cdot 10^{-1}$	$2.5 \cdot 10^{-2}$	13.2
738	"	135—145	$3.3 \cdot 10^{-1}$	$2.8 \cdot 10^{-2}$	11.7
739	100 m to south of drift 34 (ore-free)	0—7	$1.35 \cdot 10^{-1}$	$1.9 \cdot 10^{-2}$	6.5
740	Same	25—35	$1.5 \cdot 10^{-1}$	$1.7 \cdot 10^{-2}$	9
741	"	50—60	$2.4 \cdot 10^{-1}$	$2.5 \cdot 10^{-2}$	9.6
742	"	100—110	$2.1 \cdot 10^{-1}$	$1.7 \cdot 10^{-2}$	12.3
743	"	135—145	$1.9 \cdot 10^{-1}$	$1.13 \cdot 10^{-2}$	16.8
744	150 m to south of drift 34 (over ore)	0—7	$8.5 \cdot 10^{-2}$	$1.9 \cdot 10^{-2}$	4.5
745	Same	25—35	$2.1 \cdot 10^{-1}$	$7.1 \cdot 10^{-2}$	3
746	"	50—60	$3.6 \cdot 10^{-1}$	$1.5 \cdot 10^{-2}$	24
747	"	100—110	$1.3 \cdot 10^{-1}$	$1.6 \cdot 10^{-2}$	8
748	"	135—145	$2.5 \cdot 10^{-1}$	$3 \cdot 10^{-2}$	8.1

years there are: St. Johnswort Hypericum perforatum, common dock Rumex acetosa L., common nipplewort Lapsana communis L., and everlasting Xeranthemum scarrosum.

The northern slopes of Mount Pirdoudan are covered with a scrubby growth of oak (Quercus macranthera F. et M.) with an admixture of common hornbeam (Carpinus betulus L.) and others.*

The work was done on the northern, partially forested slope. A system of 11 profiles (corresponding to the geological profiles) was laid out in this area in the main sector of the deposit. These profiles were used in selecting samples of soils and plants at points spaced at 20-m intervals. The distance between profiles was 100-200 m. The profiles intersect the ore-bearing zones (veins, etc.) across their strike, that is, almost in a latitudinal direction. The sampling grid was 300 m wide and 1500 m long. In this grid a total of 250 soil samples and about 300 plant samples were obtained. The work begun on Mount Pirdoudan in 1955 was continued in the summer of 1956.

The analysis of the soils and plants was by spectral and chemical methods. Interference from copper was eliminated by using thiourea (instead of $SnCl_2$) as a molybdenum reducer; this was proposed for similar purposes by L. B. Zaichikova [1949]. The presence of copper in soils and plants not only did not hinder the reaction of color formation, but required the addition of copper (when its content was small) as a catalyst. Iron also is no hindrance to the determination and even facilitates the retention of the colored complex.

Data for colorimetric determinations for one of the eleven studied profiles (profile 4, Table 53) have been given to show the distribution of molybdenum in soils and plants over the known deposit on Mount Pirdoudan in the Kadzharan area.

The data in Table 53 show the variation in the molybdenum content in the soils of the main sector — from 6 $\cdot 10^{-3}$ to $2.04 \cdot 10^{-2}$%, that is, by a factor greater than 3. Moreover, the coefficient of concentration of molybdenum shows an excess over the mean content in soils by a factor of 50 to 60. It follows from these data that in sampling along the profile we did not go beyond the limits of the dispersion halo of the molybdenum deposit.

The molybdenum content in the ash of grassy and woody plants on Mount Pirdoudan varies from $2 \cdot 10^{-3}$ to $2 \cdot 10^{-2}$%. The coefficient of concentration of molybdenum in plants of the main sector is 20, provided the mean content of molybdenum in the ash of plants is assumed to equal $1 \cdot 10^{-3}$%. The molybdenum content in grassy plants is higher than in the leaves of the oak. With the same molybdenum content in the soil — $1 \cdot 10^{-2}$% (samples 100, 112) — the molybdenum content in the leaves of the oak is less ($4.5 \cdot 10^{-3}$%) than in the grassy plant everlasting ($1.2 \cdot 10^{-2}$%). The pattern determined was confirmed by further investigations. A comparison of the observed facts with a geological map of the deposit revealed that the high molybdenum content in soils and plants in most cases correlates with the topography of the ore-bearing zones (Fig. 61).

Samples were taken in five profiles for a study of the distribution of molybdenum and copper by horizons in the soil-geological profile over the zone of mineralization (profile 4). These samples were taken to a depth of 140 cm — from 1 to 10 cm, from 25 to 35 cm, from 50 to 60 cm, from 100 to 110 cm, and from 135 to 145 cm.

Table 54 shows the copper and molybdenum content in the soil and residual material of the mentioned profile. These data show there sometimes is an increase in the molybdenum content in the upper humus layer, then a decrease in its content at a depth from 25 to 60 cm, and a new sharp increase at a depth of 150 cm. Thus, the earlier established distribution of metals in two planes, upper and lower, is confirmed in this case as well. The intermediate layer, corresponding to the zone of maximum development of the root system, is impoverished of metals. The observed high concentrations of molybdenum and copper in the intermediate soil horizon can be attributed to the mechanical destruction of the soil layer at the time of working of cultivated area. The localization of higher contents of molybdenum in the ash of plants occurs in zones of mineralization. In oreless sectors the molybdenum content decreases sharply with depth.

There is an extremely limited downslope displacement of maxima, despite the considerable steepness (up to 30°). This phenomenon can be attributed to the relatively limited range of migration of high concentrations of molybdenum, which are concentrated and firmly held in the soil humus layer and in clayey eluvial minerals.

The appreciable accumulation of molybdenum in the soils and plants over the ore-bearing zone of Mount Pirdoudan made it possible to test the method in such promising areas as were pointed out by geologists of the Kadzharanskii Geological Exploration Party.

---

* According to data supplied by N. S. Petrunina.

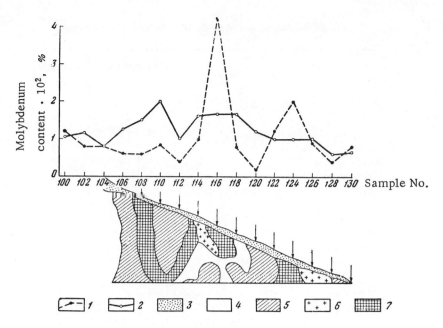

Fig. 61. Distribution of molybdenum in soils and plant ash in relationship to the geological profile (Mount Pirdoudan, profile 4). 1) Curve showing the molybdenum content in plants; 2) curve showing the molybdenum soils; 3) soil and residual material; 4) unmodified monzonites; 5) slightly modified monzonites; 6) dikes; 7) ore-bearing monzonites.

Fig. 62. Panoramic view along the left bank of the Okhchi River at Kadzharan.

For solution of the problem of the possibilities of the mentioned sectors the method used was the preliminary sampling for molybdenum of water, soils, and plants, selected for special purposes in these sectors. Two sectors were investigated in 1956 for selection of the most promising region: the left bank of the Okhchi River (Mounts Davachi, Yaglu-Zami, and Kadzharan) and Mount Dvenadtsat' Orlov at Ankavan. No molybdenum was discovered at the time

TABLE 55. Enrichment of Plant Ash with Molybdenum

Plant	Mo content, %	Concentration coeff.
Astragalus aurens W.	$2.7 \cdot 10^{-2}$	27
Thymus Kotshyanus Boiss et H o h. .	$1.8 \cdot 10^{-2}$	18
Stachys annua L.	$2.7 \cdot 10^{-2}$	27
Salvia verticillata L.	$1 \cdot 10^{-2}$	10
Teucsium alba L.	$1.4 \cdot 10^{-2}$	15
Scabiosa micrantha D e s v.	$5 \cdot 10^{-2}$	50
Scutellaria latifolia L.	$2 \cdot 10^{-2}$	20
Teucrium alba L	$1.5 \cdot 10^{-2}$	15
Scrophularia Grossheimii B. Sch. . .	$1.2 \cdot 10^{-2}$	12
Astrodaucus orientalis Dr.	$3.3 \cdot 10^{-2}$	33
Gypsophila elegans M. B.	$2 \cdot 10^{-2}$	20
Astragalus declinatus W.	$1.3 \cdot 10^{-2}$	13
Leontodon sp.	$1.2 \cdot 10^{-2}$	12
Mean	$2 \cdot 10^{-2}$	20
Mean in plant ash . . .	$1.10 \cdot 10^{-3}$	

of a preliminary sampling of the water from springs, soils, plants, and minerals of Mount Dvenadtsat' Orlov, with the exception of pyrite, taken from a drift, where hundredths and thousandths of a percent of molybdenum were discovered.

The left bank of the Okhchi River was found to be the most enriched with molybdenum and exploratory work by the biogeochemical method was undertaken there. Figure 62 is a panoramic view of this sector.

Exploration for Molybdenum on Mounts Davachi, Yaglu-Zami, and Kadzharan

The Kadzharanskii Geological Exploration Party considered the entire left bank of the Okhchi River to be promising for molybdenum. This was indicated by the geological structure of the sector, which consists of monzonite, widely represented on Mount Pirdoudan. In addition, molybdenum has been discovered in the water of springs found on the southern slopes of Mounts Davachi, Yaglu-Zami, and Kadzharan (Dolukhanova, 1957).

In the summer of 1955 the entire left bank of the Okhchi River was covered by a soil-plant biogeochemical survey on the southern slopes of Davachi and Yaglu-Zami. The sampling was done using a regular rectangular grid with grid squares measuring 20 × 100 m, that is, the distance between profiles was 100 m and the interval between samples was 20 m. The 200-g soil samples were taken from the upper A horizon, from 0 to 10 cm. The plant samples (a single species) were 100-150 g of green mass.

The preliminary data from the analyses of soils and plants for molybdenum and copper reveal the presence of major anomalies similar to those which were observed on Mount Pirdoudan. The molybdenum content in soils attained $3 \cdot 10^{-2}\%$ and exceeded the normal content by a factor of 100.

In 1956 a soil-plant biogeochemical survey covered the adjacent part of Mount Kadzharan. The resulting maps of isoconcentrations of molybdenum in the soil clearly revealed zones with a high molybdenum content on Mounts Davachi, Yaglu-Zami, and Kadzharan (Fig. 63).

The map of isoconcentrations of molybdenum in soils on the left bank of the Okhchi River and Mount Davachi were submitted to the Kadzharanskii Geological Exploration Party for use in developing a plan for mineral exploration work.

According to the theory of biogenic accumulation of metals in the soil humus layer, the maps of the soil and plant biogeochemical surveys should correlate with one another. The floristic (biogeochemical) map was compiled on the basis of data obtained by analyses of plants collected along the same profiles and at the same points at which the soil samples were taken. A study was made of grassy plants of various species: milk vetch, St. Johnswort, thyme, betony, figwort, and others. Analyses of plants collected in the same area in the zone of the dispersion halo of the ore deposit revealed an approximately equal molybdenum content in virtually all the collected plants, regardless of

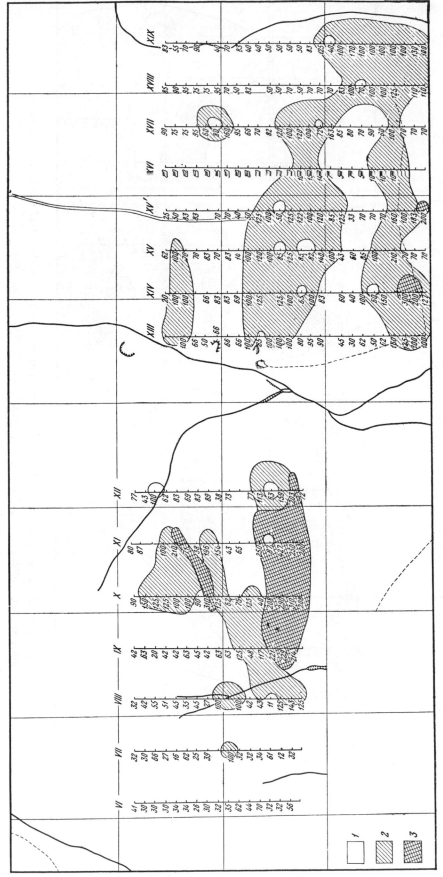

Fig. 63. Map of isoconcentrations of molybdenum in the soils of the left bank of the Okhchi River at Kadzhar-n. Molybdenum content: 1) less than 0.01%; 2) more than 0.01%; 3) more than 0.02%.

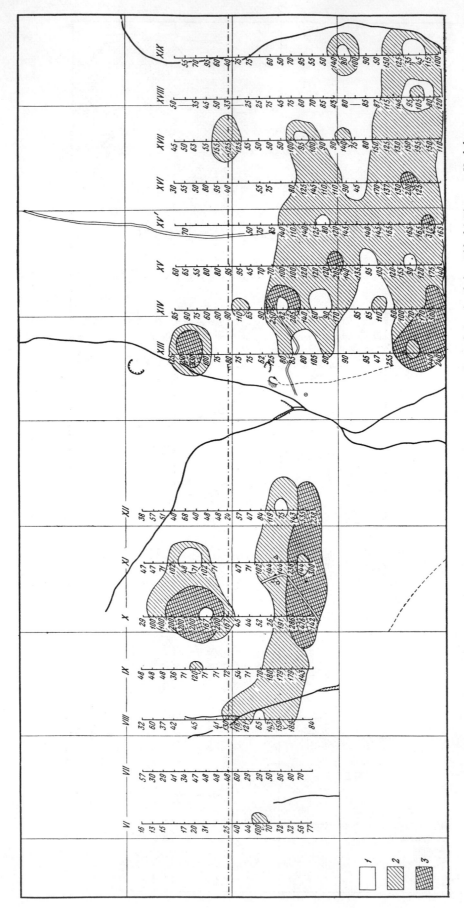

Fig. 64. Map of isoconcentrations of molybdenum in the ash of plants along the left bank of the Okhchi River at Kadzharan. Molybdenum content: 1) less than 0.01%; 2) more than 0.01%; 3) more than 0.02%.

144

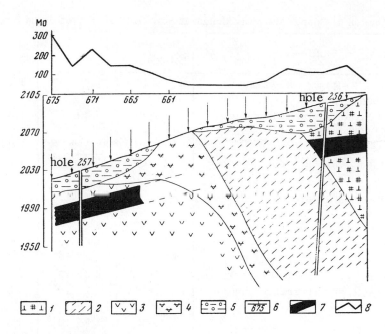

Fig. 65. Distribution of molybdenum in plant ash in relationship to the geological profile. 1) Modified porphyrite; 2) hornfels; 3) fresh monzonite; 4) modified monzonite; 5) residual material; 6) sampling points; 7) ore-bearing zone; 8) molybdenum content in plant ash, in ten-thousandths (%).

what family they belonged to. The data in Table 55 show that on the average plant ash is enriched with molybdenum by a whole order greater than the mean molybdenum content in the plants characteristic of the entire region (the geochemical background is $3 \cdot 10^{-3}\%$ of molybdenum in ash). The highest content is found in: scabiosa (teasel family), golden milk vetch (Leguminosae family), and eastern carrot (umbel family).

The smallest content of molybdenum was noted in camomel, sage, chicory, and others. Despite the known dissimilar content of molybdenum in individual species, all plants without exception accumulate molybdenum over ore deposits, that is, in areas where the soils and the underlying rocks are enriched with this element. Thus, the replacement of certain plants by others in the sampling of plants along exploration profiles is not a matter of decisive importance.

Figure 64 is a map of the isoconcentrations of molybdenum in the ash of plants from the left bank of the Okhchi River (Mounts Yaglu-Zami and Kadzaharan). The map clearly shows two zones with a high molybdenum content on the southeastern slope of Mount Yaglu-Zami and on Mount Kadzharan. These zones closely correspond to those which are observed on the map based on the soil biogeochemical survey. Thus, anomalies were detected which correlate well with the anomalies detected in the soil biogeochemical survey.

Drilling work done by the Kadzharanskii Geological Exploration Party in 1957-1958 on the left bank of the Okhchi River (Karmir-Karskii sector) confirmed our predictions as to the presence in that area of mineralization of economic importance. Of the eight deep holes (averaging 400 m in depth), sulfide ores of copper and molybdenum of economic importance were discovered at various depths. In contrast to the main sector of the deposit on Mount Pirdoudan, the mineralization was related not only to hydrothermally modified monzonites, but also to porphyrites, extending to the north and northwest.

The richest ore deposits are situated along contacts, in pulverized zones, primarily along fissures in the rock. Ore-bearing zones often are traced even in the upper horizons of the deposit, where processes of the oxidation of sulfides have not penetrated too deeply. For example, on Yaglu-Zami (Karmir-Karskii sector), mineralization of economic importance (in monzonites) is observed in hole 257 (Fig. 65), beginning at 30 m and in the interval from 37 to 47 m. The mineralization is primarily chalcopyrite and molybdenite with a mean content of copper in the rock of 0.45% and a mean molybdenum content of 0.05%. At higher levels there are partially oxidized, fissured monzonites with a smaller content of ore components, and at still higher levels there is a 15-m layer of highly weathered

TABLE 56. Distribution of Copper and Molybdenum in Soil-Geological Profiles on Mount Yaglu-Zami

Sample No.	Profile	Depth of horizon, cm	Content,%		Ratio Cu : Mo
			Cu	Mo	
1000	Chestnut soil with rock fragments, along control line	0-10	$1.8 \cdot 10^{-1}$	$1.4 \cdot 10^{-2}$	13
1001	Bright cinnamon-colored clayey loam with rock fragments	25-35	$9.5 \cdot 10^{-2}$	$1.3 \cdot 10^{-2}$	7.3
1002	The same	50-60	$4.8 \cdot 10^{-2}$	$1.2 \cdot 10^{-2}$	4
1003	Fragmented yellow monzonite	90-100	$1.4 \cdot 10^{-1}$	$1.5 \cdot 10^{-2}$	9.2
1004	The same	130-140	$1.8 \cdot 10^{-1}$	$1.4 \cdot 10^{-2}$	13
1005	Chestnut soil, 40 m to south of control line	0-10	$1.7 \cdot 10^{-2}$	$1.1 \cdot 10^{-2}$	15
1006	The same	25-35	$1.4 \cdot 10^{-1}$	$1.6 \cdot 10^{-2}$	9
1007	The same	50-60	$1.6 \cdot 10^{-1}$	$1.6 \cdot 10^{-2}$	10
1008	The same	90-100	$1.3 \cdot 10^{-1}$	$1.3 \cdot 10^{-2}$	10
1009	The same	130-140	$2.3 \cdot 10^{-1}$	$1.3 \cdot 10^{-2}$	16.4
1010	Chestnut soil, 80 m to south of control line	0-10	$1 \cdot 10^{-2}$	$8 \cdot 10^{-3}$	12
1011	The same	25-35	$8 \cdot 10^{-2}$	$7.5 \cdot 10^{-3}$	10
1012	The same	50-60	$7 \cdot 10^{-2}$	$6 \cdot 10^{-3}$	12
1013	The same	100-110	$1.1 \cdot 10^{-2}$	$1.1 \cdot 10^{-2}$	10

monzonites, covered by deposits of fragmentary material and soil. The soil cover, 70 to 80 cm thick, lies either directly on the weathered rocks or on residual material.

In hole 256 ore was found in the 34-66 m interval and at lower horizons. In hole 255 mineralization already is observed beginning at a depth of 20 m, while in others it begins at 50 to 80 m (holes 293, 253, 254).

In almost all ore holes, the upper zone of mineralization is situated under the immediate influence of descending meteoric water; the latter often can be observed in drifts at corresponding depths. The highly fissured weathered porphyrites and monzonites covering the ore are no hindrance to the ascending and descending migration of ground water, which very often moistens the soil at low elevations or emerges at the surface in the form of springs, enriched with copper and molybdenum. Naturally, under such conditions the ore elements are intercepted easily by plants which possess a deep root system (milk vetch, figwort, and others).

The formation of chemical (biogeochemical) dispersion haloes of copper and molybdenum over a zone of mineralization situated at a depth of 20-50 m therefore becomes completely understandable. Ore bodies known to exist at greater depths (80-100 m) are more difficult to detect from the surface. For example, the ore-bearing zone penetrated by hole 254 at a depth of 83 m was not noted by the biogeochemical survey. Thus, the effective depth of the exploration method based on soils and plants, as used in the Kadzharan area, apparently does not exceed 50 m; this corresponds to the mean depth of the zone of oxidation of sulfides in the Karmir-Karskii sector.

A comparison of the dispersion haloes of copper and molybdenum in soils and plants and the outlines of the ore zones at depth has made it possible to establish a correlation between biogeochemical anomalies and ore-bearing zones. The study of this dependence was facilitated by detailed mineral exploration work, making it possible to obtain geological profiles through almost the entire Karmir-Karskii sector. These profiles were used in the interpretation of copper and molybdenum anomalies in soils and plants. As an example, Fig. 65 shows the molybdenum content in the dispersion halo (e.g., in plant ash) in relationship to the geological profile associated with boreholes 256 and 257.

Figure 65 shows an appreciable increase in the molybdenum content in the lower and upper parts of the profile over ore-bearing monzonites and porphyrites. In the middle part of the profile the ore-bearing zones are disrupted by non-ore-bearing hornfels; this has been denoted by an appropriate pattern.

A study of the upper horizons of the deposit was very difficult due to the lack of samples of unconsolidated rock fragments, absent from the cores obtained in the drilling work. It was necessary to take samples from trenches, pits, and the mouths of the holes. An analysis of these samples has revealed that the molybdenum content in unconsolidated rocks over the mineralization zone decreases slowly toward the surface from hundredths of a percent in monzonite (at

146

TABLE 57. Ash Content in Newly Sampled Plants and Plants of the Preceding Year

Sample No.	Plant and site	Sampling date	% of ash in dry plant		Concentration coefficient
			Newly sampled	From preceding year	
424,425	Chicory Cichorium intybus L. (above ground), Mount Narzannaya, profile 3 , 180 m	Aug. 20, 1958	6.86	6.60	0.93
426,427	St. Johnswort Hypericum perforatum L. (above ground), Mount Narzannaya, profile 3 , 160 m	Aug. 20, 1958	3.76	2.10	0.56
421,422	Apple Malus sp. (leaves, shoots), Mount Narzannaya, profile 4, 140 m	Aug. 20, 1958	4.70	4.47	0.95

a depth of 20-30 m) to thousandths of a percent in weathered material. There is a sharp change toward the surface in the ratio of oxidized and sulfide forms of metals; there is a decrease or total disappearance of the latter. In the humus layer of the soil the copper and molybdenum content increases somewhat and attains tenths and hundredths of a percent, respectively. The accumulation of copper and molybdenum in the soil humus is due to a biogeochemical process, as is indicated by the considerable accumulation of these elements in plant ash in certain cases.

The new geological map of the Karmir-Karskii sector shows an extremely complex combination of extrusive and other rocks — porphyrites, monzonites, and hornfels. All to some extent have been modified by hydrothermal processes and often are mineralized. The study of the chemical and mineralogical composition of the rocks on the basis of data from deep drilled holes has not yet been completed. This study is being made not only by our group, but also by workers of the Moscow Geological Exploration Institute, under the direction of M. P. Isaenko.

The study of the distribution of copper and molybdenum in the soil-geological profile was made using samples selected at depths as great as 140 cm, by percussive boring. Three profiles were laid out on Mount Yaglu-Zami for selection of samples; these profiles were between profiles 8 and 9 of the exploration grid. Table 56 gives an analysis of the samples.

The data in Table 56 show an appreciable accumulation of copper and molybdenum in the humus horizon of the soil from 0 to 10 cm. In the interval from 25 to 60 cm there is some decrease in the copper and molybdenum content, and then a new increase at greater depth. It was noted that in the profiles over the zone of mineralization the increase of ore components with depth occurs more rapidly than outside the limits of the ore-bearing zones. Table 56 also shows the quantitative ratios of copper and molybdenum. For the most part they resemble those which are observed in ore. In the intermediate soil horizons there is some decrease in the ratio of copper to molybdenum. It can be attributed to the more active extraction of copper than molybdenum by the roots of plants, as can be judged from a certain change in the ratio of copper to molybdenum in plants.

As already noted, drilling and mineral exploration work in the Karmir-Karskii sector for the first time established the presence of ore in hydrothermally modified porphyrites. Thus, the promising areas for exploration for copper-molybdenum ores at Kadzharan have expanded greatly. Because of this it was possible for us to carry on exploration-survey biogeochemical investigations in adjacent sectors to the north and northwest of the Karmir-Karskii and Davachinskii sectors. As a result, new promising areas enriched with copper and molybdenum have been detected.

The outer boundaries of the rocks making up the Karmir-Karskii sector of the left bank of the Okhchi River, such as monzonites and porphyrites, are detected from the surface rather easily from the color of the soil cover. On weathered monzonites the chestnut soils are of a dark cinnamon color, on porphyrites and hornfels they assume a greenish-gray color, etc. Similarly, there is a change in the external appearance of the vegetation associations. More detailed geobotanical investigations on Mount Yaglu-Zami (Malyuga et al. [1959]) have revealed a rather rigorous relationship between individual plant groups and outcrops of corresponding rocks (see Figs. 5 and 6).

By a comparison of the geological and geobotanical maps of the Karmir-Karskii sector it is possible to observe a close relationship between a thyme-tragacanth association and monzonites, between legumes and various grasses and porphyrites, etc.

In the study of the relationship of plants to specific rocks or dispersion haloes of ore deposits, it has been noted that the milk vetch Astragalus declinatus W. is found in the Kadzharan area primarily over zones of hydrothermal mineralization. For example, this plant is found on Mount Pirdoudan and along the left bank of the Okhchi River, where copper-molybdenum ores have been discovered (Karmir-Karskii and Davachi sectors). At the same time, there has been noted a nonuniform development of black color on the petals of the poppy Papaver commutatum F. et M. In the normal forms of this poppy the black spots are at the base of the petals, while in modified forms they reach the edges of the petal, forming a black cross on the bright red background of the flower (see Fig. 2).

The modified poppy was found on Mount Yaglu-Zami (Karmir-Karskii sector), in a gully between the eighth and ninth profiles of our grid, where the soil is moistened by ground water and enriched with copper and molybdenum.

At the same time, a study was made of the seasonal influence on the accumulation of copper and molybdenum in plants. The plants collected in the same area in the Karmir-Karskii sector at different seasons revealed a higher content of copper and molybdenum in the plants sampled in August than in these same plants sampled in June. Similarly, it was established that the content of metals in dry stems of the preceding year from St. Johnswort, chicory, yarrow, and other plants, is significantly higher than in freshly sampled plants, as was discussed above.

The factor responsible for the accumulation of copper and molybdenum in the ash of plants of the previous year in comparison with the content in freshly collected samples still remains unclear. By comparing the data on copper and molybdenum in different plants, it can be noted that the greater the copper content, the less molybdenum there is, and vice versa.

In attempting to establish the reason for the increase of copper and molybdenum in the ash of plants of the preceding year, we made a study of their ash content, assuming that the increase could result from the leaching out of the more mobile chemical elements from plants which had experienced winter conditions, including such elements as potassium, sodium, calcium, etc. Table 57 gives a comparative analysis of the ash in such plants.

The resulting data do not reveal any significant decrease in the ash content in plants which have undergone winter conditions, such as chicory and the apple tree. The certain decrease in the ash content of St. Johnswort cannot explain the increase of copper and molybdenum in plants which have experienced winter conditions.

Samples of grassy plants were collected from the same area at the beginning and end of the summer in an effort to explain the change in the chemical composition of plants during the course of the growing season.

In addition to the Kadzharan deposit, similar biogeochemical investigations were undertaken by our party in the Agarakskii, Dastakertskii, and other ore-bearing regions of Armenia. The resulting data revealed the possibility of using the biogeochemical method in exploration for copper-molybdenum and polymetal deposits under the conditions prevailing in Eastern Transcaucasia.

In the mountainous dry steppe zone of southeastern Armenia the conditions for weathering and soil formation facilitate the development of an eluvial weathered crust with well-expressed secondary dispersion haloes of the ore elements in eluvium, residual material, soils, and plants. Therefore, the copper-molybdenum and other deposits of the Kadzharan, Agarak, and Dastakert type can be identified from the surface by an analysis of soils and plants in which the copper and molybdenum content exceeds by tens of times the normal content.

By a geochemical comparison of the distribution of ore elements over the zone of mineralization it has been possible to establish a correlation between the copper and molybdenum content in rocks (ores), soils, and plants. The development of a leached weathered crust to a considerable depth and the formation of characteristic sediments over the ore-bearing zone is no hindrance to this correlation. The depth to which this geochemical relationship can be detected from the surface is 50-60 m.

On the basis of a soil-plant biogeochemical survey it has been possible to obtain maps of the isoconcentrations of copper and molybdenum on the basis of their content in soils and plants. This has made it possible to outline the dispersion haloes of these elements over known ore-bearing zones (Mount Pirdoudan) and promising areas along the left bank of the Okhchi River. The detected anomalies on Mounts Yaglu-Zami and Kadzharan were checked by the drilling of holes. As a result, two major ore-bearing zones were discovered, both enriched with copper and molybdenum (Karmir-Karskii ore-bearing sector).

Additional biogeochemical survey work, done to the north of the Karmir-Karskii sector, revealed new promising zones with a high copper and molybdenum content in soils and plants. The fact that this zone is associated with porphyrites is of basic significance in solving the problem of the presence of ore in the porphyrites at Kadzharan.

The biogeochemical survey in 1957 in the extreme northwestern part of the left bank of the Okhchi River revealed the presence of high contents of molybdenum in the ash of plants at the foot of the southern slope of Mount Narzannoy. The detected anomalies are entirely characteristic of zones of mineralization. Because no appreciable increase in the copper and molybdenum content was observed in the soils and underlying residual material, it was surmised that ore was present at a considerable depth below the surface.

The biogeochemical relationship between plant associations and outcrops of monzonites and porphyrites, which in the Karmir-Karskii sector are ore-bearing, has been established. Individual species of plants — Astragalus declinatus W. and the modified poppy form Papaver commutatum (with a black cross) — are found only over a zone of copper-molybdenum mineralization. These plants can be used as indicators for copper and molybdenum ores.

It has been noted that the copper and molybdenum content increases sharply toward the end of the growing season. An analysis of dry grassy plants from the previous year reveals that in contrast to alkaline and alkaline-earth elements, copper and molybdenum are not leached out and are retained in plants until the year which follows. This observation shows that a plant biogeochemical survey can be made late in the autumn and in early spring, using dry plants for this purpose.

4. The Varaz Polymetal Deposit (Georgian SSR)*

The use of the biogeochemical method in the exploration for nonferrous and precious metals under different physicogeographic and geologic conditions in the USSR is constantly revealing new and interesting aspects of the migration of chemical elements over ore deposits. Investigations at Kadzharan in the Armenian SSR in a copper-molybdenum deposit has established the geochemical relationship between the zone of oxidation of sulfide ores at a depth of 30-40 m, the soil, and the plant cover. A dispersion halo of the ore elements is formed due to the deep penetration of weathering processes into the strata of ore-bearing rocks — monzonites, porphyrites, and others. The highest content of copper and molybdenum has been noted in the humus horizon of the soil. An especially high content of molybdenum has been found in the roots of the milk vetch, which penetrate deeply into weathered rocks.

The experience of work at Kadzharan has demonstrated the possibility of successful application of the biogeochemical method in exploration for ore over an extensive area in the Transcaucasus with bioclimatic and soil-geological conditions similar to those in the Kadzharan area. This has been pointed out in a study by A. I. Makarova [1960] of the Alaverdskii ore region (Akhtala, Armenian SSR), made under the auspices of the Institute of Geochemistry and Applied Chemistry of the Academy of Sciences of the USSR. The studied zone is in a region of moderately high mountains with broadleaf forests on brown mountain forest soils. As in the Kadzharan region, here in the Akhtal'-skii polymetal deposit it has been possible to confirm the general patterns observable in the biogeochemical accumulation of copper, zinc, and lead in the humus horizon of the soil and in plant ash. The lead content in the leaves of trees growing over the zone of mineralization exceeds by a factor of ten the normal distribution, and this, together with the soil content, makes it possible to apply such data in biogeochemical exploration of polymetal deposits under the corresponding conditions prevailing in eastern Transcaucasia. An especially high lead content has been noted in the roots of plants.

Many regions in the Caucasus, especially the very moist subtropics, have not been studied as to the applicability of the new exploration method. This problem was studied by making investigations in the Varaz copper-polymetal deposit, located in the Adzharskaya ASSR, Georgian SSR.

The Varaz deposit, where biogeochemical sampling was done, is situated in the western part of the Adzharo-Trialetskaya folded system, within the basin of the Adzharis-Tskhali River. The ore field of the deposit occupies the headwaters region of the Varaz River, which flows down the southern slope of the Shavshetskii Range. The area is one of high, severely dissected mountains with absolute elevations of 1200-1500 m within the deposit. The hydrographic system is very well developed.

With respect to geological structure, the region includes rocks of the Middle Eocene volcanic stratum, penetrated by intrusions of syenite-diorite composition, exposed 1.5 km to the north of the Varaz deposit (Fig. 66). The great thickness of volcanic rocks here for the most part consists of coarsely stratified massive tuff-breccias, tuffs, and intercalations of andesites and andesite basalts which alternate with them. This entire volcanic complex makes up the northern wing of the Shavshetskii anticlinal fold, complicated by secondary minor folding and disjunctive disloca-

---

*Published, with modifications, from an article by D. P. Malyuga, V. R. Nadiradze et al. (1960).

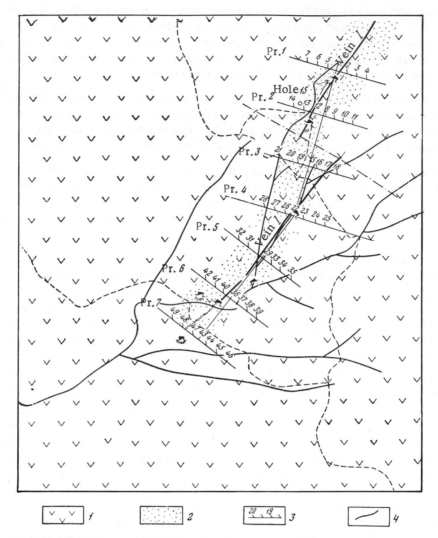

Fig. 66. Geological map of the Varaz deposit. 1) Tuff-andesites; 2) modified tuff-andesites; 3) biogeochemical sampling points; 4) lines of dislocations.

tions. The angle of dip to the northwest (300°) is 25°. The volcanic rocks and andesite-basalts are broken by systems of faults with the following dip: to the southwest (220°) at an angle of 80° and to the southeast (100°) at an angle of 20°.

The andesites and andesite-basalts are for the most part fresh, and sometimes merge into rocks with a taxitic structure. The tuff-breccias usually are of a taxitic structure and in most cases consist of large fragments.

The intrusive rocks are represented by a series of rocks from quartz syenites and granodiorites to gabbrodiorites and gabbros. Contact metamorphosed rocks have developed around the intrusive. Contact hornfels are encountered near the intrusion and at some distance from it there are bleached rocks with a considerable quantity of newly formed quartz, sericite, kaolinite, and leverrierite.

The metamorphosed rocks contain in almost all cases impregnations of pyrite, with chalcopyrite and sphalerite being less common. The following are characteristic of metamorphosed rocks: strong silification, sericitization, pelitization, and impregnation with pyrite.

Seven ore veins have been explored in the Varaz deposit area. These veins lie in the rocks of the tuff-porphyrite complex and are approximately parallel to one another, with a common northeast strike. The veins form an ore field with an area of about 1 km².

The veins are 100 to 500 m apart and are distributed in such a way that their geometric centers lie along a single line with a northeast strike. They dip southeastward at steep angles. All the veins are of the same type with respect to their morphological characteristics, structure, and chemical composition. Vein I can be traced along the surface for a distance of 650 m (see geological map, Fig. 66). For the most part the mineralization is copper-poly-metal and there is a zonal distribution. For example, the mean content for vein I is: copper, 2.8%; lead, 2.6%; zinc, 2%; with traces of molybdenum.

The ore-bearing minerals form impregnations in the vein or continuous pockets in quartz. The mineralization is uneven and is accompanied by highly mineralized sectors, alternating with poorly impregnated ores, locally merging into ore-free quartz, from time to time alternating with stringers.

Climatic and Hydrogeologic Conditions in the Region — Soils and Plants

The Varaz deposit is a zone of moist mountain forest landscapes with brown podzolized soils. The climate of the region is transitional — from high mountain to subtropical. The precipitation is heavy — from 1500 to 1800 mm. The large amount of precipitation, falling as rain and snow, has facilitated the development of the surface hydrographic network and the ground water. Despite the great steepness of the slopes, the presence of the abundant vegetation hinders the rapid erosion of the slopes and the washing down of the products of weathering and the soil cover. Alluvial deposits are represented by clays containing fragments; the latter, for the most part, are no larger than 0.3-2 m, and only in individual parts of the area do they attain several tens of meters.

The accumulation of ground water, classified here as soil and fissure water, is facilitated by the rather temperate climate and dense vegetation, both hindering direct evaporation. On the other hand, the unsorted material in the alluvium does not lead to an even distribution of ground water and a constant flow in springs. The discharge of water in the Varaz River per kilometer averages 0.1-0.35 m^3/sec; the gradient is 530 m. The influx of water into underground mines (drifts) assumes the form of slight dripping, or in a few cases small streamlets. The water temperature in the drifts ranges from 8 to 10°C.

Soils

The Varaz deposit region has weakly podzolized brown forest soils (Sabashvili [1948]). They are shallow, pebbly, and of a clayey loam composition. They are poorly differentiated by horizons. The underlying rocks in the region of the deposit are tuff-andesites and clayey alluvium of varying thickness. The soils of the drainage divide, formed on thick alluvium, are characterized morphologically by a more conspicuous differentiation by horizons. As an example, in Fig. 66 we show a soil profile for profile 4.

A, 0-5 cm. A humus horizon of brownish-black color, moist. In the lower part of the horizon there is slight podzolization. Transition to B_1 is gradual. B_1, 5-15 cm. Clayey, brownish-yellow, dense. B_2, 15-50 cm. Yellow, clayey, dense, with veins of Fe_2O_3, streamers of humus. B_2C, 50-100 cm. Clayey, dense, veins and streamers rare. Below 100 cm clayey alluvium.

The soil effervesces nowhere in the profile; the pH in the humus horizon is 5.5.

Vegetation

In the Adzharskii mountain forest zone there is a clearly expressed vertical zonality of forest species. The dominant formation up to 1500 m is a mixed forest with beech Fagus orientalis Lips, hornbeam Carpinus betulus L., oak Quercus Hartwissiana Stev., linden Tilia caucasica Rupr., and others. At greater elevations the beech forest is replaced by a coniferous forest, consisting of the spruce Picea orientalis L. and the fir Abies Nordmanniana Spach.

The undergrowth consists of evergreen brush vegetation, such as rhododendron Rhododenron ponticum L., laurel-cherry Prunus laurocerasus L., butcher's broom Ruscus hypophyllum L., and others.

A part of the deposit is covered by dense nearly impassable thickets of cherry laurel and rhododenron, within which there are scattered clumps of mixed forest, characteristic of the transitional zone. Spruce and fir are found here, together with beech, hornbeam, and oak.

The character of the ore deposit and natural conditions were extremely favorable for the application of the biogeochemical method of exploration. We now will discuss briefly the characteristic conditions for the migration of ore elements in the dispersion halo.

Geochemical Characteristics of Copper, Zinc, and Lead in the Zone of Oxidation of the Sulfide Deposit

The principal elements in polymetal deposits are copper, zinc, and lead, with a varying ratio in the composition of the ore. Copper and zinc are elements of basic magma. Their content in gabbro and basalts attains hundredths of a percent, exceeding by a factor of 2 or 3 their content in intermediate and acidic rocks (Vinogradov [1956]). The copper in basic rocks apparently is associated with high-temperature sulfides, and zinc with silicates. Copper and zinc

TABLE 58. Distribution of Copper, Zinc, and Lead in the Earth's Crust*

Distribution in	Content, %		
	Cu	Zn	Pb
Lithosphere	$7 \cdot 10^{-3}$	$5 \cdot 10^{-3}$	$1.6 \cdot 10^{-3}$
Sedimentary rocks	$4.1 \cdot 10^{-3}$	$8 \cdot 10^{-3}$	$2 \cdot 10^{-3}$
Natural surface waters	$2 \cdot 10^{-6}$	$5 \cdot 10^{-6}$	$5 \cdot 10^{-7}$
Ground water	$4 \cdot 10^{-6}$	$1 \cdot 10^{-5}$	$1 \cdot 10^{-6}$
Soils (mean)	$2 \cdot 10^{-3}$	$5 \cdot 10^{-3}$	$1 \cdot 10^{-3}$
Soddy-podzol soils	$8 \cdot 10^{-4}$	$3.5 \cdot 10^{-3}$	$5 \cdot 10^{-4}$
Chernozem soils	$1.7 \cdot 10^{-3}$	$7 \cdot 10^{-3}$	$2 \cdot 10^{-3}$
Chestnut soils	$1.5 \cdot 10^{-3}$	$4 \cdot 10^{-3}$	$1.6 \cdot 10^{-3}$
Plants (in ash)	$2 \cdot 10^{-2}$	$3 \cdot 10^{-2}$	$7 \cdot 10^{-4}$

*According to A. P. Vinogradov [1949, 1957], D. P. Malyuga [1946, 1947], H. Petterson and H. Rotschi [1951], and others.

TABLE 59. Distribution of Lead and Copper in Soil-Geological Profile No. 2

Depth of horizon, cm	Content, %		Ratio Cu:Pb	Depth of horizon, cm	Content, %		Ratio Cu:Pb
	Pb	Cu			Pb	Cu	
0-3	$6 \cdot 10^{-3}$	$9.7 \cdot 10^{-3}$	1.6	50-55	$9.8 \cdot 10^{-3}$	$1.1 \cdot 10^{-2}$	1.1
5-15	$6 \cdot 10^{-3}$	$6 \cdot 10^{-3}$	1.0	100-105	$9.7 \cdot 10^{-3}$	$1.1 \cdot 10^{-2}$	1.1
20-25	$5 \cdot 10^{-3}$	$6 \cdot 10^{-3}$	1.2	250	$9 \cdot 10^{-3}$	$1.3 \cdot 10^{-2}$	1.4

TABLE 60. Forms of Lead and Copper in the Soil of the Varaz Deposit (Depth 0-7 cm)

Metal	Content, %					
	total	water-soluble	exchange	with humates	with fulvates	in mineral fraction
Lead	0.0540	0.0024	0.0078	0.0006	0.0248	0.0170
Copper	0.0310	—	—	0.0097	0.0060	0.0150

give ore pyrite enrichments in contact processes of granodiorite magmas, as well as in acidic intrusive and effusive rocks. Copper often accompanies zinc and lead in polymetal deposits in tuff extrusives. The mineralogical composition of these ores is characterized by the presence of galena, sphalerite, pyrite, and chalcopyrite. Of similar composition are the sheet and metasomatic sulfide-polymetal deposits in calcareous rocks (Krasnikov [1959]).

In the process of the oxidation of sulfide minerals, the copper, zinc, and lead migrate with the soil and ground water. Depending on the composition of the ores and the ore-bearing rocks, the migration of the ore elements occurs jointly or separately. In cases of acidic weathering (a podzol zone), when organic acids are present in the soil and ground water, copper, zinc, and lead migrate together.

In cases when the climate is relatively dry, and when the soil pH is high (chestnut soil zone), the copper forms stable carbonaceous forms, the following minerals: malachite ($CuCO_3 \cdot Cu(OH)_2$ and azurite $2CuCO_3 \cdot Cu(OH)_2$, the lead is precipitated in the form of a sulfate and enriches barites, and the zinc — which is the most mobile — penetrates into the unconsolidated sediments of the weathered crust and enters into various isomorphic relationships in clayey minerals. In this case the lead is less mobile than the copper and zinc. This obviously explains the noncoincidence of the lines showing the isoconcentrations of copper and lead in the dispersion halo of the Uspenskii deposit in central Kazakhstan, as described by Ginzburg et al. [1960].

Copper, zinc, and lead are constant constituents of soils and plants. The study of copper, zinc, and lead in rocks and the biosphere makes it possible to give quite precise mean values of their content in rocks, soils, water, and surface plants (see Table 58).

When these values are compared with the content of copper, zinc, and lead in soils and plants taken from ore deposits, there often is a noticeable lack of correspondence, that is, there is a sharp increase in the content of these

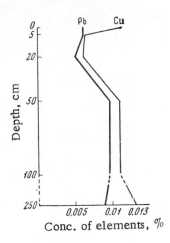

Fig. 67. Distribution of lead and copper in the soil-geological profile.

elements over the zone of mineralization, which confirms the basic principle relating to exploration for these elements using soils and plants.

As already mentioned, the Varaz veined copper-polymetal deposit, associated with the tuff-porphyrite complex, is greatly modified by hydrothermal processes related to a syenite-diorite intrusion. The heavy precipitation and the rich forest vegetation facilitate intensified weathering of the rocks. In a number of cases heavy showers result in a considerable loss downslope of unconsolidated materials to the lower-lying parts of the terrain. There are no appreciable accumulations of alluvial deposits in the area of the deposit. The weathered crust of primary rocks therefore lies in the immediate vicinity of the surface. The thickness of the residual material-eluvial deposits, together with the soil layer, extends to depths of between 4 and 20 m.

The weathered crust consists of fragments of little-modified crystalline rocks and vein material: quartz, sericite, chalcopyrite, and clayey material. In depressions, on the drainage divides, and on slopes which are not excessively steep, the soils are held in place by brush vegetation.

In the profile of the brown forest soils in the area of the Varaz deposit there is a weak process of podzolization; this is easy to observe from the distribution of sesquioxides, SiO_2, and other macrocomponents.

Profile 2, obtained beyond the boundaries of ore vein I (Table 59), is shown to illustrate the distribution of microelements in the soil-geological profile. These data reveal a nonuniform distribution of copper and lead in the various horizons of the profile; this is particularly noticeable in the diagrams shown in Fig. 67. The virtually uniform distribution of lead in the upper soil horizons is readily noticeable. Beginning at a depth of 50 cm, the lead content increases appreciably, but then drops off again at a depth of 250 cm.

In the copper content there is some decrease in the eluvial horizon in comparison with the humus horizon; there then is an increase at a depth of 50 and 100 cm. The copper content in the rock is higher than in the soil.

The copper content in the humus layer of the soil, sampled over the zone of mineralization, varies from 0.020 to 0.060%, zinc varies from 0.023 to 0.100, and lead ranges from 0.010 to 0.065%.

The accumulation of ore elements in the humus layer of the soil occurs as a result of the absorption of ions of metals by the roots of plants and their accumulation in roots and leaves; this is confirmed by chemical analysis. For example, the copper content in the ash of the leaves of the cherry laurel and rhododendron attains 0.035%, whereas in the roots it is 0.043%; the zinc content in leaves is 0.20%, and in roots 0.30%; the lead content in leaves is 0.060%, and in roots 0.25%.

The enrichment of humus by metals results from the breaking away and dying of the roots of plants and as a result of the high adsorptive properties of humus matter with respect to copper ions (Manskaya et al. [1958]) and lead ions (our data). The copper-lead balance in the humus horizon of brown forest soil, sampled in the Varaz copper-polymetal deposit, is indicative (see Table 60). The data in Table 60 show that the content of lead, present in easily mobile, water-soluble form (when the pH = 5.5), does not exceed 5% of the total. The content of exchangeable forms of lead in a brown forest soil attains 15% of the total. A considerable part of the copper and lead (about 50%) is firmly bonded to humus matter. In a "phase" analysis, almost all the lead can be separated by use of fulvic acids, whereas copper is equally bonded in the form of humates and fulvates. A total of 31.5% of the lead and 50% of the copper is in the mineral part of the soil.

The high lead content in the fulvate fraction cannot be attributed easily solely to the bonding of lead with fulvates. In this case there apparently also is a withdrawal of lead from the mineral part of the soil by an alkaline solution (0.1 N NaOH), which is used in the separation of humates and fulvates.

The study of the forms of compounds of copper and lead in the soils of the Varaz deposit illustrates the great mobility of ore elements in the natural profile over the zone of mineralization.

A biogeochemical survey of the Varaz deposit within the limits of the ore-bearing sulfide veins I and II and their postulated extensions was made for the purpose of describing the dispersion haloes of copper, zinc, and lead over the copper-polymetal deposit.

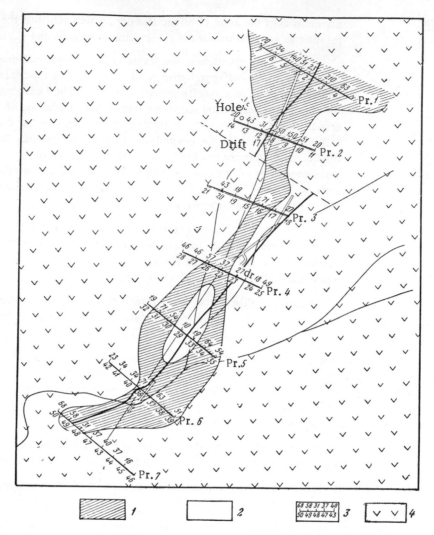

Fig. 68. Isoconcentrations of zinc in the soil in the Varaz deposit (vein I).
1) Zinc content equal to or more than 50 thousandths (%); 2) lead content
less than 50 thousandths (%); 3) numerator = zinc content, denominator =
number of sampling point; 4) tuff-andesites.

Practical Testing of the Method

The biogeochemical method is the most practical for use in a reconnaissance survey under the conditions prevailing in Adzhariya, with its continuous sodded surface and the nearly impassable brush vegetation. In this area all the factors which impeded the application of other methods were favorable for a biogeochemical survey: abundant vegetation and a rather good preservation of the soil cover.

For making the biogeochemical survey the area was broken down into grid squares measuring 10 × 50 m (see Fig. 66). At each point of intersection plant samples were taken and the soil sampled from the surface to a depth of 7 cm. The vegetation samples taken were cherry laurel and rhododendron leaves and shoots. The roots of these plants were taken as independent samples.

The soil samples were dried and passed through a fine 1-0.5 mm sieve. The material was sent to the laboratory for a study of the soil content of copper, zinc, and lead by chemical and polarigraphic methods. The plants were burned in aluminum pans on a primus stove. After calcination in an electric muffle furnace, the plant ash was studied in the same way as the soil.

About 200 samples from 7 profiles were investigated; these profiles cut through the ore veins. In the plotting of data on copper, zinc, and lead in the soils on a map the dispersion haloes with an obviously high content of these elements were clearly defined. As an example, Fig. 68 shows a map of the isoconcentrations of zinc in the soil.

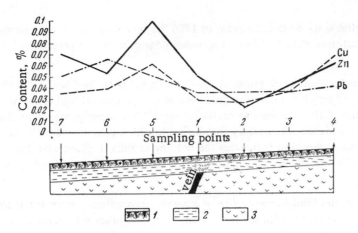

Fig. 69. Distribution of copper, zinc, and lead in soils along profile 1. 1) Soil; 2) clayey deposits; 3) tuff-andesites.

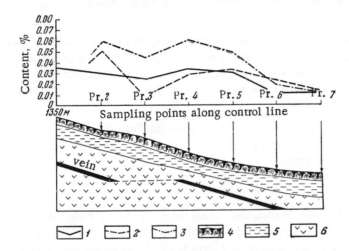

Fig. 70. Distribution of lead in the soil and in the ash of plant leaves and roots along a vein. 1) Lead in the soil; 2) lead in leaves; 3) lead in roots; 4) soil; 5) clayey deposits; 6) modified tuff-andesites.

About 200 samples from 7 profiles were investigated; these profiles cut through the ore veins. In the plotting of data on copper, zinc, and lead in the soils on a map the dispersion haloes with an obviously high content of these elements were clearly defined. As an example, Fig. 68 shows a map of the isoconcentrations of zinc in the soil.

In Fig. 68 the zinc content has been shown in thousandths of a percent. Points have been shown where the zinc content was greater than 50 units, so that the enriched zone corresponding to the extent of the ore veins has been clearly outlined.

The distribution of copper, zinc, and lead in the soils taken from profile 1 at right angles to the vein has been shown in Fig. 69. The diagrams in Fig. 69 clearly show the maxima of copper and lead content, especially downslope from the vein.

According to the data collected by a local geological exploration party in 1956, ore vein I ended approximately at the third profile of our grid. Data obtained from an analysis of the soils and plants of the succeeding profiles, 4 and 5, indicated the possibility of a continuation of vein I to the southwest (Fig. 70).

Figure 70 shows an appreciable increase in the lead content in soils and plants in profiles 4 and 5 in comparison with profiles 6 and 7, where the vein is deflected westward.

The mineral exploration work done subsequent to 1956 has revealed an ore zone in the vicinity of profiles 5 and 6 precisely on the extension of vein I. Thus, biogeochemical data on the presence of mineralization in this area have been fully confirmed.

The method of biogeochemical exploration of ore deposits has been used under the specific conditions prevailing in mountainous Adzhariya, which is under the influence of a near-coastal highly moist warm climate. The immense amount of precipitation falling in the mountains (about 2000 mm per year) favors the weathering of rocks and the strong leaching of unconsolidated sedimentary formations in which podzolized soils are developing. The strong development of brush and tree vegetation facilitates the holding of soils in place and their enrichment with humus matter. Therefore, brown soils, together with vegetation (the leaves of trees and brush), can be used in a biogeochemical exploration survey.

The behavior of copper and lead in the profile of a weakly podzolized brown forest soil, obtained beyond the limits of the dispersion halo, correlates with the iron, aluminum, and other microelements of the soil. In contrast to lead, copper is clearly accumulated in the accumulative A horizon, and lead in the B horizon.

A study of the forms in which metals are accumulated in soils has revealed that about 50% of the copper and lead is bonded with the humus matter of the soil. In this case the copper is bonded to the humic acids to a greater extent than to fulvic acids, while the reverse is true of lead. In the mineral part of the soil lead is 31.5% and copper is 50% of the total content.

The copper content in brown forest soil, sampled over the zone of mineralization, ranges from 0.020 to 0.060%, zinc content from 0.023 to 0.100, and lead content from 0.010 to 0.065%. The copper content in the ash of plants is the same as in the soil. Zinc is concentrated in the leaves and roots of plants and lead in the roots. The high content of copper, zinc, and lead in soils and the ash of plants over the zone of mineralization of the Varaz deposit corresponds to the dispersion halo of the ore vein.

The effectiveness of the biogeochemical exploration method has been demonstrated under the conditions prevailing in the high-mountain part of Adzhariya in the example of the study of the dissemination of copper, zinc, and lead in soils and plants of the Varaz deposit.

5. The Application of the Biogeochemical Method in the Exploration for Uranium under Desert Conditions *

The problem of geochemical exploration work under desert conditions long has attracted the attention of geologists and geochemists. This problem attracted the attention of A. E. Fersman in his time, and later that of A. A. Saukov and others. Much has been done to improve hydrochemical and geobotanical exploration methods for use in the desert. In an article by A. I. Perel'man and Yu. V. Sharkov [1957], deserts and semideserts are assigned to provinces with an alkaline soil reaction. Judging from the maps, these provinces occupy enormous areas. After evaluating the effectiveness of various geochemical exploration methods under desert conditions, we concluded that the biogeochemical method is the most promising. The great possibilities of exploration for ore deposits under arid conditions on the basis of an analysis of the ash of plants has been noted repeatedly both in Soviet and in foreign literature by A. P. Vinogradov et al. [1958], D. P. Malyuga [1956], H. L. Cannon [1952], and others.

Geochemical Characteristics of Uranium

Uranium, thorium, and radium are among the most dispersed chemical elements in the earth's crust. Their dispersion in rocks, natural waters, soils, and organisms is facilitated by the instability of nuclei, the volatility of certain compounds, and their appreciable solubility in natural solutions (U, Ra).

The geochemical properties of uranium are characterized by its position in group VI of the Mendeleev periodic system and its position in the horizontal row of radioactive elements of the actinide series. Uranium is similar to chromium and molybdenum and possesses variable valence: U^{3+}, U^{4+}, U^{5+}, and U^{6+}. The valences most widespread in nature are U^{4+} and U^{6+}. It is they which determine the behavior of uranium in deep and surface processes. With these valences are associated mineralogical associations of uranium with Th, Zr, Nb, Ta, RE, classified into pegmatite (uraninite, thorianite, tantalo-niobate), hydrothermal (pitchblende−nasturan), and hypergene − series of uranites $(UO_2)^{2+}$ and uranates $(UO_4)^{2-}$. Almost all minerals of uranium constitute oxygen compounds.

---

*Published with modifications and additions from an article by M. M. Botova, D. P. Malyuga, and U. I. Moiseenko (1962).

TABLE 61. Mean Content of Uranium, Thorium, and Radium in Igneous Rocks

Rocks	Content, %			Ratio Th : U	Author, year
	U	Th	Ra		
Ultrabasic	$7 \cdot 10^{-5}$	$2 \cdot 10^{-4}$	$1 \cdot 10^{-12}$	3.4	Vinogradov [1957], Davis [1947]
Basic	$9.6 \cdot 10^{-5}$	$3.9 \cdot 10^{-4}$	$2.7 \cdot 10^{-11}$	4.4	Evans and Goodman [1941], et al.
Intermediate	$2 \cdot 10^{-4}$	$7 \cdot 10^{-4}$	$6 \cdot 10^{-11}$	3.5	Evans and Goodman [1941], Senftle and Keevil [1947]
Granites	$4 \cdot 10^{-4}$	$1.2 \cdot 10^{-3}$	$1.2 \cdot 10^{-10}$	3	Evans and Goodman [1941], Senftle and Keevil [1947], Komlev [1936, 1950], Starik et al. [1945].

A characteristic feature of radioactive elements in geochemistry is their concentration in the upper part of the earth's crust, primarily in acidic series of igneous rocks, in granites, granodiorites, rhyolites, etc. A comparison of analyses of acidic and basic (ultrabasic) rocks shows a sharp predominance of uranium in granites in comparison with its content in peridotites. The mean uranium content in rocks and its ratio to thorium has been shown in Table 61. The data in Table 61 show that the mean uranium content in granites is four times greater than in basic rocks, and 100 times greater than in ultrabasic rocks. Moreover, the Th : U ratio changes little between rocks formed from acidic magma and ultrabasic rocks.

"In both elements," notes A. E. Fersman, "there are characteristic general features: first, both elements in the overwhelming number of their atoms are not in definite regular crystal structures, but rather in a dispersed or endocryptic state; second, there is a constant process of decay of individual atoms, which change into new types of atoms, partially accumulating in the old structure."

An important difference between uranium and radium, on the one hand, and thorium, on the other, is their high capacity for migration in hypergene processes.

In the process of weathering of igneous and other rocks and minerals, uranium is syngenetically and epigenetically set free in various kinds of continental and marine deposits, where it forms minerals which are stable under surface conditions: oxides and hydroxides, phosphates, silicates, vanadates, etc. More stable primary minerals containing uranium — monazite, samarskite, etc. — are ground up in the process of weathering and transport and enter into clays. Other minerals, still more resistant, such as zircon, enrich sand with uranium.

Uraninite is less resistant to the agents of weathering. Pitchblende also changes with the formation of more mobile uranyl compounds. The presence of the sulfides of accessory minerals (of the epithermal type) in ores can accelerate weathering processes, especially if climatic conditions are favorable (temperature, humidity) as a result of the formation of H_2SO_4. In granitic pegmatites, which have no sulfides, in which an alkaline weathering process is predominant, dissolved carbonic and silicic acid assume importance, giving rise to $NaHCO_3$, $Ca(HCO_3)_2$, and $Na_2Si_2O_5$, the carbonates, bicarbonates, and silicates of alkaline metals. These compounds facilitate the formation of secondary uranium minerals: gummite,* uranotyl $Ca(UO_2)_2Si_2O_7 \cdot 6H_2O$, and others (Shcherbina [1946]).

Under ordinary weathering conditions, with the participation of free oxygen of the air and CO_2, the complex uranyl-carbonates $Na_4UO_2(CO_3)_3$ are formed, which remain stable in the presence of carbonic acid. They are capable of migrating with the ground water. At the surface these compounds are destroyed rapidly with the formation of hydroxyls and uranates. In this condition uranium is sorbed by clayey particles, iron hydroxyls, manganese, and aluminum, and is held in the unconsolidated rocks of the weathered crust or is transported by the surface water for great distances, reaching the seas and oceans.

The nature of the accumulation of uranium in schists and phosphorites is not clear. According to current concepts, (Tolmachev [1943], Fredrickson [1948], McKelvey et al. [1950]), in this case there apparently is an isomorphic replacement of calcium by uranium, such as in phosphorites, while in bituminous shales there is a chemical sorption of uranium by organic and clayey material.

---

*A cryptocrystalline mixture of curite $2PbO \cdot 5UO_3 \cdot 4H_2O$ and soddyite $(UO_2)_2SiO_4 \cdot 2H_2O$.

TABLE 62. Uranium and Thorium Content in Upper Part of Earth's Crust

Contained in	Content, % Th	Content, % U	Ratio Th : U
Lithosphere	$8 \cdot 10^{-4}$	$3 \cdot 10^{-4}$	2.7
Hypogene minerals (uraninite)	–	–	1 - 0.1
Hydrothermal minerals (pitchblende)	–	–	0.001
Hypergene minerals (carnotite, etc.)	–	–	< 0.001
Clays and sandstones	$1 \cdot 10^{-3}$	$1.5 \cdot 10^{-4}$	6.6
Calcareous rocks	$1 \cdot 10^{-4}$	$1.3 \cdot 10^{-4}$	0.75
Sea water	$5 \cdot 10^{-8}$	$2 \cdot 10^{-7}$	0.25
Soils			
soddy-podzol	$1.2 \cdot 10^{-3}$	$2.6 \cdot 10^{-4}$	2.7
gray forest	$1.2 \cdot 10^{-3}$	$3.2 \cdot 10^{-4}$	3.8
chernozem	$1.0 \cdot 10^{-3}$	$4 \cdot 10^{-4}$	2.5
light chestnut	$1.0 \cdot 10^{-3}$	$3 \cdot 10^{-4}$	3
Mean in soils	$6.0 \cdot 10^{-3}$	$1 \cdot 10^{-4}$	6
Soils on uranium deposits (mean of three analyses)*	$3.2 \cdot 10^{-3}$	$2.3 \cdot 10^{-3}$	1.4
Surface plants (in ash)	–	$5 \cdot 10^{-5}$	–
Surface plants on uranium deposits	–	$5 \cdot 10^{-4}$	–

*Analyses made by K. G. Kunasheva

The biogenic accumulation of uranium in the earth's crust takes place by sorption by organic matter, buried in the sedimentary complex: bituminous shales, calcareous matter, and petroleum. According to data supplied by Manskaya et al. [1956], uranium is firmly bonded to the humus matter of peat. The experiments of Breger and Deul [1955] have demonstrated that uranium becomes a part of the organic molecule of calcareous substances (culm) and is not extracted even by acids (pH = 2.18).

It is noted that in the presence of the S^{2-} ion (H_2S and others) there can be a "precipitation of pitchblende." Constant associates of natural organic matter, sulfur compounds can facilitate the separation of uranium in the zone in which organic residue is found (Kerr [1955]).

The enrichment of bioliths with uranium also can occur by a different means, such as by the concentration of uranium (radium) by living organisms. According to data obtained by V. I. Vernadskii, A. P. Vinogradov, and the author, the concentration of radium and uranium by certain water organisms (duckweed, algae, and starfish) occurs in quantities hundreds and thousands of times greater than in the medium in which they live.

According to data obtained by Vinogradov and the author, the uranium content in soils varies from $1 \cdot 10^{-5}$ to $1 \cdot 10^{-3}\%$. The highest concentrations occur in uranium deposits, and the lowest in the upper leached horizons of soddy-podzol and gray forest soils. The upper humus horizons of forest and steppe soils of the south (mountain soils) are enriched appreciably with uranium in comparison with the underlying horizon, which obviously is associated with the presence of uranium in the organic matter of the soil, although its role in this process is unclear. In exactly the same way, there is some accumulation of uranium in the calcareous B horizon. The uranium content in the ash of plants is the same as in soils.

Table 62 shows the distribution of uranium in the earth's crust, rocks, natural water, soils, and plants. The data shown in Table 62 demonstrate that under the conditions prevailing in the surface layer the paths of uranium and thorium diverge sharply. The thorium is concentrated in the products of physical weathering (in hydrolysates — clays, sand, etc.), while uranium is accumulated in sea water, carbonates, and biotites.

Under mineralization conditions the uranium often predominates over thorium or is equal to it in primary and secondary uranium minerals (and ores). The Th : U ratio changes in exactly the same way in the soils of uranium deposits, approaching unity, whereas in ordinary zonal soils the Th : U ratio is considerably higher and the mean apparently is 5 : 1. The decrease of the Th : U ratio in soils and plants over uranium deposits is an extremely reliable indicator when doing exploration work for uranium.

The constant presence of uranium and radium in soils, natural water, and plants indicates that they have an appreciable capacity for migration under the conditions prevailing at the earth's surface. The mobile forms of uranium are sulfates, chlorides, nitrates, carbonates, and bicarbonates. Soluble compounds of radium include chlorides, iodides, and bromides. Sulfates and certain carbonates facilitate the precipitation and sorption of radium from solutions (Starik [1943]).

In acidic soils of a podzolic or soddy-podzolic profile over ore deposits, the uranium and radium are the most mobile, and as a result the near-surface horizons of the profile are greatly impoverished of these elements. However, the humus horizon of the soil, the forest litter, and especially the peaty layer, are enriched considerably with uranium and radium, which is associated with the accumulating function of plants.

Under the conditions of an arid climate, such as in the zone of desert and semidesert, the capacity for radium to migrate is reduced due to the presence of an alkaline reaction in almost the entire soil-geological profile (carbonate horizon). In this case, radium is stabilized by the carbonates and sulfates of Ca, Sr, and Ba, while uranium, despite the moisture deficit, gradually is carried downward in the profile from the upper horizons.

Thus, the migration of uranium and radium over ore deposits is determined by bioclimatic and soil conditions. In exactly the same way, the accumulation of uranium and radium in plants over ore deposits is dependent on climate, vegetation, and its selective capacity.

The history of individual radioactive elements in the earth's crust reflects the evolution of the corresponding parent family. For example, Ra^{226}, related to the uranium family U^{238}, possesses features in common with uranium and is its constant companion and indicator.

Although the radium content in the earth's crust is $3 \cdot 10^6$ times less than uranium, the presence of the latter is best indicated by radium. It is this factor which has made it possible to apply radiometric methods of exploration, especially the radioflorometric method of exploration for uranium (Anderson and Kurtz [1954], Kovalevskii [1960]).

Description of the Region and Field Methods for Uranium Exploration

This part of the book presents the results of work involved in a clarification of the possibility of applying the biogeochemical method to the exploration for uranium under desert conditions. The derived preliminary data indicate the high effectiveness of the biogeochemical method, making it possible to a considerable degree to broaden the scale of the exploration work being done.

The work zone was situated in a desert area in a low-lying part of the region. The climate in this area is sharply continental, with a relatively high mean annual temperature. The region must be classified as extremely arid, since the mean annual precipitation does not exceed 100 mm.

The formation of local ground water is influenced by the filling of tectonic zones with clayey or highly fragmented washed argillites, which hinders the process of infiltration of precipitation. The sector is characterized, therefore, by an unelutriated type of ground water.

Closer to the surface the water is slightly mineralized (3 mg/liter), but with increasing depth the mineralization increases to 50 mg/liter. In chemical respects the water circulating in the fissures can be classified as (a) chloride-sulfate-sodium to the 168-m horizon and (b) chloride-sodium below the 168-m horizon. The uranium content in the water varies from $5 \cdot 10^{-6}$ to $4 \cdot 10^{-4}$ mg/liter. The high metal content in the water can be attributed to the fact that the water apparently is in direct contact with uranium mineralization.

The soil-vegetation cover is characterized by features associated with a dry hot climate. Over extensive areas of sand the soil-forming processes occur only where the sand and clayey loam are held in place by vegetation. The most widespread of the soils are so-called gray soils — very poor in humus and rich in carbonate — forming under conditions of meager precipitation and weak leaching.

In the work area the upper soil layer, from 5 to 30 cm, is sand which is moved easily by the wind. The upper soil horizon therefore is completely devoid of organic matter. Beneath the sand there is a brownish-red sandy alluvium with fragments of aleurites, aleurolites, and argillites. The thickness of the alluvium in the sector is from 2 to 5 m, but in the direction of Takyrs it increases. A desert and semidesert vegetation has developed in the sector. This vegetation is adapted to life under conditions of inadequate moisture and high summer temperatures. The most important species is wormwood Artemisia terra-alba (Compositae family); there also are certain species of Russian thistle Salsola subaphylla, black haloxylon Haloxylon aphyllum, astragalus Astragalus villosissimus, and annual ephemerals.

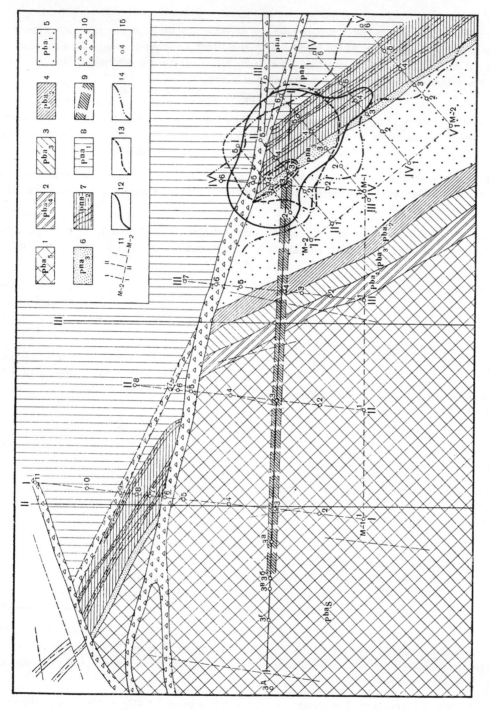

Fig. 71. Schematic geological map of a uranium deposit. 1) Upper argillite horizon; 2) upper horizon of concretions; 3) intermediate argillite horizon; 4) lower horizon of concretions; 5) lower argillite horizon; 6) sandstone horizon; 7) aleurolite-argillite horizon; 8) argillite horizon; 9) projection of ore zone; 10) zone of breccia; 11) profiles with sampling points and their numbers; 12) uranium in soil; 13) uranium in plant ash; 14) uranium as indicated by gamma survey; 15) numbers of sampling points.

The depth of the roots of plants growing in the desert is not uniform. The plant with the deepest roots is the black haloxylon, whose roots extend to a depth of 20 m. Wormwood roots penetrate 2 m and astragalus roots extend to 10 m. The depth of the roots apparently is dependent to a greater extent on the conditions of permeability of the soil and the moisture content of the rocks making up the soil-geological profile than on the individual peculiarities of the mentioned perennial plants.

According to data obtained by V. S. Kurbatov (1953), the geological structure of the region includes for the most part rocks of the Permian sandstone-argillite and upper nonargillite suites (Fig. 71). The sandstone-argillite suite is divided into three horizons (from bottom to top):

1) An argillite horizon, consisting of a thick uniform stratum of dark brown argillites, with intercalations of aleurites and sandstones in the lower part.

2) An aleurite-argillite horizon, consisting of dark brown argillites.

3) A sandstone horizon, which is the reference horizon for the entire sector; at the surface it becomes thinly plated under the influence of weathering.

The upper argillite suite consists for the most part of dark brown and dense argillites in which there are two bands with intercalations of calcareous-clayey concretions. There are five distinguishable horizons.

All rocks have a northwest strike (300-320°) and a southward dip (32-40°). Uranium mineralization has been found in fissures in the sandstone stratum which lies on the boundary of the sandstone-argillite and upper argillite suite of the Permian. Mineralization is represented by primary uranium minerals. Veins with secondary mineralization are found near a fault with a latitudinal strike and join into a single zone which also extends in a latitudinal direction. The richest mineralization is localized within the above-mentioned stratum of sandstones.

Work Method

A wide range of geophysical investigations was made in the work area. All types of geophysical work were carried on by the generally accepted methods. At the same time, samples of soils and growing vegetation were taken using a rectangular sampling grid.

The biogeochemical survey, made along experimental lines, involved the following operations:

1) Staking and tying-in of profiles in a grid with grid squares measuring 50 x 20 m and 25 x 20 m, with the distance between points decreasing to 7 m in those cases when rocks of different lithological composition are involved.

2) Sampling at each point of plants growing within a radius of 2-3 m.

3) Sampling of plants for the herbarium.

The soil samples were taken from beneath a drifted sand layer with a depth of 3-4 cm. The intensity of gamma radiation was measured after taking the soil samples; RP-1 (with an open counter) and SRP-1^a instruments were used. The sampling profiles passed not only over known ore zones, but also in sectors where the ore body was covered by deposits of other rocks and had been detected by core drilling.

The profiles of the biogeochemical survey were run in two directions: across the strike of the rocks and across the strike of the ore zone, which had been traced at depth. The following problems were thereby clarified: 1) whether desert plants assimilate uranium; 2) what plants are concentrators of uranium; 3) the importance of the normal geochemical background of uranium in the plants of the region; and 4) the uranium content in the ash of plants growing on different rocks. A study also was made of the dependence of the uranium content in the ash of plants on the depth of the mineralized zone, that is, the effective depth of the method. While the biogeochemical survey was being made, a comparison was made of the results obtained by different methods in order to clarify the advantages of each of them.

As mentioned, the intensity of beta and gamma radiation was measured at each point where plant samples were taken. At the same time, soil samples were obtained and their uranium content was determined subsequently by the pearl-luminescent method. All the growing plants at a staked point were selected. A total of eight species were selected in the sector: wormwood Artemisia terra-alba (Compositae family), small-leafed saltwort Salsola subaphylla, astragalus Astragalus villosissimus, brushlike saltwort (itsegek) Anabasis aphylla, black haloxylon Haloxylon aphyllum, and various kinds of ephemerals.

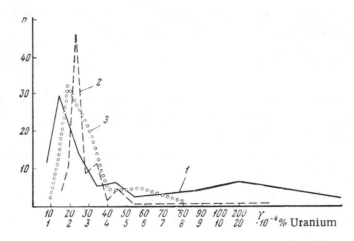

Fig. 72. Variation curves of gamma activity and uranium content in soils and plants. 1) Uranium content in plant ash; 2) uranium content in soil; 3) gamma activity of soil. n) Number of analyses.

The surface parts of the plants were selected (leaves, branches, stems) and the roots. The plant samples were burned in a special incinerator, the ash collected into a packet, and the uranium content in the ash then determined by the fluorescent method.

Results of the Work

According to the data obtained in the gamma survey, as well as on the basis of the results of a fluorescent analysis of the soil and ash of plants, it was possible to outline the area of the dispersion halo over the known zone of uranium mineralization; this is shown in Fig. 71.

We will now consider certain results obtained by use of the various methods. The gamma survey along profiles where plant samples were selected revealed several anomalies with a rock activity exceeding 100 gammas, the greater part of which is related to outcrops of sandstones (Fig. 71): profile I (points 3, 4), profile II (points 3, 4), profile III (points 3, 4), all of which were revealed by a prospect hole.

A clarification of the possibility of using the biogeochemical method for detecting an ore body buried in depth and discovered by core drilling is of basic interest. The data from the gamma survey reveals that the presence of an ore body at depth cannot be detected from the surface. The value of the activity over a known ore-bearing zone falls within the background range established for the investigated sector (about 10 gammas). On the basis of the completed biogeochemical survey, it has been established that the normal uranium content in soils is $2\text{-}3 \cdot 10^{-4}\%$, and the maximum is $8\text{-}12 \cdot 10^{-4}\%$.

An analysis of the variation curve of the uranium content in the ash of plants (Fig. 72) gives the following results: normal (background) uranium content in plants — $3 \cdot 10^{-4}\%$; maximum content in samples of plants selected in this same sector over sandstones with uranium mineralization attained $80 \cdot 10^{-4}\%$ of the uranium in the ash of the astragalus Astragalus villosissimus.

Table 63 is a list of plants with a high uranium content. The data in Table 63 show that in the investigated sector there are many samples of plants whose ash contains a high quantity of uranium in comparison with the background ($3 \cdot 10^{-4}\%$) and the uranium content in the ash of plants is higher than in the soils; in only three cases is the reverse relationship observed.

A high content of uranium is noted in the ash of plants growing over outcrops of sandstones containing uranium mineralization. A high content of uranium also has been discovered in plants selected at points where the gamma activity of rocks at the surface does not exceed the background values (Figs. 71 and 73).

Only four points with a high uranium content in plants correspond to high values of gamma activity of rocks and the soil. At these points ore-bearing sandstones outcrop at the surface. However, at the other points where plant samples were selected and high uranium contents were recorded in the ash of plants, the ore body withdraws to a depth as great as 20 m (Fig. 74).

TABLE 63. Uranium Content in Plant Ash and in the Soil

Plant	Content in plant ash, $n \cdot 10^{-4}\%$	Soil content, $n \cdot 10^{-4}\%$	Plant	Content in plant ash, $n \cdot 10^{-4}\%$	Soil content, $n \cdot 10^{-4}\%$
Wormwood, gray soil, Artemisia terra-alba (family Compositae)	5.3	1.8	Oligophyllous saltwort Salsola subaphylla	3.9	—
The same	3.4	1.4	The same	18	5.1
" "	5.5	2.1	" "	3.1	5.2
	1.7	1.8	Shrubby saltwort Anabasis aphylla	4.5	2
" "	3.1	1.4	The same	7.9	—
" "	3.2	3.2	" "	20	13
" "	4	2.2	" "	75	—
" "	4.1	1.4	" "	4.5	1.7
" "	4.5	2.5	" "	8.5	7.5
Oligophyllous saltwort Salsola subaphylla	3.4	2.7	" "	15	13
The same	5.2	2.1	" "	3.9	—
" "	4.5	5.1	Milk vetch Astragalus villosissimus	12	—
" "	20.5	5.8	The same	80	—
" "	4.1	5.1	" "	20	5.3
" "	8.9	—	" "	14	3.2
" "	3.2	3.2	Black haloxylon Haloxylon aphyllum	5.6	2
			Ephemerous plants	5.2	5.3

Thus, the first desert use of the biogeochemical survey method reveals that under these singular conditions, the same as has been established for other regions, the ash of plants growing over ore bodies is characterized by a high uranium content. Since plants with a high uranium content are found over a considerable area, the contamination of plants by uranium is of an areal, rather than of a point character. Individual mineralized zones are therefore traced on the basis of a high uranium content in the ash of plants. Under desert conditions we are concerned primarily with the possibility of using plants for the exploration of deep-lying ore bodies which cannot be detected from the surface by other methods.

The results of study of the profile over the projection of the ore body are of basic interest. It seemed to us that it was precisely here that it was possible to clarify the value of a biogeochemical survey in the general complex method for the exploration of uranium deposits. Despite the fact that mineralization cannot be detected by a gamma survey, in the profile above the ore-bearing zone it was possible to detect three points with a high uranium content in the ash of plants ($4.5 \cdot 10^{-4}$ and $12 \cdot 10^{-4}\%$). A uranium content of $12 \cdot 10^{-4}\%$ has been noted in the ash of astragalus. At a depth of 25 m in a borehole, gamma logging data indicate the presence of an anomaly of 140 μr (microroentgens)/hour, related to the upper horizon of uranium-bearing concretions.

At point 3a (to the west of point 3 in profile 1) there is a high uranium content in the ash of wormwood ($4.5 \cdot 10^{-4}\%$). At a depth of 20 m in the borehole at this point gamma logging revealed an anomaly of 100 μr/hour, related to the upper argillite horizon. At point 2 in profile 1 the uranium content in the ash of Russian thistle* is $4.1 \cdot 10^{-4}\%$. Here, in the borehole, there was an anomaly of 400 μr/hour in the sandstones of the sandstone-argillite suite.

The ash of Russian thistle at point 3 of profile 4 contains $4.6 \cdot 10^{-4}\%$ uranium. Figure 74 shows that in this interval there are active sandstones at a depth of 7 m. Anomalous contents of $20 \cdot 10^{-4}$ and $75 \cdot 10^{-4}\%$ in the ash of the Russian thistle have revealed sandstones at a depth of 2 and 3 m.

The uranium content in plants does not exceed the background value over the ore-bearing zone which dips downward from the surface. In profile 3 (points 1 and 2) there are high contents of uranium in plants; no other method reveals any excess over the background value (Fig. 73). As already mentioned, several species of plants were sampled in the sector. All the plants growing on areas known to be anomalous contain uranium, but it is assimilated to a different degree.

---

*The names "Russian thistle" and "Oligophyllous saltwort" are used interchangeably in the Russian text.

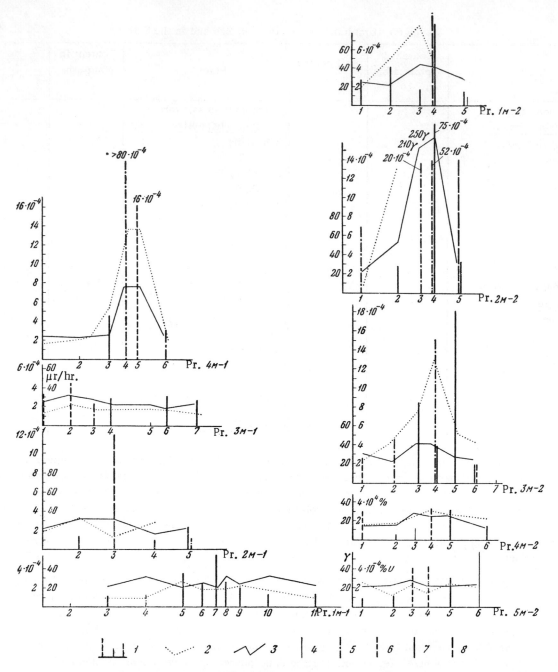

Fig. 73. Diagrams of readings of biogeochemical, metallometric, and gamma surveys along profiles of the exploration network. 1) Uranium content in plants; 2) curves showing the uranium content in soils; 3) curves from the gamma survey; 4) black haloxlon; 5) different plants; 6) wormwood; 7) shrubby saltwort; 8) milk vetch.

It also has been established that individual parts of the plant concentrate uranium to different degrees. This problem was solved by selecting all the plants in an area measuring 10 x 10 m and separately analyzing the roots, the cortex of the root, the wood, and the tops of plants (leaves and upper part of the stems). The uranium content in different parts of the plants is characterized by the data shown in Table 64.

The higher accumulation of uranium in the roots and wood of plants is confirmed in the studied of O. P. Golikova [1960] who studied the content of uranium and potassium in various crops, in different parts of plants, at different periods of their growth. She established that the assimilation of uranium by plants takes place from the very beginning of the growing season, and the uranium content increases with growth. She also noted that uranium in plants is concentrated for the most part in old organs.

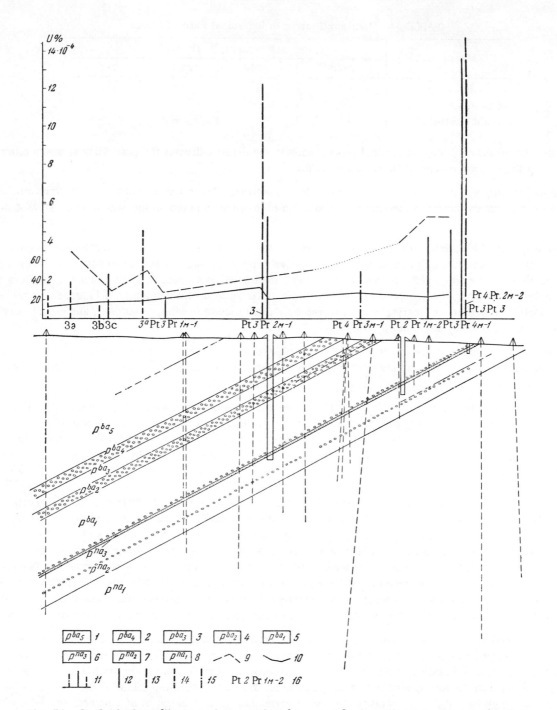

Fig. 74. Geological profile in a plane cutting the zone of mineralization along profile 1-1.
1) Upper argillite horizon; 2) upper horizon of concretions; 3) intermediate argillite horizon;
4) lower horizon of concretions; 5) lower argillite horizon; 6) sandstone horizon; 7) aleurolite-
argillite horizon; 8) argillite horizon; 9) uranium content in soils; 10) survey curve; 11) uranium content in plant ash; 12) shrubby saltwort; 13) astragal; 14) wormwood; 15) various plants;
16) profiles, points.

TABLE 64. Uranium Content in Individual Parts of Plants

Plant	Ash content, $n \cdot 10^{-4}\%$			
	leaves	wood	roots	bark
Black haloxylon	1.2	1	12	110
Milk vetch	2.7	–	1.9	6.7
Shrubby saltwort	0.9	14	–	–

Thus, the results of a biogeochemical survey made in the desert indicates the possibility of discovering ore bodies from a high uranium content in the ash of plants.

Plants growing over ore-bearing zones contain high quantities of uranium, attaining $8 \cdot 10^{-3}\%$ in ash, which considerably exceeds the normal geochemical background of uranium in plants in the region of the studied deposit ($2 \cdot 10^{-4}\%$).

The dispersion halo, determined from the uranium content in plants, is greater in area than indicated by the data of the gamma survey, which indicates a high effective depth of a biogeochemical survey for uranium under desert conditions. For example, the plants growing over ores situated at a depth of 25 m contain anomalous quantities of uranium, exceeding the geochemical background by a factor of 4. Consequently, a biogeochemical survey makes it possible to detect ore-bearing zones covered by a thick mantle of sand, sandstones, and clayey loams, which it is impossible to detect by any other halo method.

The uranium content in the ash of plants always is higher than in the soil. Moreover, different parts of plants assimilate uranium differently. The greatest quantities of uranium are contained in the cortex of the roots of the haloxylon, brushlike Russian thistle, and others.

A biogeochemical survey for uranium must be made using plants which possess deep-reaching root systems: haloxylon, brushlike Russian thistle, peganum, astragals, wormwood, and others. For this purpose it is necessary to select samples from the tops of the stems of perennial plants, taken either with or without the leaves. There is no limitation on the season when samples can be taken, that is, a biogeochemical survey in a desert or semidesert zone can be made at any time during the year.

* * *

The principal objective of this study was to demonstrate the exploration possibilities of the biogeochemical method in the different zones of the Soviet Union. The following therefore were studied: 1) the zone of dry steppe landscapes of the Trans-Ural province, with dark chestnut and chestnut soils (Orenburgskaya, Aktyubinskaya, and other regions); 2) the geochemical landscape zone of the mountain steppe and mountain forest oblasts of Tuva with chestnut and gray forest soils; 3) the mountain dry steppe and mountain dry forest regions of the Armenian Transcaucasus with chestnut and brown mountain forest soils (Kafanskii, Megriliiskii, and Alaverdskii ore-bearing regions); 4) the zone of moist high-mountain forest landscapes of Adzhariya, with brown mountain-forest podzolized soils; 5) the zone of desert landscapes of Soviet Central Asia which are characterized by the gray soils of deserts and semideserts.

In the Trans-Ural province a study was made of the possibilities of undertaking biogeochemical exploration for nickel, cobalt, copper, and chromium. The distinguishing geochemical characteristic of the studied zone is a dry continental climate, and therefore an alkaline process of recent weathering and soil formation. The process of migration of ore elements in the soil-geological profile is difficult due to the shielding effect of the carbonate horizon. There is an accumulation of ore elements in the humus horizon of the soil to tenths of a percent (nickel), which is due to the biogenic influence of the xerophytic vegetation. It is recommended that exploration work be done using the sodded humus horizon of the soil. The effective depth of the exploration method is about 20 m.

The distinguishing characteristic of the landscape zonality of Tuva is the influence of exposure to the sun, with the result that the southern slopes of the mountains have a steppelike character and are drier than the forested northern slopes. In the studied copper-nickel-cobalt deposit the ore elements are more mobile under the conditions prevailing in the northern forested sector, so that there is a higher accumulation of metals in the ash of plants than in the soil. In the southern sector, on the other hand, the migration of nickel, cobalt, and copper in the profile is difficult due to the presence of a calcareous weathered crust. There is therefore an appreciable concentration of ore elements in the sodded part of the humus horizon of the soil. Because of these circumstances, it is recommended that a biogeochemical survey be made with proper allowances for the landscape geochemical peculiarities of the area: on the southern steppe slopes the humus layer of the soil should be used, and on the northern forested slopes plants. The effective depth of the method averages 10-15 m.

The Kadzharanskii ore-bearing region (Armenian SSR) falls in a zone of mountainous dry steppe (lightly forested) landscapes. The climate is characterized by a nonuniform distribution of moisture – a dry and hot summer and autumn and cold and moist the remainder of the time. The specific conditions of climate, and therefore of weathering and soil formation, have favored the development of a thick eluvial (calcareous) weathered crust, with well-expressed dispersion haloes of ore elements. Due to the sodded character of the soil, under perennial xerophytic plants (golden astragal, etc.), the copper and molybdenum conveyed by the plant roots from the ore halo are concentrated in the humus layer of the soil. The great effective depth of the method is facilitated by the ground water reaching the upper horizons of the profile on steep slopes and the well-developed root system of plants, extending as deep as 12-15 m (milk vetch). The effective depth of the biogeochemical method attains 50 m in the Karmir-Karskii sector. As a result of the biogeochemical survey on the left bank of the Okhchi River, it was possible to detect a large copper-molybdenum ore-bearing zone. Under similar conditions it is recommended that a joint soil-plant survey be made. The detected anomalies can be checked against one another by these two methods, and this provides an unambiguous indication as to the presence or absence of ore. The zone of moist high-mountain forest landscapes of Primorskaya Adzhariya (Georgian SSR) is characterized by an abundance of precipitation, a moderately warm climate, and well-developed forest and brush vegetation. Climatic conditions favor the deep weathering of rocks and considerable leaching, resulting in some podzolization of the brown forest soils.

Because the upper soil layer is well sodded, the upper layer is enriched with humus and contains appreciable quantities of polymetals. This obviously is facilitated by the dying part of the forest vegetation (leaves, branches, roots), containing high concentrations of copper, zinc, and lead. It has been established that 50% of the copper and lead are bonded to the soil humus. Up to 80% of the lead is bonded to fulvic acids. The uniform accumulation of polymetals in soils and plants makes it possible to recommend a joint soil-plant biogeochemical survey under these particular conditions. The effective depth of the method apparently does not exceed 10 m.

The high effectiveness of the biogeochemical method under arid conditions has been noted repeatedly in Soviet and foreign literature. It is attributed to the capacity of desert xerophytic vegetation (haloxylon, milk vetch, and brushlike Russian thistle) to penetrate deeply through the overlying sands and clayey loams into the zone where the dispersion haloes of ore deposits are found.

Because of this, attempts have been made to use the method in uranium exploration in a desert zone. It has been established that the uranium content in soils and overlying clayey loams is much lower than in the ash of plants. The uranium content in ash attains $1 \cdot 10^{-2}\%$ and exceeds the value of the geochemical background by a factor of ten. The effective depth of the method is 20-25 m. It is measured by the depth of the root systems of individual desert plants. It therefore is recommended that in such areas the exploration should be based primarily on plants.

In the conclusions and recommendations (Chapter XI) the author also has taken into account the extremely valuable experience of the field parties and detachments of the Geological Exploration Trust No. 1, the Eastern Kazakhstan Geological Exploration Administration, the Main Geological Exploration Administration of the Ministry of Geology and Conservation of Mineral Resources of the USSR, the Geological Institutes of the Academy of Sciences of the Uzbek SSR and the Academy of Sciences of the Ukrainian SSR, and others. The authors of these investigations are: E. A. Astrakhan, L. I. Grabovskaya, V. I. Nemchinov, A. D. Aivazyan, M. M. Botova, A. L. Kovalevskii, I. Kh. Khamrabaev, R. M. Talipov, B. F. Mitskevich, as well as others.

CHAPTER VIII

PRACTICAL PROBLEMS INVOLVED IN A PLANT-SOIL
BIOGEOCHEMICAL SURVEY

As already mentioned, depending on the character of the dispersion haloes of ore deposits, it is desirable to employ one of the following halo methods: lithochemical, hydrogeochemical, or biogeochemical. The selection of one of these or a reasonable combination of well-known geochemical methods is determined by geologic, physicogeographic, geomorphological, and biopedological weathering conditions, i.e., the environmental geochemical conditions for the migration of chemical elements in a specific area on the earth's surface. Sufficient detail has been given with respect to the best conditions under which the biogeochemical exploration method can be used; this information was given in the discussion on the problem of the formation of secondary dispersion haloes. We note that the chemical or salt dispersion haloes exceed by tens of times the dimensions of the ore bodies over which they have formed, and therefore can be detected easily by a biogeochemical survey. At the same time it is necessary to take one important circumstance into account. It has been noted that in any metallogenic province, polymetal, precious metal, uranium, etc., there is an increase in the "normal background" of the content of metals in soils, water, and plants, characteristic of the particular bioclimatic zone. Its origin can be attributed to the dispersion of chemical elements in the process of weathering of rocks containing ores.

The higher the geochemical background, such as the content of Co, Ni, Cu, Zn, and Mo in soils and plants, the more difficult it will be to localize the haloes, that is, detect anomalies indicating the nearness of ores.

However, experience shows that high values of the background are more characteristic of mechanical dispersion haloes, especially in mountainous regions. In the case of chemical haloes, an increase of the metal content by a factor of only 2 or 3 in comparison with the local geochemical background already is sufficient for the detection of ore bodies. This can be attributed to the more local manifestation of biogeochemical haloes at the surface, for example, due to the contact of plant roots with ore at depth, etc.

The biogeochemical survey method involves: 1) familiarization with the geological structure of the region to be studied and familiarization with the character of hydrogeological, soil, and geobotanical conditions; 2) a preliminary geochemical sampling at scales from 1 : 50,000 to 1 : 100,000 for determining the possibilities of the selected area on the basis of the content of ore elements in the soils, water, and plants and their ratio; 3) the laying out of an exploration grid for a detailed biogeochemical survey based on soil and plant sampling in the selected area at a scale of 1 : 2000 to 1 : 5000 by means of subdividing the grid used for the small-scale biogeochemical survey or by means of laying out a new grid; 4) the selection of soil and vegetation samples and their preparation for analysis under field conditions; 5) an analysis of soils and plants for their content of metals; and, 6) a geochemical and cartographic processing of the derived data. We will discuss all the enumerated problems in sequence.

1. Geological, Hydrogeological, Pedological, and Geobotanical Study of the Region

In the study of the geological structure of a region it is customary to use a geological map of a suitable scale and then become familiarized with the region's geological, geomorphological, and hydrogeological conditions in the field with certain ore manifestations (in outcrops of mother rock, in old mine workings, etc.).

The study of the type of weathered crust, the character and thickness of covering deposits, their age and interrelationships with present-day sedimentary formations, is the initial task of the geologist before undertaking a geochemical and biogeochemical survey.

Similarly, the determination of the ground water level and the direction of migration of underground water should be used in a preliminary analysis of the character and means by which ore elements migrate. All these

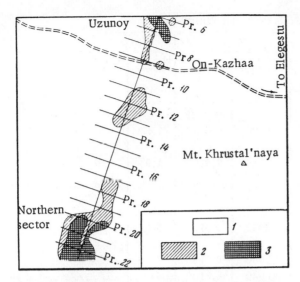

Fig. 75. Schematic map of the On-Kazhaa River region with isoconcentrations of copper in soils. Copper content: 1) less than $2 \cdot 10^{-3}\%$; 2) from $2 \cdot 10^{-3}$ to $1 \cdot 10^{-2}\%$; 3) more than $1 \cdot 10^{-2}\%$.

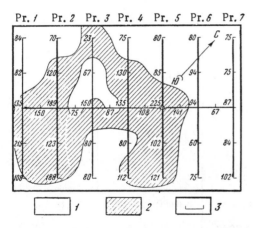

Fig. 76. Plan of the biogeochemical sampling on Mount Khrustal'naya with isoconcentrations of copper in soils. 1) Copper content of less than 100 ten-thousandths (%); 2) copper content more than 100 ten-thousandths (%); 3) sampling profiles, with indication of copper content in soils.

observations must be related to the characteristics of the climate, the soil cover, and the vegetation. A knowledge of the strike of geological structures, fault lines, and other tectonic dislocations can be of help in determining the direction of circulation of ground and fissure water, which in turn facilitates the problem of the proper laying out of the exploration grid.

Geomorphological characteristics should not be overlooked in the preliminary familiarization with the region. These include the exposure of slopes relative to the sun and the direction of removal of products of weathering and their thickness.

Particular attention should be given to a study of the soil cover, determination of the character of soil processes, the depth of the soil layer, the soil pH, etc. As already noted, the lithological-geobotanical study of the distribution of vegetation can be of great importance in the preliminary sampling of the new sector. But the most important factor in these investigations is a small-scale biogeochemical sampling at scales from 1:50,000 to 1:100,000 of the content of ore elements in soils and plants.

2. Preliminary Geochemical Sampling for Evaluation of the Possibilities of the Sector

Preliminary sampling excludes from the plan for detailed exploration work immense areas which are hopeless from the point of view of ore finds, making it possible to concentrate on more promising sectors.

A complex of lithochemical, hydrochemical, soil, and geobotanical observations is used when making a preliminary sampling. Rocks and minerals are sampled, as well as water from springs, and a preliminary geobotanical survey is made. Soil and plant samples are taken for chemical or spectral analysis in a field laboratory. For a preliminary biogeochemical sampling the entire area is covered by a small-scale survey grid.

Experience shows that the most effective grid for use in preliminary sampling is a square or rectangular exploration grid with grid squares measuring 250×500 m or 100×500 m, corresponding to a map at a scale of 1:50,000. The scale can be modified, depending on the size of the area. We will discuss one specific example of a preliminary biogeochemical sampling in a region of a known copper-nickel-cobalt deposit. We did this work in the Tuvinian ASSR on Mount Khrustal'naya, 5 km to the northeast of the northern sector.

In geological respects, the area which we explored is a mountainous complex 1340 m above sea level. It is dissected in different directions by deep dry ravines, covered by a nearly impassable larch forest. The northern slopes on Mount Khrustal'naya are wooded, but slopes with a southern exposure are covered by steppe. The geological structure of the complex includes basic extrusives and tuffs of the Lower Devonian. If it is taken into account that these rocks are impregnated by numerous veins of quartz and in certain cases have a skarn character, it is possible to surmise that there is a geological affinity of the structure of this complex to the adjacent deposit.

At first acquaintance with the new sector we noted a whole series of outcrops of rocks on the southern side of the complex. On this side there were outcrops of quartz veins rich in rock crystal. This is the reason that the new complex was named Mount Khrustal'naya.

TABLE 65. Cobalt, Nickel, and Copper Content in Soils of Mount Khrustal'naya

Sample No.	Soil and its origin	Content, %			Ratio	
		Co	Ni	Cu	Ni:Co	Cu:Co
25	Meadow chernozem, profile 7, 200 m to south of control line	0.0015	0.0025	0.0220	1.6	15
27	The same, profile 7, 400 m to south of control line	0.0024	0.0036	0.0110	1.5	5
38	Dark gray forest soil, profile 7, 400 m to north of control line	0.0010	0.0010	0.0100	1.0	10
18	Dark gray forest soil, profile 6, along control line	0.0014	0.0030	0.0190	2.1	13.5
31	The same, profile 6, 200 m to south of control line	0.0022	0.0070	0.0123	3.2	5.6
29	The same, profile 6, 400 m to south of control line	0.0020	0.0040	0.0190	2	9.5
11	The same, profile 4, along control line	0.0010	0.0040	0.0150	4	15
88	The same, profile 4, 200 km to south of control line	0.0008	0.0025	0.0080	3	10
5	The same, profile 5, along control line	0.0016	0.0021	0.0135	1.3	8.4
43	Dark gray forest soil, profile 4, 200 m to north of control line	0.0004	0.0008	0.0067	2	17
44	Dark gray forest soil, profile 4, 400 m to north of control line	0.0012	0.0010	0.0123	0.9	10
86	Meadow chernozem, profile 5, 200 m to south of control line	0.0012	0.0030	0.0082	2.5	7
46	The same, profile 5, 400 m to north of control line	0.0010	0.0033	0.0075	3.3	7.5
1	The same, profile 3, at triangulation station, on control line	0.0016	0.0010	0.0224	0.6	1.4
80	The same, profile 3, at triangulation station, 200 m to south of control line	0.0010	0.0030	0.0100	3	10
75	The same, profile 3, 400 m to north of control line	0.0010	0.0008	0.0060	0.8	6
18	Dark gray meadow soil, profile 6, along control line	0.0014	0.0030	0.0189	2.1	13.5
	Mean	0.0013	0.0023	0.0133	2	10.2

Dark gray forest soils with an abbreviated profile predominate on the northern slope of Mount Khrustal'naya. The soils lie on eluvium which is stony, with a transition to weathered rock. The southern slopes are covered with steppe vegetation, which also is partially true of the eastern slopes; these have chernozem meadow and chestnut soils. The chestnut soils are very stony on the steep southern slopes. The vegetation cover is very well expressed, except on rock outcrops, where there are mosses and lichens. The location of the sector is shown on the schematic map of the On-Kazhaa region (Fig. 75).

We first took samples of soils, rocks, and plants for a preliminary evaluation of the possibilities of the new sector. The sector was completely lacking in pits and trenches which would indicate that geological exploration work had been done here. Similarly, we did not find any traces of old mine workings. Consequently, the surface of Mount Khrustal'naya remained completely free of any extraneous contamination by metals.

Due to the absence of structures oriented in a definite direction, the preliminary evaluation was based on a square exploration grid with grid squares measuring 200 x 200 m. For control of the sector a reference line was run approximately from the middle of the sector, from a triangulation station atop a mountain, on the spoil bank of the No. 12 drift in the northern sector; this line ran in an azimuth of 230°. Seven exploration profiles were run at an azimuth of 320° at a right angle to the control line. The length of the grid was 1200 m and it was 800 m wide (Fig. 76).

TABLE 66. Cobalt, Nickel, and Copper Content in Plants Sampled on Mount Khrustal'naya*

Sample No.	Plant and its origin	Content, % Co	Content, % Ni	Content, % Cu	Ratio Ni : Cu	Ratio Cu : Co
28	Melanocarpous cotoneaster, profile 7, 200 m to south of control line (leaves)	0.0010	–	0.0201	–	
39	Warty birch (leaves), profile 7, 400 m to south of control line	0.0010	0.0020	0.0270	2	27
17	Warty birch (leaves), profile 6, along control line	0.0010	0.0038	0.00168	3.8	18.6
32	Gray-blue wormwood (above ground), profile 6, 220 m to south of control line	0.0013	0.0048	0.0252	3.7	20
10	Pasqueflower (above ground), profile 4, along control line	0.0004	0.0016	0.0072	4	18
89	Pasqueflower (above ground), profile 5, along control line	0.0008	0.0022	0.0120	2.7	15
42	Larch (needles), profile 4, 200 m to north of control line	0.0005	0.0022	0.0180	4.4	38
45	Larch (needles), profile 4, 400 m to north of control line	0.0004	0.0028	0.0160	7	40
87	Dwarf Caragana, profile 5, 200 m to south of control line	0.0005	0.0005	0.0084	1	17
47	Warty birch (leaves), profile 5, 400 m to north of control line	0.0004	0.0042	0.0200	10	50
2	Pasqueflower (above ground), profile 3, at triangulation station on control line	0.0010	0.0022	0.0300	2.2	30
81	Average oxytropis (above ground), profile 3, 200 m to south of control line	0.0014	0.0017	0.0270	1.3	20
77	Larch (needles), profile 3, 400 m to north of control line	0.0020	0.0008	0.0198	0.4	10
76	Pasqueflower (above ground), same site	0.0010	0.0008	0.0270	1	**10**
16	Wild milkvetch, profile 6, along control line	0.0026	0.0010	0.0270	0.4	10.4
	Mean	0.0010	0.0021	0.0205	2.1	20.5

*Plants sampled on June 25, 1959.

At each point samples were taken of soils and the most common plants (Caragana, dark blue wormwood, anemone, the leaves of the birch, the needles of the larch, etc.). A total of 100 samples were obtained. These data were prepared for analysis and immediately conveyed to the Kyzyl laboratory for determination of their nickel, cobalt, and copper content. Tables 65 and 66 give the content of these elements in the upper soil horizon from 0 to 10 cm. The data in Table 65 show that the cobalt content in the soils on Mount Khrustal'naya varies from 0.0004 to 0.0024%, nickel content from 0.0008 to 0.0070%, and copper content from 0.0060 to 0.0230%. By comparing the mean contents of cobalt (0.0013%), nickel (0.0023%), and copper (0.0130%) in the soils on Mount Khrustal'naya with the mean abundance ratios of these elements in soils (0.001, 0.002, and 0.004%, respectively) it is possible to note that their content in the soils on Mount Khrustal'naya exceed the abundance ratio; this is particularly true of copper.

The sharp variations in copper content in the soils on Mount Khrustal'naya and the appreciable excess over the abundance ratio were the first indications of the possibility of mineralization on Mount Khrustal'naya. The appreciable excess of copper over nickel and cobalt (the Co : Ni : Cu ratio was 1 : 2 : 10) obviously indicates the predominance of copper mineralization.

We endeavored to confirm these assumptions by sampling the vegetation which, by penetrating into the soil and the underlying rocks, intercepts metals and often indicates the presence of mineralization. Table 66 gives data from analyses of the ash of plants collected at the same points where the soils were sampled.

The maximum cobalt content in the ash of plants on Mount Khrustal'naya is 0.0026%, nickel content 0.0048%, and copper content 0.0300%. The Co : Ni : Cu ratio is 1 : 1.9 : 11.5. Table 66 gives the mean cobalt and copper content in plant ash (the mean of 16 determinations). Comparison with data in Table 65 shows an appreciable increase of the copper content in plant ash in comparison with soils. The nickel and cobalt content in soils is greater than in plants. Thus, under the conditions prevailing on Mount Khrustal'naya exploration for cobalt, nickel, and copper is equally successful whether soils or plants are used.

For a preliminary judgement as to the relationship of the high concentrations of metals in soils and plant ash, the derived data were plotted on schematic maps of the same scale. As an example we cite maps showing the iso-concentrations of copper in soils and plants.

Figure 76 shows that the highest concentrations of copper in soils are associated with the central, most elevated part of Khrustal'naya and its southern and southwestern slopes. It was in this area that we subsequently discovered signs of copper mineralization in the fissures of outcrops.

In Fig. 77 it is possible to note a correlation of high contents of copper in soils and plants for a whole series of points, although the copper in the plant ash usually is twice as abundant as in the soil.

The derived data from the preliminary check of the cobalt, nickel, and copper content in soils and plants revealed that Mount Khrustal'naya was not without possibilities with respect to copper. A detailed sampling was made using a subdivided grid, with grid squares measuring 50 × 100 m.

On the basis of data from a preliminary sampling, a sector for a detailed survey was selected in the southern part of the quadrangle, thereby greatly decreasing the amount of subsequent work involved in the localization of anomalies.

3. Layout of the Exploration Grid for a Detailed Biogeochemical Survey

In a detailed survey a square or rectangular grid is laid out. The orientation of the geological structures and the surmised configuration of the zone of mineralization are taken into account. The dimensions of the grid and the interval between sampling points are dependent on the conditions prevailing in the region, tectonics, relief, the thickness and character of the soil cover, and the vegetation. The dimensions of the postulated zones of mineralization and the dispersion haloes also are taken into account in laying out the grid. The distance between profiles is determined on the basis of the survey scale. In the case of a 1 : 20,000 small-scale survey the distance between profiles is 200 m and the sampling interval is 50 m. In a 1 : 2000 detailed survey the distance between profiles is decreased to 100 m and samples are taken every 20 m.

It also is the practice to lay out exploration lines, oriented in such a way that they probably will intersect the ore-bearing structures and extend beyond the limits of the surmised ore-bearing zone. This method is used primarily in the preliminary sampling of the sector for the content of metals in soils and plants and when checking the presence of the correlation of ore bodies situated at depth from the surface (the exploration geologist should not pass over even the weakest anomalies when making a survey).

The techniques involved in laying out the grid and establishing its topographic "control" are very simple. The area over which the survey is made is divided into two parts by a line running at a particular azimuth along the geological structure or the surmised orientation of the ore zone. The reference line is marked by signals, or in the forest by slash marks on trees. A pillar is set up at one end of the line; this is precisely tied in with landmarks shown on the map. Profiles are laid off at right angles along this line, at 100- or 200-m intervals. Sampling along the profile is done in both directions from the reference line. For example, a sample with a plus (+) denotes the right side of the profile, and one with a minus (-) the left side. The exploration grid is plotted on a map of an appropriate scale which shows outcrops of rocks with known manifestations of ore, old mine workings, etc.

The problem of the most desirable grid to be used in a detailed biogeochemical survey is solved by using data from a preliminary sampling, with the experience gained in a metallometric survey or geological exploration work taken into account.

Because the nature of the biogeochemical dispersion haloes of ore elements determined by soil and plant sampling are identical, the dimensions and character of the survey grid for the humus layer of the soil and for the analysis of plant ash are the same, making it possible to compare the results. As a result, the sampling of soil and vegetation is done simultaneously and insofar as possible at the same points on the profile. Figures 76 and 77 show examples of a joint (square) exploration grid for a plant-soil survey.

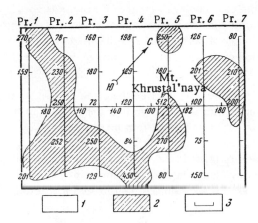

Pr. 1 Pr. 2 Pr. 3 Pr. 4 Pr. 5 Pr. 6 Pr. 7

Fig. 77. Plan of the biogeochemical sampling on Mount Khrustal'naya with isoconcentrations of copper in plant ash. 1) Copper content in ash less than 200 ten-thousandths (%); 2) copper content equal to or more than 200 ten-thousandths (%); 3) numbers of profiles and copper content.

The character of the exploration grid for a detailed exploration survey, the distance between profiles, and the sampling interval are dependent upon the above-mentioned characteristics of the studied area. The best method for the selection of the correct procedure is to make investigations on well-explored deposits belonging to a specific metallogenetic province. In this case it is possible to study the tectonic peculiarities of the region, the character and dimensions of the ore bodies, etc. Examples of this type of investigation are numerous; in particular, they have been described in studies by the author (Malyuga [1954, 1958]).

The density of the exploration grid is dependent on the configuration and dimensions of the ore bodies, as well as on their depth. Experience shows that vein ore manifestations of minimum depth often have haloes at the surface, that is, in soils and plants, with a width not less than 20-30 m. This makes it possible when intersecting veins to use a corresponding sampling interval, without fearing an oversight of ore veins. As an example, Fig. 53 shows the width of a secondary dispersion halo, detected from the content of cobalt, nickel, and copper in the humus layer of the soil over a sulfide-arsenide vein, intersected by profile 561, in the northern sector of a copper-nickel-cobalt deposit in Tuva.

A high cobalt, nickel, and copper content was noted in samples 102, 104, 105, 112, and 113; these samples were 10 to 20 m apart. The total width of the halo is 60-70 m, and the length along the profile is about 200 m. Proceeding on the basis of specific data for the studied deposit, it has been established that this type of ore manifestation cannot be overlooked when the survey is based on a rectangular grid with grid squares measuring 20 × 100 m.

The exploration grid, laid out in the field by the reference line and the profiles, is plotted on a plan corresponding to the map of the sector at a scale of 1:2000 or 1:5000. The plan shows future profiles with sampling points. In practice, the plotting of sampling points is done in the field at the time of collecting soil and plant samples. In this case the direction of the profiles is determined using a compass, in accordance with an earlier established azimuth.

The sampling points are marked by markers or slashes on trees. The ends of the profiles are marked by stakes which bear the number of the profile, the distance from the reference line, and the sampling dates. The marking of the exploration grid by means of reliable landmarks and stakes is of considerable importance for resampling purposes or for checking anomalies by test pits and other kinds of mineral exploration work.

4. Selection of Soil and Plant Samples and Their Preparation for Analysis under Field Conditions

A biogeochemical survey or an ordinary metallometric survey is made, depending on the method of soil sampling. This problem, seemingly simple to many engaged in geochemical investigations, nevertheless has not been fully studied.

If the sample is selected from the uppermost soil layer, which is enriched with considerable humus, it is used in a biogeochemical survey; if the sample is taken from beneath the humus layer or residual material, it is used as a metallometric sample. The selection of the most representative soil sample for a biogeochemical survey requires that the following conditions be observed: the soil is selected from the uppermost humus horizon (from 0 to 7 cm), and also from beneath bushes, hillocks of feather grass, the roots of trees, etc., that is, where the soil is held most firmly in place by roots. When sampling soils it is possible to use material from a single site or a joint sample, using material from several sites. These methods do not exert an appreciable influence on the results of the analyses.

The soils in desert and semidesert zones are not suitable for use in a biogeochemical survey, because they contain no humus. Soils in coniferous forests in a podzol zone with a slight humus layer require sampling jointly with the forest litter layer with the maximum humus content.

In order to avoid errors in the selection of the material to be sampled — soils or plants — a joint soil-plant survey is made. In deserts the plant analysis data are compared with the results of analyses of lithochemical samples.

173

Large roots and rock fragments are removed from the material sampled. The net weight of a sample is about 250 g. The sample is placed in a bag made from fine cotton fabric, to which is attached a tag which gives the sampling site, a description of the sample, and the date. The same data are noted simultaneously in the field book, including a description of the characteristics of the sampling site: condition of the soil, cases of outcropping of the bedrock, presence of mine workings, peculiarities of the relief and vegetation, etc.

The soils are transported separately from the rocks and vegetation samples. At the field base the sacks containing the soil samples are suspended to a stretched rope and dried in the sun. After thorough drying, the samples in the bags are crumbled by hand and passed through an aluminum or wire sieve with a 0.5- to 1-mm mesh (taking care that the samples are not contaminated by metal). The small fraction of the soil, in a quantity of 50-60 g, is placed in a paper envelope made of strong wrapping paper, the envelope is carefully tagged, and in this form is sent to the field laboratory for analysis. The old tag must be enclosed in the paper envelope. In the laboratory a part of the quatered soil sample is pulverized carefully in an agate mortar, dried, and weighed samples then taken for spectral analysis.

Surface plants (grasses, brush, woody species), like soils, can be used for exploration of ore deposits. Until now it has been assumed that due to the nonuniform selectivity of plants growing on ore deposits such plants are not of equal value for exploration work. However, the experience of our work with copper and molybdenum at Kadzharan, in the Armenian SSR, and elsewhere, reveals that all plants, without exception, experience an increase in the metal content of their ash, regardless of what family or genus they belong to. In this case the appreciable differences in the selectivity of individual plants, such as legumes to molybdenum (Vinogradova [1954]), disappear on the general background of high metal concentrations in plants.

In the preliminary sampling of plants it is necessary to compare the metal content in the individual species characteristic of a particular zone. Thereafter, in taking samples along the profiles in the exploration grid we endeavored to take samples from the most common species, but without fearing to replace them by others. In principle, when making biogeochemical surveys it is possible to use leaves, stems, bark, wood, and even roots, depending on the character of the distribution of a particular metal in a plant. Experience along these lines is still limited. However, certain patterns have been noted. It is known that all grassy plants, without exception, accumulate Ni, Co, Cu, Mo, Zn, Cr, Pb, B, U, and other elements in the stems and leaves. An appreciable increase of uranium has been noted in the roots of mosses and sedges, and an increase of lead has been found in the bulbs of certain plants growing over a zone of mineralization, whereas there is a low content in the stems.

Data show that the highest molybdenum content is in the stems of grassy plants and in leaves, taken together with young shoots of trees and bushes.

It should be noted that there is a general seasonal accumulation of heavy metals in the parts of plants involved in photosynthesis. This is why, when selecting samples, in exploration work the leaves (needles) should be taken together with young shoots.

Many data show that the content of mobile elements in the green parts of plants increases until the time of blossoming. After blossoming there is some redistribution of mobile elements. A part of these elements enters the seeds, fruits, and tubers, and another part remains and in the autumn is lost with the falling of the leaves and returns to the soil. Thus, there is an accumulation of heavy metals in the humus layer of the soil. With respect to certain deviations from this rule, they still are not clear and should be clarified with respect to each individually studied element.

In all cases it is necessary to take into account the age of the plants. The capability of plants to accumulate elements increases with age. Their roots penetrate more deeply into the soil and therefore can come into contact sooner with ground water which is enriched with metals or directly into contact with ore.

The use of the biogeochemical method for ore exploration, based on an analysis of plants, is possible at any season of the year: in winter and spring by analysis of branches, bark, and cellulose of trees, and in summer and fall by analysis of the leaves of trees and grassy plants.

Plant samples (leaves, needles, grasses) are taken at points marked along the profile. In the event there are no plants at the point the samples are taken at some distance to one side, but by no more than 5 m. One or two samples of grassy plants (one or two species) are cut at a height of 10-15 cm above the soil surface. Leaves and needles with young shoots or bark and wood are sampled from trees and bushes, depending on the season of the year and other circumstances. It is necessary to use a branch trimmer (garden shears at the end of a long stick) for taking samples from large trees). The weight of the sample should be not less than 260-300 g to yield 30-50 g of dry matter. The size of the sample can be changed, depending on the sensitivity of the analytical method used.

The collected plants are dried in the sun to a flammable state. The dry sample is placed in an aluminum vessel and burned in the open air on a kerosene or primus stove. Poorly burned ash containing carbon is compacted and left for final combustion.

The raw ash is placed into paper packets and sent to the field laboratory. There the ash is roasted in porcelain crucibles in an electric muffle furnace at 450-500°C. Experience shows that in determining nickel, cobalt, iron, manganese, molybdenum, tungsten, and uranium there is no appreciable loss even when the ash is roasted at higher temperatures. In individual cases it is necessary to maintain the recommended roasting temperature, for example, for determining zinc, tin, and lead. For a number of elements — antimony, mercury, boron, germanium, selenium, and tellurium — precautionary measures are in order. The resulting ash is placed into small packets made from tracing paper and sent for spectral analysis or investigated in the chemistry laboratory.

5. Analysis of Soils and Plants for Metal Content

The determination of metals in geochemical exploration work should be divided rigorously into two categories: 1) precise determination, done in permanent laboratories, and 2) spectral determination. Spectral determinations can be made under field conditions in temporarily outfitted quarters (tents, huts) or at mine laboratories. Mobile generators can be used as the power source for the spectrograph.

The author has developed polarographic methods for precise determinations of cobalt, nickel, copper, zinc, cadmium, and other elements (Malyuga [1946, 1957]). Speedy field determinations of cobalt, nickel, and copper have been made jointly and separately using rubeanic acid. In addition, speedy methods have been developed for colorimetric determinations of cobalt, nickel, copper, molybdenum, and other elements, and rapid determinations by the spectral method have been made for such metals as chromium, molybdenum, and lead (Belyaev and Pavlenko [1954]). Uranium has been determined by the polarographic and luminescent methods.

The speedy method for determination of the total content of the metals cobalt, nickel, and copper was used by the author while working in the sulfide-arsenide deposits of the Tuvinskaya ASSR and proved very successful.

A weighed soil sample or sample of plant ash is melted with potassium bisulfate ($KHSO_4$), the melt is dissolved in 20% HCl, and the solution is reduced to a volume of 15 ml. Part of the solution (5-10 ml) is poured into a beaker and diluted with up to 50 ml of water, several ml of 10% potassium citrate is then added, together with 2 ml of a 0.5 alcohol solution of rubeanic acid. After a weak alkalization with ammonia the sample is heated to 50°C (before the solution becomes cloudy) and left standing until the rubeanates are precipitated fully (in 1-2 hours). When the precipitate is filtered care must be taken that it is distributed evenly over the entire filter. After drying of the filters they are removed from the funnels and the precipitate is compared with reference samples obtained from standard solutions of cobalt, nickel, and copper. A conventional scale — 0, 0.5, 1, 1.5, 2, 3, 4, 6, 8, 10 — is used for estimating the gross content of metals in the sample, in milligrams. The method makes it possible for one laboratory worker to make 60 analyses in 8 hours.

The spectral method can be used for mass field determinations of copper, zinc, molybdenum, and lead in soils and plants (Tuva, Eastern Transbaikalia, etc.). The spectrograph is set up for this purpose near the power source. A portable generator is used when no electricity is available. An 8 A dc-arc is used for exciting the spectrum. The spectrum is registered on type 2 "spectral" plates (4-minute exposure; for plant ash, 3 minutes). Before spectral analysis the soils are roasted in an electric muffle furnace (500°C) and carefully pulverized.

The reference samples (standards) used are soils which do not contain the sought-for elements, and artificial mixtures of oxides, imitating the composition of a soil to which metals have been added in accordance with the scale of the standards — from $1 \cdot 10^{-3}$ to 0.1%. The standards were studied on the same plate with the samples. The results were evaluated using calibration curves by the three-standard method. In this case a direct dependence was maintained between the concentrations of metals in the samples and the difference in the blackening of the lines, except for cases of an excessively high content of chromium in soils (more than 0.1%). However, such a content of chromium is rarely observed in soils and plants.

Nickel was determined using the 3414.7 A line; cobalt, the 3405.1 A line; copper, the 3273.9 and 3247.5 A lines; chromium, the 4254.34 and 2677.15 A lines; molybdenum, the 3170.35 A line; and lead, the 2833.07 A line. The

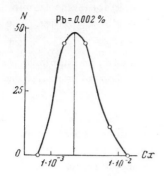

Fig. 78. Variation curve of the lead content in the normal geochemical background at Karatau (according to Solovov [1959]). N) Number of studied samples; Cx) lead content, %.

sensitivity of the method was $1 \cdot 10^{-3}\%$ and the error ± 15-20%. The rate of determination was 60 samples per 8-hour work day.

6. Geochemical Processing and Mapping of the Accumulated Data

The content of ore elements characteristic for a particular metallogenetic province (for example, $Co - Ni - Cu$, $Cu - Zn - Pb$, $Mo - Cu$, etc.), is computed in percent of the dry weight of the soil or the dry ash of plants and tabulated separately for soils and plants, in the order of sampling along the profiles.

When a search is being made for 2 or 3 elements, such as cobalt, nickel, and copper, the data on these elements are entered in a single row and the quantitative relationships are computed. When the relationship is found, the least significant element, such as cobalt, is assigned the value 1. The established sequence makes it possible to note deviations in the content of various elements for the expected concentrations and thereby detect possible errors in analysis or anomalies associated with mineralization. If the relationships showing metal content in plants and soils agree, they are considered reliable. In the event of a discrepancy they are compared with nearby points and the analyses repeated. If there is again a discrepancy, the point is visited for additional samples and additional studies are made of the conditions for migration of ore elements at a particular point in the profile.

The data then are plotted on a map of the required scale: $1:2000$ or $1:5000$. If the required topographic base or geological map is unavailable, it is necessary to compile a plan or layout of the sector and plot thereon the biogeochemical survey grid. Separate maps are compiled for plotting soil and plant data. The profiles and sampling sites (numbering of the samples) are plotted on the map at the appropriate scale, as well as the metal content in fractions of a percent. In many cases, in order to avoid cluttering of the map, only the metal contents are plotted or only the lines showing isoconcentrations of metals are drawn.

It is best to plot data for only one metal on one map, such as the soil content of copper. A second map of the same scale is compiled for plants. This results in several maps showing the distribution of the various metals in soils and plants for the same area explored.

In order to represent the distribution of the necessary element in the survey area graphically, the sectors with an identical or nearly identical content are circled with lines showing areas of equal concentration. The so-called local geochemical background is used for the minimum content. The background value is determined in several ways: by a study of the metal content in soils and plants sampled at a considerable distance along the extensions of the exploration profiles, or by a study of areas known to have no ore but with identical geological and bioclimatic conditions. In the latter case an adequate number of samples is obtained — several hundred — and they are studied for their content of the necessary elements.

The derived data are subjected to statistical processing, and the results plotted on a variation curve. The peak of the curve shows the value of the geochemical background (Fig. 78). Figure 78 shows that sometimes only a relatively small number of determinations, several dozen, is required in order to obtain reliable results from the background value. This was demonstrated, for example, using the example of the lead content in the normal background of metallometric samples at Karatau. The value of the geochemical background of lead at Karatau is 0.002%, which can be accepted as unity for drawing maps of isoconcentrations. Exactly the same method is used in compiling maps of isoconcentrations of metals in a soil-plant biogeochemical survey.

In comparison with the geochemical background, the anomalies with a higher content of metals in soils and plants over ore deposits usually stand out clearly. For example, the geochemical background of molybdenum in soils in the Kadzharanskii copper-molybdenum deposit is 0.005%, and anomalies with a 0.01 and 0.02 molybdenum content stand out clearly. On the map these are shown by different colors or made to stand out by use of an appropriate pattern.

As examples we can cite the maps of isoconcentrations of molybdenum in the soils of the Karmir-Karskii sector at Kadzharan (Armenian SSR), shown as Figs. 63 and 64. Consulting these maps it is easy to confirm that there is a close coincidence of the biogeochemical anomalies detected by soil and plant analysis. Diagrams are prepared for individual profiles of the studied area for a more graphic presentation. The metal content in the soil (ash) in % is plotted along the y axis and the distance between sampling points is plotted along the x axis. Such diagrams clearly reflect the appearance of biogeochemical haloes, as has been shown in Fig. 53.

* * *

Depending on the character of the dispersion haloes, that is on geological, physicogeographic, geomorphological, and bioclimatic conditions, it is appropriate to use lithochemical, hydrogeological, or biogeochemical methods of exploration.

The biogeochemical survey method involves: 1) familiarization with the geological structure of the region; 2) preliminary small-scale geochemical and biogeochemical sampling; 3) a detailed biogeochemical survey of the content of useful elements in soils and plants; 4) the selection, preparation, and analysis of samples; and, 5) geochemical processing, mapping, and interpretation of survey data.

The preliminary sampling is carried out to check the prospects of the region and exclude those areas which have little prospect of showing ore from the plan for detailed exploration. A complex of lithochemical, hydrochemical, soil, and geobotanical observations is employed for this purpose.

It is necessary to adhere to a number of requirements when obtaining a soil biogeochemical sample: the soil is sampled from the uppermost humus horizon, from 0 to 7 cm. The sample is obtained from beneath bushes, hillocks, of feather grass, and under the roots of trees, in places where the soil is best held in place by roots. The soil sample is dried in the air and passed through a 0.5- to 1-mm sieve and in that form is sent for analysis to a field laboratory.

Woody, grassy, and brush vegetation (perennials) are used in a joint biogeochemical survey involving analysis of soils and plants, or plants alone. It has been noted that all plants growing over ore deposits have a higher metal content and therefore all can be used in a biogeochemical survey. Stems of grass, leaves of trees and brush vegetation, taken together with young shoots, are selected for analysis. Plant material weighing 250-300 g is dried in the sun, then burned in aluminum pans on a kerosene or primus stove. Before analysis the ash is subjected to final combustion in electric furnaces.

Rapid field methods — chemical and spectral — are used for an analysis of soils and plant ash. The resulting data are tabulated and plotted on a map showing the isoconcentrations of ore elements. These maps are used in the further geochemical processing of the accumulated survey data.

CHAPTER IX

GEOCHEMICAL INTERPRETATION OF THE RESULTS
OF A BIOGEOCHEMICAL SURVEY

An important aspect of the work is the geochemical interpretation of the accumulated data. This involves the solution of problems associated with an evaluation of the ore content of the investigated area: 1) the extent and intensity of anomalies; 2) the value of the surrounding geochemical background; and, 3) the correlation in the distribution of ore elements in soils, plants, and underlying rocks and ores, etc.

The extent and intensity of anomalies are determined from maps of isoconcentrations and corresponding diagrams showing the distribution of metals in soils and plants. A comparison of soil and plant data makes it possible to evaluate the correlation.

The degree of concentration of metals in an anomaly is determined by a comparison of maximum content with the minimum content in the surrounding background. The background is established by a study of rocks, soils, and plants sampled at a considerable distance from the exploration profiles, along their extensions. The value of the geochemical background, as already noted, can be above or below the abundance ratio. Thus, the abundance ratio in this particular case will be the ratio not to the clarke, but to the geochemical background.

For a proper evaluation of the detected anomalies, it is necessary first to consider the experience of the geochemical exploration investigations made under different geological, physicogeographic, and bioclimatic conditions. In each specific case these data will help to correctly determine the conditions for migration of the chemical elements over ore deposits. These conditions have been discussed in detail in the preceding chapters.

The influence of geochemical processes on biogeochemical and other anomalies can be manifested in many ways. It is expressed in the degree of concentration of ore elements in the weathered crust, in soils, water and plants, as well as in the position of secondary haloes relative to the ore deposit and the configuration of these haloes. Most importantly, it is necessary to take into account internal and external migration factors facilitating an increase or decrease in the concentration of chemical elements in soils and plants. The most important external factors leading to anomalies of high intensity are: the nearness of the ore to the surface, not deeper than 5-10 m; 2) a high metal content in the ore; 3) the degree of development of the zone of oxidation; 4) the presence of conditions ensuring the migration of metal ions to the surface – the capillary rise of ground water, vegetation with deep root systems, etc.

Dispersion haloes (chemical or mechanical) over ores lying close to the surface usually stand out more clearly on the plan and are characterized by a high metal content. The extent of such anomalies at the surface often corresponds to the value of an ore deposit situated at some depth (3-4 m). Such cases were encountered in the Southern Urals, in the Kimpersaiskii nickel deposits (Malyuga [1954]), and in Tuva in a copper-nickel-cobalt deposit (Malyuga and Makarova [1956]). In the event that the ore deposit is at a greater depth, from 30 to 60 m, as was observed in Armenia in the Kadzharanskii copper-molybdenum deposit (Malyuga [1958]), the dispersion haloes detected by analysis of plants and soils had a fanlike form, with an appreciable attenuation of the intensity of the anomaly on the flanks. The dispersion haloes detected from soils and plants correlated well with one another, which is a good indicator of the presence of an ore deposit, although the absolute content of copper and molybdenum rarely exceeded the geochemical background by a factor of 4-5.

A slight displacement of dispersion haloes in soils in relation to the topography of an ore body lying close to the surface can be attributed to the sorption of metal ions by organomineral soil colloids. The latter constitute an obstacle to the migration of metals beyond the boundaries of the ore field. This is the explanation for the extremely slight displacement of the soil dispersion haloes of cobalt, nickel, and copper observed in the Southern Urals and Tuva.

The factors responsible for attenuation of geochemical anomalies at the surface are: 1) the ore bodies are at a great depth; 2) a low ore content of metals; 3) elutriation and leaching of the upper horizons of the soil-geological profile; 4) the attenuating influence of the covering clayey loams; 5) the screening effect of the carbonate horizon, inherent in the profile of dry steppe and other regions.

As already mentioned, xerophytic vegetation, possessing a deep root system, overcomes unfavorable conditions in the profile, forming a biogeochemical connection between the deep horizons and the surface. It is this factor which explains the anomalously high content of metals in the ash of plants growing over ore deposits.

A whole series of examples of correlation in the content of metals in ore, soil, and plants was given in the chapter devoted to the effectiveness of the biogeochemical method in the different bioclimatic zones of the Soviet Union.

When making lithochemical and biogeochemical surveys it is common to observe a displacement of anomalies in soils and plants relative to the subsurface position of the ore body. This phenomenon occurs most frequently in mountainous regions, especially in areas where there are acidic podzol and podzolized gray forest and soddy soils. Experience shows that the chemical dispersion halo is localized at some distance (in the plane of the field sheet) from the zone of mineralization, and usually downslope. It is characteristic that the haloes for different chemical elements in this case do not coincide.

The displacement of the dispersion haloes, and therefore the biogeochemical haloes, complicates the work on localization of ore bodies causing the formation of the anomalies. Because of this it is difficult to distinguish a real dispersion halo from a false one, which can owe its origin to various factors: the presence of old spoil banks or the surface wash of rocks and minerals enriched with ore elements.

An appropriate interpretation scheme for the data accumulated during a biogeochemical survey has been devised for the correct interpretation of biogeochemical anomalies.

1. Comparison of the Results of Soil-Plant Biogeochemical Surveys

As already mentioned, the accumulation of metals in the humus layer of the soil is due to the absorbing role of plants; after the death of these plants the metals are retained in humus matter. Thus, data from a survey on the content of metals in the humus layer of the soil and in the ash of plants are of a common origin and they can be compared for the purpose of interpreting the reliability of the detected anomalies by two different methods. However, for such a comparison to be possible it is necessary to know the biogeochemical activity of the studied plant, on the one hand, and the conditions under which metals are retained in the soil, on the other. Both processes are zonal and therefore should be taken into account when considering the bioclimatic zonality of the studied area.

When compiling maps of the isoconcentrations of metals in plants it is therefore necessary to take into account the nonuniform concentrating capacity of individual species in relation to various metal indicators. It was noted earlier that almost all plants over ore deposits have a high content of copper, molybdenum, nickel, and cobalt. Nevertheless, in precise biogeochemical mapping it is necessary to know the effect of concentration by each species taken for analysis, which should be expressed in the form of a coefficient. Steppe plants, despite some general increase in the nickel content in the ash, concentrate metal to a different degree. The least concentrating capacity is characteristic of the shaggy goldilocks (normal form), feather grass, and bedstraw; the maximum concentrating capacity is characteristic of St. Johnswort and agnus castus. The principal factors responsible for the nonuniformity in the accumulation of metals, as already noted, are the selectivity of plants and the nonuniformity in depth of root systems. Therefore, when compiling maps of the isoconcentrations, the metal content in the ash is divided by the coefficient of the concentrating capacity of the plants used in the survey.

The coefficients are computed in advance on the basis of an analysis of plants collected at several sites staked out over the deposit and beyond its limits. The nickel content in the plant most frequently encountered in the mapped region is used as the unit for concentrating capacity, such as in sheep's fescue (Shcherbakovskii deposit), which has a 0.015% nickel content in the ash. In this case the concentrating capacity of yarrow will be 2, agnus castus 3, etc. When analytical data for various plants are plotted on the map, the metal content is divided by this coefficient.

It should be mentioned that the concentrating capacity of the species with respect to the same element changes in dependence on the bioclimatic and other conditions in the region. The established coefficients of concentrating capacity therefore can be used only for the region for which they were derived.

According to data collected by the Systematic Experimental Party of the Altaiskii Geophysical Expedition of the VKGU (Nemchinov and Okoneshnikova [1960]), the biogeochemical activity of a species increases from the mountain forest zone to the dry steppe zone. Thus, certain rare elements which have not been noted in a moist mountain-forest zone appear in deposits in the steppe zone. At the same time, there is an increase in the sensitivity of the biogeochemical method in relation to individual elements (gold, molybdenum, etc.).

When compiling maps of the isoconcentrations, expressed in geochemical backgrounds, the value of the relative concentrating capacity of plants is expressed in these units.

As already mentioned, the biogeochemical method involves the making of a joint survey using the humus layer of the soil (0-5 cm) and plant ash. For these data to be comparable, the soil samples are taken from the most humus-enriched layer of the soil. In this case the soil samples will be the most representative from the biogeochemical point of view. However, it is not always possible to select soil samples which are sufficiently enriched with humus. In mountain regions, where the soils are unstable and often washed down by currents of water, it is necessary to take samples from any natural centers of humus accumulation – from beneath bushes, near tree roots, etc. This possibility is usually excluded in desert and semidesert areas of gray soils due to the deflation of humus particles and their rapid oxidation.

Both in certain mountainous regions with unstable soils and in zones with gray soils, the principal object of biogeochemical mapping is plants. Therefore, in such areas it is impossible to make a joint soil-plant survey. In those zones where such a survey is possible, such as in areas where there are gray mountain forest and meadow soils with a well-sodded surface, especially in a steppe zone with well-developed chernozem, dark chestnut, and chestnut soils, the making of a joint survey is most desirable, since it makes it possible to check the results of the biogeochemical survey, that is, give a more correct interpretation.

The zonal factors involved in the migration of chemical elements over ore deposits stand out more clearly when comparing the cartographic data obtained on the basis of a plant and soil analysis. For example, the displacement of an anomaly in the soil layer indicates instability of the soil-geological profile (in the upper part). On the other hand, vegetation with a well-developed and deep root system (milk vetch) more precisely reflects the localization of the ore deposit.

The observed considerable accumulation of certain ore elements in the humus layer of the soil in comparison with plant ash, as is characteristic of certain steppe regions (Aktyubinskaya Oblast, and elsewhere), is evidence of the relative stability of the soil layer and the long-term character of the process of metal accumulation in the soil, which is not comparable to their brief seasonal concentration in steppe plants. According to our observations, steppe fires facilitate the accumulation of ore elements in soils from ash enriched with metals.

The necessity for a joint soil-plant survey becomes completely obvious. An example of the successful use of a joint soil-plant survey for the prediction of the presence of mineralization has been revealed in the work in the Karmir-Karskii sector, discussed in greater detail in Chapter VII.

2. Geochemical Interpretation

When making a soil-plant biogeochemical survey it also is necessary to take samples of water and samples of soil and rock from the soil-geological profile in the best exposures and, taking into account the stratigraphic sequence and the possible presence of mineralized zones. In each area studied it is necessary to have not less than three such profiles, and the soils and unconsolidated rock of the weathered crust must be described for such profiles. The depth and thickness of the flocculated horizon also are determined under field conditions.

The presence of a carbonate horizon hinders the direct migration of ore elements to the surface. As already mentioned, the root system of vegetation easily overcomes the carbonate geochemical barrier, penetrating through cracks and the passages made by moles and earthworms into the deeper layers of the soil and underlying rocks, thereby facilitating the migration of metals to the surface.

The diagram (Fig. 79) graphically represents the influence of the carbonate horizon on the migration of nickel and cobalt. The diagram shows two maxima in the accumulation of nickel and cobalt: in the upper humus horizon from 0 to 10 cm and in leached serpentinite at a depth of 470 cm. In the layers between these maxima there is some increase in the nickel and cobalt content directly under the carbonate horizon, at a depth of 170 cm. Thus, when making a lithochemical survey under environmental conditions in which a carbonate horizon is formed it is possible to use samples from the upper humus horizon of the soil and, of course, samples from plants with a sufficiently deep root system, capable of breaking through the shielding carbonate layer of the profile.

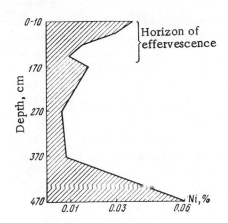

Fig. 79. Distribution of nickel in carbonate profile (Shcherbakovskii deposit).

The same deposit may have sectors where the effervescent horizon either emerges at the soil surface or is situated at some depth, depending on geomorphological conditions. On steep slopes with a well-washed crust there may be no carbonate horizon at all. On the other hand, on leached drainage divides the carbonate horizon is best developed, with a thickness of 2 m or more. Thus, under the same bioclimatic conditions there can be sharply different conditions for the migration of calcium carbonates, and of ore elements as well.

A study of the distribution of metals and their ratios in the vertical profile greatly facilitates the interpretation of the detected biogeochemical anomalies, and sometimes the digging of a test pit or shallow drilling provides a direct answer as to the presence or absence of mineralization. In such cases it is of great assistance to analyze the ratios of ore elements in rocks, soils, water, and plants.

The ratio of the individual elements in the soils and plants over ore deposits must be used in the interpretation of the collected data. It is known that the ratios of the geochemical pairs Ni : Co, Th : U, U : Ra, and others, can be used for the solution of genetic problems in lithology (Vinogradov [1944, 1950, 1954]; Malyuga [1947, 1949, 1954]). In exactly the same way it is possible to classify ore formations on the basis of the predominance of certain elements.

When studying the content of heavy elements in soils and plants it is possible to observe ratios characteristic of a particular intrusion or ore zone. Experience shows that geochemical pairs of elements often retain their ratios in dispersion haloes. For example, in the ore of nickel silicate deposits the Ni : Co ratio is 30-40, and in soils and plants sampled over the deposit 15-20, that is, very much higher than normal. In sulfide-arsenide deposits, where cobalt very frequently is equivalent to nickel, the plants and soils have the same ratios of these elements. Copper is an equally important indicator of the closeness of mineralization, especially when its content is compared with cobalt. In normal soils copper usually predominates over cobalt by a factor of 2-3, but in copper-cobalt deposits the cobalt content in soils is equivalent to the copper content. However, in the case of typical copper mineralization, the copper sharply predominates over cobalt. These phenomena are so regular that on this basis it is possible to trace regional transitions from one type of mineralization to another, as was demonstrated above.

The ratio between geochemical pairs can be used advantageously in those areas where ore anomalies are manifested poorly, such as in cases where the ore body is at a great depth, covered by a mantle of sedimentary and other rocks. In such cases there will be no clearly expressed anomaly at the surface and it can be overlooked and not plotted on the map. The ratios of the ore elements characteristic of a particular type of mineralization can help in the recognition of such anomalies.

3. Structural, Geomorphological, and Hydrogeological Analysis

The experience of exploration work includes certain cases in which the biogeochemical method has been used for the detection of geological structures — faults, thrusts, and fractured zones of folding.

In addition, we have studied the possibility of using the biogeochemical method for determining the boundary between two different metallogenetic zones: predominantly copper and copper-nickel-cobalt. The work was done in a 20-km long interval between the northern sector of the copper-nickel-cobalt deposit and the Uzunoiskii copper deposit in the Tuvinian ASSR in the On-Kazhaa River sector. These two metalliferous provinces differ in the content and ratio of chemical elements in the primary ores and in the zone of oxidation. The change in the content and ratio of cobalt, nickel, and copper in the humus layer of the soil in the On-Kazhaa River sector was traced in this way.

The processing of numerous data, collected in the field, on the content of cobalt, nickel, and copper, revealed that the southwestern part of the sector (along the On-Kazhaa channel) is characterized by a Co : Ni : Cu ratio in the soil of 1 : 1 : 2, close to that which was found in the copper-nickel-cobalt deposit, whereas the northeastern part has a Co : Ni : Cu ratio of 1 : 2 : 6, similar to that in the soils of the Uzunoiskii deposit. In this way it was possible to delimit two metallogenetic zones of different age, in essence separate and distinct.

Extent and configuration are important criteria for use in interpretation of biogeochemical anomalies. Most commonly, the anomalies have the same configuration as the secondary dispersion haloes, but not always and not for

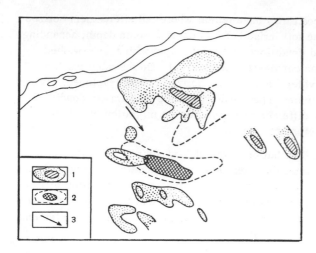

Fig. 80. False biogeochemical anomalies of zinc in the region of the Nokian deposit (according to Marmo [1953]). 1) Hydrochemical anomalies in the mineralization zone; 2) biogeochemical anomalies; 3) direction of flow of ground water.

all elements. As an example, we can cite the dissimilar dimensions of the soil haloes for copper and lead described by Ginzburg et al. [1960], as well as the different configurations of soil anomalies of cobalt, nickel, and copper which we observed in the Chugaevskii nickel deposit in the Kimpersaiskii region of Aktyubinskaya Oblast (Malyuga [1954], and others).

The simplest and smallest anomalies occur in open secondary dispersion haloes. Exceptions are mechanical haloes. These acquire a specific, downward elongated configuration and a surface manifestation of oxidation products enriched with ore components. Experience shows that such haloes are easily identified using even the simplest mining methods.

Large biogeochemical haloes are observed both in level areas with impregnated ores and on gentle slopes. They usually produce extensive anomalies, often poorly defined. By a careful analysis of the collected data it is possible to define more local sectors. By correlation of soil and plant anomalies it is possible to localize the zones of mineralization precisely, sometimes to a considerable depth – from 30 to 60 m – as the Karmir-Karskii sector at Kadzharan (Malyuga [1958]).

As noted by S. M. Tkalich [1959], biogeochemical anomalies sometimes are distant from ore bodies, which complicates their interpretation. This can be attributed to the well-known phenomenon of migration of ore elements from the zone of mineralization by means of underground and surface water into regions of stagnation – to greater depths or to areas with no surface runoff. Such complex anomalies are observed for uranium, molybdenum, radium, and other highly mobile elements. V. Marmo [1953] has described an example of the noncoincidence of the maxima of hydrochemical and biogeochemical anomalies. The noncoincidence of the chemical anomaly of zinc, detected from plants in the Nokian deposit in Finland, can be attributed to the migration of mineralized mine water in the direction shown in Fig. 80.

4. Preliminary Checking of Detected Anomalies

The final checking of detected biogeochemical anomalies is accomplished by exposure of the zones of mineralization by mining methods: intersection of the ore bodies by trenches; tracing their strike by test pits or drilling. The checking technique therefore differs in no way from that used in a lithochemical survey.

By knowing the geochemical peculiarities of indicator elements, as well as by evaluating the environmental characteristics of the exploration area (climate, presence of an effervescent horizon), it is possible to make a preliminary check of the detected anomalies long before formulating serious mine exploration work. A sampler which we developed in the laboratory (Malyuga, [1955]) can be used for this purpose. The instrument has a simple design and can be used for obtaining samples to any desired depth (to 150 cm) (Fig. 81).

By using this sampler it is quite easy to make a series of profiles through the anomaly quickly. These shallow profiles will be at specified intervals (10-20 m) along a single line or at any point in the anomaly, at option, thereby making it possible to study the distribution of metals in the profile, establish the presence of an effervescent horizon, find the depth of the bedrock, etc.

The systematic increase in the content of ore elements with depth is evidence of the presence of an open secondary dispersion halo at a relatively shallow depth. A decrease in the metal content of a sample taken below the illuvial horizon indicates the absence of mineralization or that mineralization is at a great depth. A further study of the anomaly is made using ordinary mine exploration methods, as provided for in the instructions for a metallometric survey (Solovov [1959]).

* * *

When evaluating the anomalies detected in a biogeochemical survey, it is necessary to be guided by the experience of zonal exploration work carried out under nearby geological and environmental-geochemical conditions.

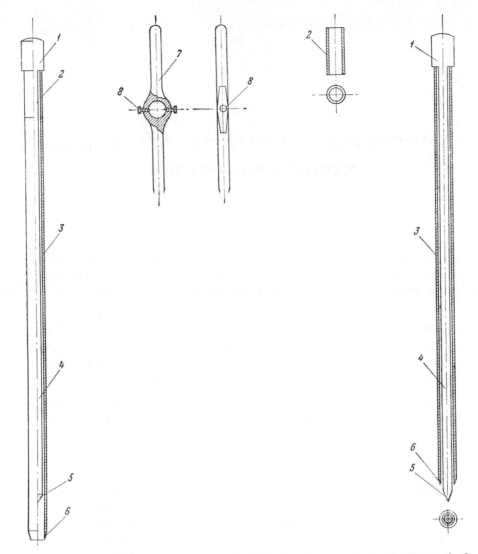

Fig. 81. Sampler for taking samples from the soil layer and subsoil. 1) Head of shaft; 2) bushing; 3) tube; 4) body of shaft; 5) point of shaft; 6) point of tube; 8) bolt.

The evaluation of internal and external migration factors of the selected elements of the indicators is of appreciable assistance in the interpretation of anomalies.

When analyzing the accumulated data, it is necessary to take into account the possibility of using the coefficients of the ratio of the elements of the geochemical companions (pairs, triads) Ni : Co, Tu : U, U : Ra, etc. The proper evaluation of these ratios is an extremely effective means for making a geochemical interpretation of the detected anomalies.

In the process of the study of biogeochemical anomalies it also is necessary to deal with false anomalies, whose origin can be attributed to a variety of factors — the influence of old spoil banks, the activity of underground and surface water flow, etc.

Among the methods for interpretation of biogeochemical anomalies are the following: 1) comparison of results (soil and plant survey maps); 2) study of the distribution and ratios of indicator elements in the soil-geological profile; 3) analysis of the geological and structural characteristics of the region and the direction of flow of ground and surface water; and, 4) a preliminary checking of anomalies at depth using simple manual drilling apparatus.

CHAPTER X

A CRITICAL EVALUATION OF THE BIOGEOCHEMICAL
EXPLORATION METHOD

An analysis of data from the Soviet and foreign scientific literature and our own experience shows that the characteristics of the biogeochemical method and its effective depth are determined by the conditions for interaction between surface vegetation and the surrounding "chemical" medium, that is, bioclimatic and physicogeographic zonality. In the geochemical literature this has been called "environmental-geochemical zonality," a term which we will use hereafter.

Problems in the practical application of the biogeochemical method are solved on the basis of a determination of its most important characteristics (specific properties, great effective depth): the advantage of its use in preference to other geochemical methods — lithochemical, hydrogeochemical, and others — and the advantages from the use of a soil or plant biogeochemical survey. In individual cases a joint soil-plant survey is made.

On the basis of the specific properties of the biogeochemical method, and taking into account the character of environmental-geochemical zonality, it is necessary to make recommendations on the methods for selecting soil and vegetation samples when making a survey.

1. Evaluation of the Specific Properties and Effective Depth of the Biogeochemical Method

The geochemical characteristics of the biogeochemical exploration method result from a number of internal and external factors involved in the migration of chemical elements inherent only in biogenic processes. These include 1) the biogenic (general) concentration of chemical elements by surface vegetation (the Vernadskii principle); 2) the well-expressed specific behavior of individual plant species (concentrator plants) in the accumulation of certain chemical elements, including heavy metals — manganese, nickel, copper, zinc, molybdenum, radium, and others; 3) the bioclimatic zonality of geochemical processes of migration of chemical elements under the conditions prevailing in the upper part of the earth's crust; 4) the accumulation of ore elements in two position of the soil profile: in the upper humus horizon from 0 to 10 (20) cm, and in the lower illuvial, sometimes subcarbonate horizon at various depths from 50 to 150 cm.

An extremely graphic example of the biogeochemical characteristics of the method is the disruption of the ratios of the chemical elements of geochemical pairs (Ni : Co, U : Ra, and others) in soils and plants over ore deposits, which are used in the process of interpretation of anomalies detected in a biogeochemical survey.

A peculiarity of the biogeochemical method which is of practical value is its great effective depth in exploration work, in this respect superior to the metallometric survey method, now employed by the geological services.

Many pages of this book, devoted to the theory of the biogeochemical method, adequately illustrate the specific properties of the new method and its difference from the lithochemical, hydrogeochemical, and other geochemical methods. Therefore, without further discussion of this fully clarified problem, we will proceed to a description of the effective depth of the biogeochemical method.

The effective depth of the method is determined by the thickness of the layer of barren rock, which makes it possible to detect indications of mineralization — an increase of the content of various elements in soils and plants, a change in their ratios, etc. Deviations in the content of ore elements in soils and plants cause the appearance of dispersion haloes of ore deposits closer to the surface, which is favored by the presence of zones of fracturing in massive and sedimentary rocks, jointing of rocks, and development of the weathered crust. The possibility of a capillary rise

184

of solutions, characteristic of dry and hot regions, is dependent on the permeability of the roof, as is the deep penetration of plant roots. Thus, the effective depth of the biogeochemical method is determined by geological, climatic, and geobotanical factors. In most cases they can be taken into account in the specific conditions prevailing in an area.

Experience shows that the permeability of rocks is characterized to a certain degree by floristic criteria, since rocks, like other phenomena, are an important edaphic factor. For example, the presence of Tamarix hispida (Viktorov et al. [1955]) indicates the presence of fractures and other tectonic dislocations, accompanied by the emergence of ground water; a "drunken forest" is evidence of the nearness of permafrost; psammophytes in deserts (haloxylon, thrift) are indicators of unconsolidated saliferous deposits which are waterlogged at depth, etc. An experienced geobotanist therefore can easily predict the probable effective depth of the biogeochemical method for any particular area.

Proceeding on this basis, it is possible to determine the effective depth of the biogeochemical method precisely, for the tundra and taiga zones over permafrost it does not exceed 1-2 m; for the zone of coniferous forests of the temperate zone it ranges from 2 to 5 m; for the dry steppes (Southern Urals, Northern Kazakhstan) it ranges from 10 to 20 m; etc. Xerophytic steppe vegetation of the arid zone (lucerne, camel's thorn, and others) possesses a long, virtually unbranching root system which penetrates to a depth of 5 to 15 m. The roots of desert plants attain still greater depths.

The depth of the root system of plants in mountainous regions conforms to natural zonality and to appropriate gradients. It is important to note that bare rocks and stony talus does not hinder the deep penetration of individual plants. The roots sometimes penetrate to depths of 10-15 m in cracks and zones of fracturing. In the Caucasus the author has seen plant roots in mine shafts at a depth exceeding 10 m.

The biogeochemical investigations which we have made in the different climatic zones of the USSR have confirmed the above-discussed aspects of determination of the effective depth of the biogeochemical method. For example, the depth at which the presence of nickel silicate ores can be detected in the Southern Urals is 20-30 m. The great effective depth of the method under the conditions prevailing in the arid Trans-Ural province can be attributed to the ore nontronites, which have a high moisture content, to which plant roots are attracted. In part the water migrates to the surface by capillary action (6 to 7 m), making it easier for plants to enter into contact with solutions enriched with ore elements. The effective depth of the method, as established in mountainous regions with respect to cobalt, nickel, copper, and uranium deposits, for the most part does not exceed 10-15 m. Minimum effective depth has been observed in the taiga on the lead and molybdenum deposits of Tuva and Eastern Transbaikalia over permafrost (1-2 m).

The foregoing text explains the reason for the nonuniform effective depth of the biogeochemical method, indicated by individual authors even on the basis of the same element, as can be seen from Table 67. The data in Table 67 show that the method makes it possible to explore for ore to a depth of 50 m. The experience gained in work in Tuva and elsewhere reveals that the ores in mountainous regions usually approach closer to the surface and are easier to detect by a soil and plant survey. It has been found that in such cases not even permafrost is a hindrance on southern slopes. In areas of poorly expressed relief, permafrost constitutes a serious obstacle in exploration work.

A comparative evaluation of the effective depth of the biogeochemical method and other exploration methods indicates that the only serious competitor with respect to effective depth is the hydrochemical method. However, the area of application of the latter is limited due to the absence of natural surface emergence of water in a number of promising regions. In addition, the hydrochemical method does not make it possible to precisely define the dispersion haloes, even when there is an abundance of water in the region. This explains why hydrochemists often have recourse to other halo methods, especially to the study of water extracts from soils, etc. (Dolukhanova [1958]).

2. Advantages of a Soil-Plant Biogeochemical Survey

The problem of selecting the method used in a biogeochemical survey, whether to use soils or plants, and the selection and development of methods for geochemical exploration in general, is a basic problem for geological exploration organizations at this time. The experience of use of the metallometric survey method in various zones of the USSR has shown that it is necessary to have a differentiated approach in the recommendations for exploration in different regions of our country. At the All-Union Conference on Geochemical Exploration of Ore Deposits in 1956 the speakers pointed out the specific conditions confronting geochemical exploration work in various environmental-geochemical zones of the Soviet Union (Vinogradov et al. [1957], Perel'man et al. [1957], Glazovskaya [1957], and others).

TABLE 67. Effective Depth of Biogeochemical Method as Stated by Different Authors
(According to A. P. Vinogradov[1954])

Element	Thickness of cover, m	Soil or plant	Author, year
Ni, Co, Cu	30	Soils and plants	Malyuga [1951]
Ni	5	Plants	Rankama [1954]
Zn, Cu	10	Plants	Warren [1932]
Zn, Cu	10	Plants	White [1950]
Cu	5	Soils	Sokolov [1951]
Cu	50	Soils and plants	Clarke [1953]
Zn	15	Soils and plants	Fulton [1954]
Zn	30	Plants	Harbaugh [1950]
Mo	5	Plants	Vinogradova [1950]
Au	10	Plants	Lundberg [1941]
V, U	10	Plants	Cannon [1952]

As already mentioned, one or another geochemical exploration method can be used, depending on the weathering conditions, the character of the dispersion haloes, and the properties of the metals. We have also already mentioned two cases of the great effectiveness of the biogeochemical method in comparison with a lithochemical survey: in the Kimpersaiskii ore region, in the Shcherbakovskii nickel deposit, and at Kadzharan on a copper-molybdenum deposit. In both cases the use of the exploration method was successful, making it possible to localize the secondary dispersion haloes, with such results as the discovery of an important copper-molybdenum ore zone in the Karmir-Karskii sector at Kadzharan.

Similar results have been noted in the studies of E. D. Astrakhan, L. I. Grabovskaya, and others (1960), in the deposits of rare metal pegmatites in Eastern Trans-Baikalia and V. I. Nemchinov et al. [1960] in the polymetal deposits of the Rudnyi Altai (Vostochno-Kazakhstanskaya Oblast).

In these investigations the problem of the relative advantage of a biogeochemical survey based on analysis of the humus layer of the soil or plant ash was not considered, since a soil survey was made along lithological lines, with sampling in accordance with the instructions for metallometric surveys prepared by A. P. Solovov [1959], that is, somewhat below the upper humus layer of the soil. Likewise, in the studies of foreign investigators — Cannon and Kleinhampl [1956] in a desert zone, Rankama [1954] in a zone of forested mountains in Finland (Makola), and Warren and Delavault (1954) in a permafrost zone (Canada), and elsewhere — biogeochemical exploration investigations usually made on the basis of the content and distribution of ore elements in plant ash.

We were the first to raise the problem of the necessity of making a joint biogeochemical survey using the humus layer of the soil and plants, so that the method was named the soil-plant method (Malyuga [1954]).

When making investigations for the study of the effectiveness of the biogeochemical exploration method in various zones of the USSR, the use of the plant and soil-plant survey methods should be selected in dependence on zonality conditions (vertical and latitudinal) and the character of the dispersion haloes. Definite techniques and procedures have been worked out for the use of these two methods.

We will now give information as to when the soil biogeochemical survey should be made, and when a plant biogeochemical survey is in order. To begin, a discussion of latitudinal zonality, starting in the north. A survey on the basis of woody vegetation (leaves, shoots) is recommended in zones of abundant or excess moisture in the northern taiga (European and Asiatic parts of the USSR, Fenoscandia, North America) with acidic podzolized soils on sialic leached weathered crusts. The studies of K. Rankama, V. Marmo, V. B. Aleksovskii, and others have demonstrated that the effective depth in such cases varies from 5 to 10 m.

The accumulation of lead, tin, molybdenum, and tungsten in the forest litter and fallen leaves, and their appreciable accumulation in swamp peat, indicates a possibility of using the upper humus layer of podzols, sampled together with the forest litter and peaty swamp soils when making a biogeochemical survey in northern forested regions (Palmqvist and Brundin [1939], Moiseenko [1959]).

In zones of moderate or inadequate moisture, which extend prominently in an E-W direction in the Kazakh SSR, such as along the line Petropavlovsk-Kokchetav-Tashkent, there are three principal environmental-geochemical provinces: a zone of moderately moist steppe and wooded steppe (Petropavlovskaya and Kokchetavskaya Oblasts); a zone of moderately dry steppes (Aktyubinskaya, Tselinogradskaya, and Karagandinskaya Oblasts); and a zone of desert and semidesert. The distinguishing characteristics of these zones, other than the distribution of precipitation, are climate, the character of the soil and vegetation cover, the presence and depth of inwash of $CaCO_3$ and $CaSO_4$, and the soil pH.

The zone of moderately moist steppe and wooded steppe is characterized by the presence of chernozems and gray wooded steppe soils (Alekseev, 1958), neutral at the surface, but with a deep-lying horizon of inwash of carbonates. Woody vegetation (birch, pine), brush (dog rose, spirea), and perennial grassy plants (wormwood, lucerne) are good objects for study in a biogeochemical survey.

The content of ore elements in the ash of leaves of woody species often is higher than in the upper humus layer of the soil. A biogeochemical soil survey therefore is less effective and is made for secondary purposes in order to facilitate the interpretation of data obtained in the plant survey.

In this particular case the effective depth of biogeochemical exploration method is determined by the length of the root systems of woody species and grassy steppe plants, as well as by the fluctuating water table. In general, the effective exploration depth exceeds 10 m.

The zone of moderately dry steppes is characterized by a continental climate and an eluvial weathered crust on which dark chestnut and chernozem soils have developed under xerophytic vegetation consisting of various kinds of grasses and wormwood. The carbonate horizon often emerges at the surface or lies very close to the surface.

In the Kimpersaiskii region, which we studied, the soils often were found on an ancient weathered crust of ultrabasites. The pH in the soil profile shows a neutral to an alkaline reaction. The upward and downward migration of ore elements is screened by a carbonate horizon. As a result, there are favorable conditions for the biogenic accumulation of metals in the humus layer of the soil by their transfer by plant roots from the deeper horizons of the profile (below the carbonate horizon).

The content of nickel, cobalt, and copper in plant ash is almost a whole order lower than in the humus horizon of the soil. Therefore, it is recommended that in a zone of moderately dry steppe the more desirable survey method is that based on the humus layer of the soil. Checking of the effective depth of the method in the Oktyabr'skii deposit indicated that it was possible to detect ore zones covered with a 20-m thickness of recent and ancient sedimentary formations.

The zone of desert and semidesert is characterized not only by aridity, but also a singular heat regime and the significant effect of the wind. Because of these conditions in the desert, semidesert, and the adjacent dry saline steppe, the soils which form are virtually lacking in humus, do not have an ordinary differentiated profile, and have been called gray soils of deserts or semideserts.

The widespread salinification of the soil-geological profile by the carbonates and sulfates of alkaline and alkaline-earth metals hinders the migration of ore elements to the surface. The covering clayey loams, sands, and sandstones therefore are impoverished of metals and cannot be of value in a lithochemical or other type of survey. However, desert plants, possessing a well-developed root system (haloxylon, saltwort, peganum, and others), reach the zone of moisture, often associated with zones of mineralization, and thereby are enriched with metals. Desert vegetation therefore should be used in a biogeochemical survey (Khamrabaev et al. [1960]). The effective depth of the method in the desert and semidesert zone attains 20-25 m.

3. Joint Soil-Plant Survey

Work in mountainous regions is the most graphic example of the need for making joint use of geochemical methods (hydrogeochemical, lithochemical, and biogeochemical) in the search for and exploration of ore deposits. When the relief is dissected and the geological, climatic, and bioclimatic pattern is complex, it is necessary to employ every possibility of biogeochemical indication, that is, soils and plants.

As already mentioned, exploration work in a mountainous area is complex because of the frequent change of natural conditions, with a consequent change in the conditions for the migration of ore elements. Typical examples of work in mountainous areas were the regions in Tuva, Armenia, and Adzhariya, described in this book. To recall certain of the most important external factors characteristic of the discussed mountainous regions: (1) The influence of exposure to the sun, which results in different conditions for the formation of dispersion haloes in the same deposit, depending on the orientation of the slopes; (2) The frequent change of climatic (microclimatic) and geomorphological conditions exerts an influence on the variability of the soil and vegetation cover. There is a particularly sharp change in the conditions for root formation. The maximum depth of root penetration is attained on dry, well-heated slopes, where plants with a deep root system develop. For example, on the dry southern and southeastern slopes at Kadzharan it is common to find golden or slanting milk vetch, whose roots penetrate as deep as 10-15 m. The same plants, trees, and shrubs on dry southern and moist northern slopes have root systems which penetrate to different depths, (3) Still another migration factor, difficult to take into account under mountainous conditions, is the composition of the humus substances in the soil. We have noted that in dependence on bioclimatic conditions there is a change in the content of individual humic acids in the humus, the humic acids vary in solubility, depending on the content of bases, the pH, and the humus moisture content, and thereby influence the mobility of heavy metals in the soil-geological profile.

A study of the forms of chemical compounds of metals in the soils of mountainous Adzhariya (Georgian SSR) revealed that about 50% of the copper and lead are found in the form of organometallic compounds with humus soil substances. In this case almost all "organic" lead is bonded with fulvic acids, that is, with the most mobile part of the humus, while copper is bonded equally in humate or fulvate form. This indicates that the mobility of ore elements is dependent on many factors which cannot always be evaluated correctly when interpreting a biogeochemical survey.

For a more correct evaluation of the results of a survey made in a mountainous area we recommend that a joint soil-plant survey be made, basing the interpretation of detected anomalies on all available geochemical, geological, and hydrogeological data. The effective depth of the biogeochemical method in mountainous areas is determined by many factors, principally geomorphological and bioclimatic conditions. For example, the effective depth of the method in the Armenian Transcaucasus was as great as 30-40 m, in Tuva it was 10-15 m, while in Adzhariya and elsewhere it was no greater than 10 m.

4. Zonal Characteristics Affecting the Sampling of Soils and Plants

The most important condition for the proper sampling of the soil in a biogeochemical survey is that the sample be obtained from the best sodded, that is, the most stable humus layer, specifically, in such places where the soil has long withstood processes of erosion: where there is a continuous sod cover, under thickets of grass and brush vegetation, and in the forest between the roots of trees. This ensures samples which are enriched with humus to the highest degree possible, a matter of appreciable significance when making a soil biogeochemical survey. This rule of course cannot be adhered to when a survey is made in cultivated areas.

When working in a mountainous taiga region, for which we have recommended a joint soil-plant biogeochemical survey, the selection of the soil sample should be made together with the upper humus-rich part of the forest litter: 2-3 cm of litter, 2-3 cm of the upper layer of a podzol or a gray podzolized mountain forest soil. Such samples have a high content of organic matter and they therefore must be burned in a muffle stove prior to spectral or other analysis and the metal content determined from the roasted soil. The enrichment of the sample with the useful element which takes place in this process increases the sensitivity, and therefore the effectiveness of the biogeochemical method, for example, for uranium, radium, copper, and other elements. Such a phenomenon has been observed in peaty soils, where an appreciable enrichment of soil samples with uranium has been noted (Moiseenko [1959]).

Taking soil samples in areas of gray desert and semidesert soils is of no essential significance for a biogeochemical survey because these samples in essence are "metallometric" samples which, as mentioned earlier, are lacking in metals and cannot reveal the presence of mineralization.

It must be acknowledged that any surface plants can be used as ore indicators in principle, since to one degree or another they reflect the properties of the surrounding chemical medium over the deposit. The experience of our studies has revealed that without exception all plants growing over ore deposits have an increased metal content. At the same time, differences in selectivity, such as the affinity of legumes and members of the thistle family to molybdenum, existing under normal conditions (outside the boundaries of ore deposits) disappear on the general background of high molybdenum contents.

Nevertheless, in actual practice it is necessary to take into account a certain nonuniform capacity of individual species of plants to concentrate ore elements. The following must be considered: the selectivity of the species, depth of the root system, age of the plants, etc. All these factors are taken into account in a plant survey. If several species with a dissimilar metal content are sampled along a survey profile, it is necessary to introduce a correction factor which is found by a study of the plants collected over the same area, over the ore body, and beyond its limits.

With respect to the zonal characteristics of importance in collecting plant samples in a florometric biogeo-chemical survey, it should be noted that when working in the taiga it is necessary to sample the leaves of trees and bushes together with branches not over 15-20 cm in length. In the winter the survey should be based on year-old shoots. A method has been developed for this purpose which employs the bark and wood of trees (Terekhova [1957]). Samples of brush and grass are obtained in a zone of moderately moist steppe and wooded steppe. Because the metal content in the vegetative organs of plants increases toward the second half of the summer, the plant samples (leaves and stems) must be selected late in summer and in the autumn. In the early spring it is possible to use grassy plants from the preceding year in the survey.

In the desert and semidesert zone, as well as in adjacent areas of dry steppe, it is necessary to sample perennial xerophytic vegetation having a deep root system. This includes grassy plants, shrubs, and subshrubs. The most wide-spread of these plants are: wormwood, peganum, desert grasses, haloxylon, saltwort, acacia, milk vetch, and others. The upper vegetative parts of the plants are selected.

In southern mountainous regions there are woody and grassy species of plants which possess a valuable property for exploration work — a well-developed root system, which makes a high content of ore elements possible. In such areas it is possible to use woody and shrub forms: rhododendron, cherry laurel, brush forms of oak, acacia (Caragana), spirea, milk vetch, thyme, St. Johnswort, sage, and others. The samples are obtained in the summer and autumn months. The remainder of the year it is necessary to sample young shoots and grasses from the preceding year.

Of the more than 30 chemical elements investigated with respect to the applicability of the biogeochemical exploration method, only 10 have been studied relatively well: boron, iron, manganese, cobalt, nickel, copper, zinc, lead, molybdenum, and uranium. The others have been studied intermittently or only once: zirconium, niobium, thorium, and mercury. Thus, recommendations can be made in the instructions only for those elements for which there is more or less reliable information, that is, for the 10 elements mentioned above.

In the instructions for zonal biogeochemical exploration we give general recommendations for all dispersed and rare chemical elements, since their individual migration properties still are known inadequately. Among the peculi-arities known at the present time, the following should be noted as examples. In the study of the results of biogeo-chemical investigations in a zone of inadequately moist steppes in the Trans-Ural province, it was established that there is a nonuniform behavior of ore elements — chromium and nickel — in the soil-geological profile. The chromi-um in soils for the most part is in the form of the stable mineral chromite, which is distributed in conformity to the laws of formation of mechanical dispersion haloes. On the other hand, chromium is accumulated in plants from the lower horizons of the profile, being absorbed from mobile compounds. That is why the dispersion haloes of chromium, determined from soils and plants, do not coincide. The latter more accurately reflect the position of the zone of mineralization. With respect to other elements, such as nickel, cobalt, and copper, under these conditions they be-have as ordinary mobile chemical elements. The current instructions therefore recommend that a biogeochemical survey for chromium be based on plants, and a survey for nickel, cobalt, and copper be based on an analysis of the humus layer of the soil.

In the zones of excess moisture, such as in the tundra where there are acidic soils, copper and molybdenum also behave differently. Copper, like nickel, cobalt, lead, and other elements, is mobile in the podzol profile and there-fore is reflected clearly in woody vegetation. Molybdenum, on the other hand, is less mobile, is assimilated poorly, and is virtually absent in plant ash (needles, leaves). Therefore, in exploration for copper, cobalt, lead, and other similar elements it is recommended that plant samples be obtained for analysis, whereas in exploration for molyb-denum the humus layer of the soil should be sampled, along with the forest litter. There are other examples too, but they require further investigation.

5. Exploration of Ore Deposits Using Companion Elements in Areas of Mineralization

When formulating plans for biogeochemical exploration work based on soil and plant analysis, it is customary to determine the elements — metals, characteristic of a particular paragenesis. These elements are known in advance from metallogenetic maps of the region or from data obtained by a preliminary chemical and spectral analysis of rocks, water, soils, and plants. In many cases the exploration geologist will find it more convenient to use data on an element present in macroquantities and more easily determined by the method used, rather than the content of the ore element which is of interest in the particular case.

Experience with exploration for the principal components on the basis of elements — indirect indicators — is common in metallometric surveys. In biogeochemical exploration this method has been used by S. M. Tkalich [1956] in exploration of arsenopyrite deposits for the content of manganese and iron in the plants in the Unashinskii, Nikol'skii, Oktyabr'skii, Belorechenskii , and other deposits. Nemchinov et al. [1960] employed the method of indirect indicators (arsenic, copper, nickel, lead) in a biogeochemical survey for gold in the Rudnyi Altai. In the same area we made an attempt to use the distribution of iron in soils and plants for the same purpose. Abroad, the method of exploration of sulfide deposits for the content of manganese and iron has been studied by Warren et al. [1954].

It should be noted that experience with indirect indicators in biogeochemical exploration is still too limited. Virtually no study has been made of problems relating to the influence of the zonality factor on the content of iron, manganese, and other ore elements, the competition of ions of heavy metals during their assimilation by plants, etc. On the other hand, the possibilities for broad utilization of the indirect indicators method are very attractive and require the most careful study.

APPENDIX I

Relative Content of Chemical Elements in Rocks and Soils in % (According to Vinogradov, 1957)

Element	Rock					
	ultrabasic (dunites, peridotites)	basic (basalt, gabbro, etc.)	intermediate (diorites, andesites)	acidic (granites, rhyolites, etc)	sedimentary rocks	soils
Li	$2 \cdot 10^{-4}$	$1.5 \cdot 10^{-3}$	$2 \cdot 10^{-3}$	$7 \cdot 10^{-3}$	$6 \cdot 10^{-3}$	$3 \cdot 10^{-3}$
Be	$2 \cdot 10^{-5}$	$1.5 \cdot 10^{-4}$	—	$5.5 \cdot 10^{-4}$	$7 \cdot 10^{-4}$	$6 \cdot 10^{-4}$
B	$4 \cdot 10^{-3}$	$1 \cdot 10^{-3}$	—	$1.5 \cdot 10^{-3}$	$1.2 \cdot 10^{-3}$	$1 \cdot 10^{-3}$
C	$1 \cdot 10^{-2}$	$1 \cdot 10^{-2}$	—	$3 \cdot 10^{-2}$	1.2	2
N	—	—	—	$3.6 \cdot 10^{-3}$	$1 \cdot 10^{-1}$	$1 \cdot 10^{-1}$
O	43	44.80	46.10	48.66	51.84	49
F	$1 \cdot 10^{-2}$	$3.7 \cdot 10^{-2}$	$5 \cdot 10^{-2}$	$8 \cdot 10^{-2}$	$5 \cdot 10^{-2}$	$2 \cdot 10^{-2}$
Na	$5.7 \cdot 10^{-1}$	1.94	3	2.77	0.66	0.63
Mg	14.10	4.50	2.18	0.56	1.34	0.63
Al	2.88	8.76	8.85	7.70	10.45	7.13
Si	20.20	22.80	26	32.30	24.80	33
P	$1.2 \cdot 10^{-1}$	$1.4 \cdot 10^{-1}$	$1.6 \cdot 10^{-1}$	$7 \cdot 10^{-2}$	$7.7 \cdot 10^{-1}$	$8 \cdot 10^{-2}$
S	$3 \cdot 10^{-1}$	$2 \cdot 10^{-1}$	$1 \cdot 10^{-1}$	$4 \cdot 10^{-2}$	$3 \cdot 10^{-1}$	$8.5 \cdot 10^{-2}$
Cl	$2 \cdot 10^{-2}$	$2 \cdot 10^{-2}$	$2 \cdot 10^{-2}$	$2.4 \cdot 10^{-2}$	$1.6 \cdot 10^{-2}$	$1 \cdot 10^{-2}$
K	$5 \cdot 10^{-1}$	$8.3 \cdot 10^{-1}$	2.31	3.34	2.28	1.36
Ca	7.70	6.72	4.65	1.58	2.53	1.37
Sc	$1 \cdot 10^{-3}$	$2.4 \cdot 10^{-3}$	$1.5 \cdot 10^{-3}$	$7 \cdot 10^{-4}$	$1 \cdot 10^{-3}$	$7 \cdot 10^{-4}$
Ti	$3 \cdot 10^{-1}$	$9 \cdot 10^{-1}$	$8 \cdot 10^{-1}$	$2.3 \cdot 10^{-3}$	$4.5 \cdot 10^{-1}$	$4.6 \cdot 10^{-1}$
V	$1.4 \cdot 10^{-2}$	$2 \cdot 10^{-2}$	$1 \cdot 10^{-2}$	$4 \cdot 10^{-3}$	$1.3 \cdot 10^{-2}$	$1 \cdot 10^{-2}$
Cr	$2 \cdot 10^{-1}$	$3 \cdot 10^{-2}$	$5.6 \cdot 10^{-3}$	$2.5 \cdot 10^{-3}$	$1.6 \cdot 10^{-2}$	$2 \cdot 10^{-2}$
Mn	$1.3 \cdot 10^{-1}$	$2.2 \cdot 10^{-1}$	$1.2 \cdot 10^{-1}$	$6 \cdot 10^{-2}$	$6.7 \cdot 10^{-2}$	$8.5 \cdot 10^{-2}$
Fe	9.85	8.56	5.85	2.70	3.33	3.80
Co	$2 \cdot 10^{-2}$	$4.5 \cdot 10^{-3}$	$2 \cdot 10^{-3}$	$5 \cdot 10^{-4}$	$2.3 \cdot 10^{-3}$	$8 \cdot 10^{-4}$
Ni	$1.2 \cdot 10^{-1}$	$1.6 \cdot 10^{-2}$	$5.5 \cdot 10^{-3}$	$8 \cdot 10^{-4}$	$9.5 \cdot 10^{-3}$	$4 \cdot 10^{-3}$
Cu	$8 \cdot 10^{-3}$	$1.4 \cdot 10^{-2}$	$3.5 \cdot 10^{-2}$	$3 \cdot 10^{-3}$	$5.7 \cdot 10^{-3}$	$2 \cdot 10^{-3}$
Zn	$5 \cdot 10^{-3}$	$1.3 \cdot 10^{-2}$	$7.2 \cdot 10^{-3}$	$6 \cdot 10^{-3}$	$8 \cdot 10^{-3}$	$5 \cdot 10^{-3}$
Ga	$4 \cdot 10^{-4}$	$1.8 \cdot 10^{-3}$	$2 \cdot 10^{-3}$	$3 \cdot 10^{-3}$	$4 \cdot 10^{-3}$	$3 \cdot 10^{-3}$
Ge	—	$1.5 \cdot 10^{-4}$	$1.5 \cdot 10^{-4}$	$3 \cdot 10^{-4}$	$7 \cdot 10^{-4}$	$n10^{-4}$
As	$2.8 \cdot 10^{-4}$	$2 \cdot 10^{-4}$	$2.4 \cdot 10^{-4}$	$1.5 \cdot 10^{-4}$	$6.6 \cdot 10^{-4}$	$5 \cdot 10^{-4}$
Se	—	—	—	—	$6 \cdot 10^{-5}$	$1 \cdot 10^{-6}$
Br	$1 \cdot 10^{-4}$	$3 \cdot 10^{-4}$	$4.5 \cdot 10^{-4}$	$1.7 \cdot 10^{-4}$	$6 \cdot 10^{-4}$	$5 \cdot 10^{-4}$
Rb	$2 \cdot 10^{-4}$	$4.5 \cdot 10^{-3}$	$7 \cdot 10^{-3}$	$4 \cdot 10^{-2}$	$4 \cdot 10^{-2}$	$1 \cdot 10^{-2}$
Sr	$2.7 \cdot 10^{-3}$	$4.4 \cdot 10^{-2}$	$8 \cdot 10^{-2}$	$3 \cdot 10^{-2}$	$4.5 \cdot 10^{-2}$	$3 \cdot 10^{-2}$
Y	$4.5 \cdot 10^{-4}$	$1.8 \cdot 10^{-3}$	$3 \cdot 10^{-3}$	$2 \cdot 10^{-3}$	$3.3 \cdot 10^{-3}$	$5 \cdot 10^{-3}$
Zr	$3 \cdot 10^{-3}$	$1 \cdot 10^{-2}$	$2.6 \cdot 10^{-2}$	$2 \cdot 10^{-2}$	$2 \cdot 10^{-2}$	$3 \cdot 10^{-2}$
Nb	$1.5 \cdot 10^{-3}$	$2 \cdot 10^{-3}$	$3.5 \cdot 10^{-4}$	$2 \cdot 10^{-3}$	$2 \cdot 10^{-3}$	—
Mo	$4 \cdot 10^{-5}$	$1.4 \cdot 10^{-4}$	$9 \cdot 10^{-5}$	$1.9 \cdot 10^{-4}$	$2 \cdot 10^{-4}$	$2 \cdot 10^{-4}$
Pd	$1.5 \cdot 10^{-5}$	$3.5 \cdot 10^{-6}$	—	1.10^{-6}	—	—
Ag	$3 \cdot 10^{-5}$	$3 \cdot 10^{-5}$	—	$1.5 \cdot 10^{-5}$	$9 \cdot 10^{-5}$	10^{-5}
Cd	—	$1.9 \cdot 10^{-5}$	—	$1 \cdot 10^{-5}$	$3 \cdot 10^{-5}$	$5 \cdot 10^{-5}$
In	$1.3 \cdot 10^{-6}$	—	—	$1.2 \cdot 10^{-5}$	—	—
Sn	—	$6 \cdot 10^{-4}$	—	$4.5 \cdot 10^{-3}$	$3 \cdot 10^{-3}$	$1 \cdot 10^{-3}$
Sb	$1 \cdot 10^{-5}$	$1.5 \cdot 10^{-5}$	$2 \cdot 10^{-5}$	$4 \cdot 10^{-5}$	$1 \cdot 10^{-4}$	—
I	$8 \cdot 10^{-5}$	$5 \cdot 10^{-5}$	$3 \cdot 10^{-5}$	$4 \cdot 10^{-5}$	$1 \cdot 10^{-4}$	$5 \cdot 10^{-4}$
Cs	—	—	—	$1.9 \cdot 10^{-3}$	$1.2 \cdot 10^{-3}$	$5 \cdot 10^{-4}$
Ba	$1.5 \cdot 10^{-3}$	$2.7 \cdot 10^{-2}$	$6.5 \cdot 10^{-2}$	$8.3 \cdot 10^{-2}$	$8 \cdot 10^{-2}$	$5 \cdot 10^{-2}$
La	—	$2.7 \cdot 10^{-3}$	$4 \cdot 10^{-3}$	$4.6 \cdot 10^{-3}$	$4 \cdot 10^{-3}$	$4 \cdot 10^{-3}$

(continued)

Element	Rock ultrabasic (dunites, peridotites)	basic (basalt, gabbro, etc.)	intermediate (diorites, andesites)	acidic (granites, rhyolites, etc.)	sedimentary rocks	soils
Ce	—	10^{-3}	$3\cdot10^{-3}$	$6\cdot10^{-3}$	$3\cdot10^{-3}$	$5\cdot10^{-3}$
Pr	—	$1.3\cdot10^{-4}$	—	$1\cdot10^{-3}$	$5\cdot10^{-4}$	—
Nd	—	$1\cdot10^{-3}$	$2\cdot10^{-3}$	$4\cdot10^{-3}$	$1.8\cdot10^{-3}$	—
Sm	—	$1.5\cdot10^{-4}$	—	$6\cdot10^{-4}$	$5\cdot10^{-4}$	—
Eu	—	—	—	$1.7\cdot10^{-4}$	$1\cdot10^{-4}$	—
Cd	—	$2\cdot10^{-4}$	—	$1\cdot10^{-3}$	$5\cdot10^{-4}$	—
Tb	—	—	—	$2.5\cdot10^{-4}$	$9\cdot10^{-4}$	—
Dy	—	$1.5\cdot10^{-4}$	—	$5\cdot10^{-4}$	$4\cdot10^{-4}$	—
Ho	—	—	—	—	$1\cdot10^{-4}$	—
Er	—	$1\cdot10^{-4}$	—	$2.5\cdot10^{-4}$	$2.5\cdot10^{-4}$	—
Tu	—	—	—	$2\cdot10^{-4}$	$2\cdot10^{-5}$	—
Yb	—	$1\cdot10^{-4}$	—	$2\cdot10^{-4}$	$2.2\cdot10^{-4}$	—
Lu	—	—	—	$2\cdot10^{-4}$	$2\cdot10^{-5}$	—
Hf	$6\cdot10^{-5}$	$2\cdot10^{-4}$	$5\cdot10^{-4}$	$4\cdot10^{-4}$	$4\cdot10^{-4}$	$6\cdot10^{-4}$
Ta	$7.5\cdot10^{-5}$	$1\cdot10^{-4}$	$7\cdot10^{-5}$	$3.5\cdot10^{-4}$	$3.5\cdot10^{-4}$	—
W	—	$1\cdot10^{-3}$	$1\cdot10^{-4}$	—	—	—
Re	—	$6\cdot10^{-6}$	—	$6\cdot10^{-7}$	—	—
Au	$1\cdot10^{-5}$	$3.5\cdot10^{-6}$	—	$1\cdot10^{-6}$	—	—
Hg	—	$9\cdot10^{-6}$	—	$4\cdot10^{-6}$	$4\cdot10^{-5}$	$1\cdot10^{-6}$
Tl	$6\cdot10^{-6}$	$2\cdot10^{-5}$	$1.5\cdot10^{-5}$	$2.5\cdot10^{-4}$	$2\cdot10^{-4}$	—
Pb	—	$8\cdot10^{-4}$	$1.5\cdot10^{-3}$	$2\cdot10^{-4}$	$2\cdot10^{-3}$	$1\cdot10^{-3}$
Bi	—	—	—	$2\cdot10^{-4}$	$1\cdot10^{-4}$	—
Po	$2.2\cdot10^{-16}$	$5.9\cdot10^{-15}$	$1.3\cdot10^{-14}$	$2.6\cdot10^{-14}$	$2.4\cdot10^{-14}$	—
Rn	$6.5\cdot10^{-18}$	$1.7\cdot10^{-16}$	$3.9\cdot10^{-16}$	$7.6\cdot10^{-16}$	$6.9\cdot10^{-16}$	—
Ra	$1\cdot10^{-12}$	$2.7\cdot10^{-11}$	$6\cdot10^{-11}$	$1.2\cdot10^{-10}$	$1\cdot10^{-10}$	$8\cdot10^{-11}$
Ac	$6.4\cdot10^{-16}$	$1.7\cdot10^{-14}$	$3.8\cdot10^{-14}$	$7.4\cdot10^{-14}$	$6.8\cdot10^{-14}$	—
Th	$6\cdot10^{-4}$	$3\cdot10^{-4}$	$7\cdot10^{-4}$	$1.8\cdot10^{-3}$	$1.1\cdot10^{-3}$	$6\cdot10^{-4}$
Pa	$1\cdot10^{-12}$	$2.7\cdot10^{-11}$	$6.2\cdot10^{-11}$	$1.2\cdot10^{-10}$	$1.1\cdot10^{-10}$	—
U	$3\cdot10^{-6}$	$8\cdot10^{-5}$	$1.8\cdot10^{-4}$	$3.5\cdot10^{-4}$	$3.2\cdot10^{-4}$	$1\cdot10^{-4}$

APPENDIX II

D. I. Mendeleev Periodic Table of the Elements

Periods	GROUPS OF ELEMENTS										
	I	II	III	IV	V	VI	VII	VIII			0
1	H 1 Hydrogen 1.00797						(H)				He 2 Helium 4.0026
2	Li 3 Lithium 6.939	Be 4 Beryllium 9.0122	5 B Boron 10.811	6 C Carbon 12.01115	7 N Nitrogen 14.0067	8 O Oxygen 15.9994	9 F Fluorine 18.9984				Ne 10 Neon 20.183
3	Na 11 Sodium 22.9898	Mg 12 Magnesium 24.312	13 Al Aluminum 26.9815	14 Si Silicon 28.086	15 P Phosphorus 30.9738	16 S Sulfur 32.064	17 Cl Chlorine 35.453				Ar 18 Argon 39.948
4	K 19 Potassium 39.102	Ca 20 Calcium 40.08	Sc 21 Scandium 44.956	Ti 22 Titanium 47.90	V 23 Vanadium 50.942	Cr 24 Chromium 51.996	Mn 25 Manganese 54.9381	Fe 26 Iron 55.847	Co 27 Cobalt 58.9332	Ni 28 Nickel 58.71	
	29 Cu Copper 63.54	30 Zn Zinc 65.37	31 Ga Gallium 69.72	32 Ge Germanium 72.59	33 As Arsenic 74.9216	34 Se Selenium 78.96	35 Br Bromine 79.909				Kr 36 Krypton 83.80
5	Rb 37 Rubidium 85.47	Sr 38 Strontium 87.62	Y 39 Yttrium 88.905	Zr 40 Zirconium 91.22	Nb 41 Niobium 92.906	Mo 42 Molyb-denum 95.94	Tc 43 Technetium [97]	Ru 44 Ruthenium 101.07	Rh 45 Rhodium 102.905	Pd 46 Palladium 106.4	
	47 Ag Silver 107.87	48 Cd Cadmium 112.40	49 In Indium 114.82	50 Sn Tin 118.69	51 Sb Antimony 121.75	52 Te Tellurium 127.60	53 J Iodine 126.9044				Xe 54 Xenon 131.30
6	Cs 55 Cesium 132.905	Ba 56 Barium 137.34	La* 57 Lanthanum 138.91	Hf 72 Hafnium 178.49	Ta 73 Tantalum 180.948	W 74 Tungsten 183.85	Re 75 Rhenium 186.20	Os 76 Osmium 190.2	Ir 77 Iridium 192.2	Pt 78 Platinum 195.09	
	79 Au Gold 196.967	80 Hg Mercury 200.59	81 Tl Thallium 204.37	82 Pb Lead 207.19	83 Bi Bismuth 208.98	84 Po Polonium 210.0	85 At Astatine [210]				Rn 86 Radon 222
7	Fr 87 Francium [223]	Ra 88 Radium 226.0	Ac** 89 Actinium 227	(Th)	(Pa)	(U)					

* LANTHANIDES

Ce 58 Cerium 140.12	Pr 59 Praseo-dymium 140.907	Nd 60 Neo-dymium 144.24	Pm 61 Pro-methium [145]	Sm 62 Samarium 150.35	Eu 63 Europium 151.96	Gd 64 Gado-linium 157.25	Tb 65 Terbium 158.924	Dy 66 Dys-prosium 162.50	Ho 67 Holmium 164.93	Er 68 Erbium 167.26	Tu 69 Thulium 168.934	Yb 70 Ytterbium 193.04	Lu 71 Lutetium 174.97

** ACTINIDES

Th 90 Thorium 232.038	Pa 91 Protactin-ium 232	U 92 Uranium 238.03	Np 93 Neptun-ium [237]	Pu 94 Plutonium [242]	Am 95 Ameri-cium [243]	Cm 96 Curium [247]	Bk 97 Berkelium [247]	Cf 98 Californ-ium [249]	Es 99 Einstein-ium [254]	Fm 100 Fermium [253]	Md 101 Mendel-eevium [256]	No 102 Nobelium [253]?

REFERENCES*

Aidinyan, R. Kh. "Detection of Soil Colloids Without Chemical Processing." Kolloid. Zhur. 9(1), 1947.

Akopyan, N. A. Mineralogy of the Zone of Oxidation of the Copper-Molybdenum Deposits of Armenia. Yerevan, Izd-vo Akad. Nauk Arm. SSR, 1948.

Aleksovskii, V. B., Mokhov, A. A., and Spirov, V. A. "The Use of the Biogeochemical Method for Exploration of Nickel on the Kola Peninsula." Geokhimiya, No. 3, 1959.

Anderson, R. Y., and Kurtz, E. B., Jr. "Factors Influencing Uranium Accumutation in Plants." Bull. Geol. Soc. of Amer. 65(12), 1954.

Anderson, R. Y., and Kurtz, E. B., Jr. "Biogeochemical Reconnaissance of the Annie Laurie Uranium Prospect." Santa Cruz County, Arizona Econ. Geol. 50(2):227, 1955.

Antipov-Karataev, I. N. "The Mobility of Copper in Soils." Pochvovedenie, No. 11, 1947.

Aschan, O. "Om Vattenhumus och dess medverkan vid sjömalmsbildningen." Arkiv Kemi mineralogy och geologi, 10A(15), 1932.

Babichka, I. "Gold in Organisms." Geochemical Methods for Exploration of Ore Deposits (collection of articles) Moscow, IL, 1954.

Balandin, V. N. "Formulation of the Problem of Indicator Plants." Sovet. Botan., No. 6, 1936.

Banerjee, D. K., Bray, R. H., and Melsted, S. W. "Some Aspects of the Chemistry of Cobalt in Soils." Soil Sci., 75(6), 1953.

Baranov, V. I. "The Problem of Measurements of Atmospheric Electricity and Radioactivity at Health Resorts." Trudy-Balneological Inst. on the Caucus Mineral Spas, 3(65), 1926.

Baranov, V. I. Radiometry, Moscow, Izd-vo Akad. Nauk SSSR, 1956.

Baranova, V. V., "Molybdenum Dispersion Haloes in One of the Sectors of the Tyrny-Auzskoye Deposit." Geokhimiya, No. 2, 1957.

Barsanov, G. P. (Ed.) "Mineralogy and the Genesis of Pegmatite." (collection of articles) Moscow, Izd.-vo Akad. Nauk SSSR, 1960.

Barsukov, V. L., and Pavlenko, L. I. "The Distribution of Tin in Granitoid Rocks." Doklady Akad. Nauk SSSR, 109(3), 1956.

Basitova, S. M. "The Geochemistry of Rhenium." Dissertation, V. I. Vernadskii Institute of Geochemistry and Analytical Chemistry,Akad. Nauk SSSR, Moscow, 1950.

Bazilevich, N. I. "Characteristics of the Cycle of Ash Elements and Nitrogen in Certain Soil-Vegetation Zones of the USSR." Pochvovedenie, No. 1, 1955.

Bazilevich, N. I. "The Small Biological Cycle of Ash Matter and Nitrogen in Meadow-Steppe and Steppe Soil Formation." Pochvovedenie, No. 12, 1958.

Bazilevskaya, N. A., and Sibirtseva, Z. P. "Change in the Color of the Corolla in Eschscholtzia under the Influence of Microelements." Trudy-Glavn. Botanichesk. Sada, No. 6, 1950.

Beath, O. A., Eppson, H. F., and Gilbert, C. S., "Selenium and Other Toxic Minerals in Soils and Vegetation." Wyo. Univ. Agr. Expt. Sta. Bull., 206:55, 1935.

Belov, N. V. The Structure of Ion Crystals and Metal Phases, Moscow, Izd-vo Akad. Nauk SSSR, 1947.

Belyaev, Yu. I., and Pavlenko, L. I. "Determination of Small Quantities of Chromium in Soils and Plants by the Spectral Analysis Method." Trudy-Biogeokhim. Lab. Akad. Nauk SSSR, Vol. 10, 1954.

Bertrand, G., and Mokragnatz, M. "Sur la présance générale du nickel et du cobalt dans la terre arable." Bull. Soc. Chim. France, 4(37), 1925.

Bertrand, G., and Sillerstein, L. "Sur la teneur du sol en bore." G. R., Vol. 28, 1939.

Bertrand, G., and Yonesuke, Okoda. "Sur l'éxistance du Pb dans la terre arable." Bull. Soc. Chim. France, 4(53):1933.

Betekhtin, A. G. Mineralogy, Moscow, Gosgeolizdat, 1950.

Bolotina, N. I. "Supplies of Humus and Nitrogen in the Principal Soils of the USSR." Pochvovedenie, No. 5, 1947.

---

* The text contains some references for which no citations appear in this list. In the translation, for all text references that are listed here, the year is printed in square brackets.

Botova, M. M., Malyuga, D. P., and Moiseenko, U. I. "Experience with the Use of the Biogeochemical Method for Exploration for Uranium under Desert Conditions." Geokhimiya, No. 4, 1963.

Breger, J. A., Deul, M., and Rubinstein. "Geochemistry and Mineralogy of Uraniferous Lignite." Econ. Geol., 50(2), 1955.

Buck, L. J. Garden Jour. N. Y. Bot. Garden Publ., Jan./Feb.:22, 1951.

Burkser, E. S., and Mitskevich, B. F. "Geochemical Methods for Exploration of Rare Elements." Doklady Akad. Nauk Ukr. SSR, No. 3, 1960.

Burstall, F. H., Davies, G. R., Linstead, R. P., and Wells, R. A. "Inorganic Chromatograph. on Cellulose. Part II. The Separation and Detection of Metals and Acid Radicals on Stips of Adsorbent." J. Chem. Soc., 44(516):7182, 1950.

Duyalov, N. I., and Chvyryaeva, A. M. "Geobotanical Methods of Exploration for Borates." Geobotanical Methods in Geological Research, Moscow, Gosgeoltekhizdat, 1955.

Byers, H. G. "Selenium Occurrence in Certain Soils of the United States with a Discussion of Certain Related Topics." U. S. Dept. Agric. Tech. Bull., 482:1, 1935.

Cannon, H. L. "The Effect of Uranium-Vanadium Deposits on the Vegetation of the Colorado Plateau." Am. J. Sci. 250:735, 1952.

Cannon, H. L. "Geobotanical Reconnaissance near Grants, New Mexico." U. S. Geol. Survey Circ., p. 264, 1953.

Cannon, H. L. "Geochemical Relations of Zinc-Bearing Peat to the Lockport Dolomite, Orleans County, New York." U. S. Geol. Survey Bull. 1000-D, 1955.

Cannon, H. L. "Botanical Prospecting for Ore Deposits." Science, 132(3427):591, 1960.

Cannon, H. L., and Kleinhampl, F. J. "Botanical Methods Used in Exploration for Uranium." Geology of Atomic Raw Materials, Moscow, Gosgeoltekhizdat, 1956.

Chebaevskaya, V. S. "Dynamics of the Content and Distribution of Microelements in Plants in a Green Conveyer." Izvest. Timiryaz. Sel'khoz. Akad., No. 5(36), 1960.

Chukhrov, F. V. Colloids in the Earth's Crust, Izd-vo Akad. Nauk SSSR, 1955.

Clarke, F. W. "The Data of Geochemistry." U. S. Geol. Survey Bull., 770, 1924a.

Clarke, F. W., and Washington, H. S. "The Composition of the Earth's Rock Crust." U. S. Prof. Paper, p. 124, 1924b.

Clark, O. M. "Geochemical Prospecting for Copper at Ray, Arizona." Econ. Geol., 48(1), 1953.

Cooper, J. G., and Huff, L. S. "Geological Investigations and the Experience Obtained in Geological Exploration at Johnson, Arizona." Geochemical Methods for Exploration for Ore Deposits, Moscow, IL, 1954.

Dadykin, V. P. Characteristics of the Behavior of Plants on Cold Soils, Moscow, Izd-vo Akad. Nauk SSSR, 1952.

Dingwall, McKibbin, and Beans. Can. J. Research, Vol. 11, 1934.

Doksopulo, E. P. "Nickel in Rocks, Soils, Waters, and Plants Adjacent to the Talc Deposits of the Chorchanskaya Group." (author's abstract), Tbilisi, Izd-vo Tbilisskogo Univ., 1961.

Dokuchaev, V. V. "Study of Natural Zones (Horizontal and Vertical Soil Zones)." Selected Writings of V. V. Dokuchaev, Moscow, Izd-vo Akad. Nauk SSSR, 1949.

Dolukhanova, N. I. "Experience in the Use of a Soil-Hydrochemical Survey for the Exploration of Molybdenum Deposits." Geochemical Exploration for Ore Deposits in the USSR, Moscow, Gosgeoltekhizdat, 1957.

Dolukhanova, N. I. Experience with the Application of a Hydrochemical Survey in the Copper-Molybdenum Deposits of the Armenian SSR, Yerevan, Izd-vo Akad. Nauk Arm. SSR, 1958.

Dorn, P. "Pflanzen als Anzeichen für Erzlagerstätten." Der Biologi, 6(1), 1937.

Duvigneaud, P. Plant "Cobaltophytes" dans le Haut Katanga. Bull. Soc. Royale de Botanique de Belgique, 91(2), 1959.

Épshtein, E. F. "The Florogeochemical Method for the Exploration of Mineral Deposits (Florometry)." Izvest. Dnepropetrovskogo Gornogo Instituta im. Artema, Vol. 20, Dnepropetrovsk, 1948.

Épshtein, E. F., and Hendricks, S. B. "Absorption and Migration of Mineral Nutrients in Plant Roots." The Use of Radioactive Isotopes in Industry, Medicine, and Agriculture, Moscow, Izd-vo Akad. Nauk SSSR, 1956.

Ermolenko, N. F. Soil Microelements and Colloids, Minsk, Izd-vo Akad. Nauk BSSR, 1960.

Evans, R. D., and Goodman, C. "Radioactivity of Rocks." Bull. Geol. Soc. Amer., p. 52, 1941.

Fersman, A. E. "Geochemical Problems of the Soviet Union." Trudy — Soviet Study of Production Powers (Series on Useful Ores, No. 2), Leningrad, Izd-vo Akad. Nauk SSSR, 1931.

Fersman, A. E. Geochemistry, Vol. 2, Leningrad, Goskhimtekhizdat, 1934.

Fersman, A. E. Geochemistry, Vol. 4, Leningrad, Goskhimtekhizdat, 1939.

Fersman, A. E. Geochemical and Mineralogical Methods of Exploration of Minerals (Selected papers. Vol. 2), Izd-vo Akad. Nauk SSSR, 1955.

Figurovskii, I. Climatic Description of Northeastern Armenia and Adjacent Regions, Tiflis, 1920.

Flerov, B. L. "The Use of a Stannometric Survey in the Exploration of Primary Tin Deposits." Redkie Metal., No. 1, 1935.

Flerov, B. L. "Methods for Exploration for Primary Tin Deposits." Sovet. Geol., 8(10):3, 1938.

Forchhammer, J. Pogg. Ann., 95(90), 1865.

Fredrickson, A. F. "Some Mechanisms of Fixation of Uranium in Certain Sediments." Science, Vol. 108, 1948.

Fowler, G. M. "Geochem. Prospecting in the Mississippi Valley." Mining, 36(12), 1950.

Fox, M. H., and Ramage, H. "A Spectrographic Analysis of Animal Tissues." Proc. Soc. B., Vol. 108, 1931.

Fulton, R. B. "Prospecting for Zn using Semiquantitative Chemical Analyses of Soils." Economic Geology, 45:654, 1950.

Gedroits, K. K. "Study of the Absorbing Capacity of Soils." Selected Articles, Vol. 1, Moscow, 1955.

Gerasimovskii, V. I. "The Geochemistry of Rare-Earth Elements." Rare Earth Elements, Moscow, Izd-vo Akad. Nauk SSSR, 1958.

Gilbert, R. E. "Geochemical Prospecting in the Park City District." Mining Congr. J., No. 9, 1951.

Ginzburg, I. I. "The Ancient Weathered Crust on the Ultrabasic Rocks of the Urals. Part 2. The Geochemistry and Geology of the Ancient Weathered Crust in the Urals." Trudy — Inst. Geol. Sci., No. 81, Moscow, Izd-vo Akad. Nauk SSSR, 1947.

Ginzburg, I. I. Experience in Developing the Theoretical Principles of Geochemical Methods of Exploration, Moscow, Gosgeoltekhizdat, 1957.

Ginzburg, I. I., Mukanov, K. M., and Poluzerov, N. P. "Copper and Lead in the Soil of the Uspenskoye Copper Deposit in Central Kazakhstan." Geokhimiya, No. 4, 1960.

Glazovskaya, M. A. "Unconsolidated Products of Weathering of Rocks and the Primary Soils in the Nival Zone of the Terskey-Alatau Range." Trudy — Inst. Geog. Akad. Nauk SSSR, No. 2, 1952.

Glazovskaya, M. A. The Weathered Crust, No. 2, Izd-vo Akad. Nauk SSSR, 1956.

Glazovskaya, M. A. "The Metal Content in Soils of Different Type." Geochemical Exploration for Ore Deposits in the USSR, Moscow, Gosgeoltekhizdat, 1957.

Glebovich, T. A. "Boron in the Sea." Trudy — Biogeokhim. Lab. Akad. Nauk SSSR, 8, Moscow, 1946.

Goldschmidt, V. M. "Die Naturgeschichte der Eisen Familie." Stahl und Eisen, No. 18, 1929.

Goldschmidt, V. M., and Peters, C. "Über die Anreicherung seltener Elemente in Steinkohlen." Nachr. Ges. Wiss. Göttingen. Math — physik Kl. 111, 38 — IV., 1933.

Goldschmidt, V. M. "Geochemische Verteilungsgesetze der Elemente, IX — Die Mengenverhältnisse der Elemente und der Atom-Arten." Skr. Norske Vid. Akad. Oslo, 1, Math.-Naturv. Kl., No. 4, 1937.

Goldschmidt, V. M. "Principles of Distribution of Chemical Elements in Minerals and Rocks." Uspekhi Khim. 7(2), 1938.

Golikova, O. P. "The Influence of Different Forms of Potassium Fertilizers on the Natural Radioactivity of Plants." Research Inst. on Plant Physiology. (author's abstract), Kiev, Izd-vo Akad. Nauk Ukr. SSSR, 1960.

Gorbunov, N. I. "Minerals of the Fine Fraction of the Soil. Patterns in their Distribution and Methods for their Study." Pochvovedenie, No. 10, 1952.

Gottschalk, V. H., and Buchler, H. A. "Oxidation of Sulphides." Econ. Geol., 7:15, 1912

Gudima, N. V., and Krutov, G. A. Industrial Requirements with Respect to the Quality of Raw Materials, No. 55, Moscow-Leningrad, Gosgeolizdat, 1948.

Harbaugh, J. W. "Biogeochemical Investigation in the Tri-State District." Econ. Geol., 45(6), 1950.

Hasler, A. "Retention of Copper in Soil." Mitt. Lebensm. u Hyg., 34(1/2), 1943.

Hawkes, H. E. "What Geochemistry Is and What It Can Do." Mining, 37(9), 1951.

Hawkes, H. E. "Geochemical Prospecting for Ores. — A Progress Report." Econ. Geol., 44(8), 1949.

Hawkes, H. E., and Lakin, H. W. "Vestigial Zinc in Surface Residium Associated with Primary Zinc Ore in East Tennessee." Econ. Geol., 44:286, 1949.

Henwood, W. J. Edinburgh New Phil . J., p. 5, 1857.

Hill, A. C., Toth, S. I., and Bear, F. E. "Cobalt Status of New Jersey Soils and Forage Plants, and Factors Affecting the Cobalt Content of Plants." Soil. Sci., 76(4), 1953.

Hjarne, U. Tentaminorum chemie in K. Laboratorie Hafn perfect, Vol. 2, Ed. 1. Wallerius.

Hoffmann, J. "Experimentale Erfassung von Uran in lebenden Süsswasseralgen." Naturwissenschaften, 29(27), 1941.

Hoffmann, J. "Detection of Uranium in Plants." Bodenkunde und Pflanzenernährung, 1942.

Hoffmann, J. "Bioelement Uran im Pflanzen und Tierischen sowie im menschlichen Organismus." Biochem. Zeitschr., 313(5/6), 1943.

Holmes, R. S. "Determination of Total Copper, Zinc, Cobalt, and Lead in Soils and Soil Solution." Soil. Sci., Vol. 59, 1945.

Huff, L. S. "Anomalous Content of Copper, Lead, and Zinc in Soils Near Ore Veins." Geochemical Methods for Exploration of Ore Deposits, Moscow, IL, 1951.

Hunt, E. C., North, A. A., and Wells, K. A. "Application of Paper Chromatography Methods of Analysis to Geochemical Prospecting." Analyst, 80(948), 1955.

Iordanskaya, N. I. "Root Systems of Certain Water-Indicating Plants of the Kalmykh Steppes." Problems in the Geobotany of Indicator Plants, Moscow, Izd-vo MOIP, 1960.

Ivanov, D. N. "Dissemination of Copper in Soils and the Role of Copper Fertilizers in Increasing the Yield of Agricultural Crops." Trudy — Soil Inst. Akad. Nauk SSSR, Vol. 34, 1950.

Jenny, Hans. Soil-Forming Factors, Moscow, IL, 1948.

Jenny, H., and Leonard, C. D. "Functional Relationship between Soil Properties and Rainfall." Soil Sci., Vol. 38, 1934.

Jensch, F. "Beitrage zur Galmeiflora von Oberschlesien. I." Angew. Chem., No. 17, 1894.

Kabata, A. "Zagadnicnie Sorpeje miedzi i kobaltu w glebie." Pastepy nauk rolniczych., 2(9), 1955.

Karbukh, D. V. "Biogeochemical Investigations in the Tri-State Region." Geochemical Methods for the Exploration of Ore Deposits (collection of articles), Moscow, IL, 1954.

Kapustinskii, A. F. "Affinity of Metals to Sulfur." Zhur. Fiz. Khim., (5):85, 1934.

Karpinskii, A. M. "Can Living Plants be Indicators of Rocks and Formations on which They Grow and does their Occurrence Merit the Particular Attention of the Specialist in Structural Geology?" Zhur. Sadovodstva, Nos. 3; 4, 1841.

Karstens, É. É. "Radioactivity of the Waters and Rocks of the Pyatigorsk Region and the Resulting New Possibilities for Development of the Pyatigorsk Resort." Zapiski Bal'neologicheskogo obshchestva v Pyatigorske, No. 2, 1912/1913.

Katz, G., and Rabinovich, E., Chemistry of Uranium, Moscow, IL, 1954.

Kerr, P. F. "The Natural Occurrence of Uranium and Thorium." Intern. Conf. on the Peaceful Uses of Atomic Energy, Geneva, 1955.

Khamrabaev, I. Kh., and Talipov, R. M. "Certain Results of Biogeochemical (Geobotanical) Investigations in Western Kazakhstan." Uzbekskii Geologicheskii Zhurnal, No. 5, Tashkent. Izd-vo Uzb. SSR, 1960.

Khitarov, N. I., and Ivanov, M. A. "The Geochemistry of Molybdenum in a Zone of Oxidation." Materialy TsNIGRI, Sbornik 1, 1936.

Kidson, E. "Cobalt Status of New Zealand Soils." New Zeal. J. Sci. and Technol., 18(9), 1937.

Klopotovskii, B. A. Radium in Plants as an Exploration Indicator for Uranium Deposits, NIIGGiMS, Novosibirsk, 1960.

Koczy, F. F. "Thorium in Sea Water and Marine Sediments." Geol. Fören i Stockholm Förn., Vol. 71, 1949.

Komlev, V. A. "Certain Problems in the Geochemistry of Uranium and Thorium in Granite Magmas." (collection of articles dedicated to Academician V. I. Vernadskii on the 50th anniversary of his activity as a scientist and teacher, Vol. I). Izd -vo Akad. Nauk SSSR, 1936.

Kononova, M. M. Problems Involved in Soil Humus, and Present-Day Problems in Its Study, Moscow, Izd-vo Akad. Nauk SSSR, 1951.

Kononova, M. M. Soil Humus and Its Fertility. Priroda, No. 12, 1955.

Korzhinskii, D. S. "The Concept of the Geochemical Mobility of Elements." Zapiski Vsesoyuz. Mineral. Obshchestva, Nos. 3;4, 1942.

Kovalevskii, A. L. Radium in Plants as a Sign in Prospecting for Uranium Deposits, NIIGG and MS, Novosibirsk, 1960.

Koval'skii, V. V. "Biogeochemical Provinces of the USSR and Methods for their Study." Trudy — Biogeokhim. Lab. Akad. Nauk SSSR, 11, Moscow, 1960.

Koval'skii, V. V., and Chebaevskaya, V. S. "The Importance of Cobalt in the Nutrition of Romanov Sheep." Doklady Vsesoyuz. Akad. Sel'skokhoz. Nauk im. V. I. Lenina, No. 2, 1949.

Kovda, V. A. Geochemistry of the Deserts of the USSR, Moscow, Izd-vo Akad. Nauk SSSR, 1954.

Kovda, V. A. "Mineral Composition of Plants and Soil Formation." Pochvovedenie, No. 1, 1956.

Krasnikov, V. I. Principles of a Rational Method for the Exploration of Ore Deposits, Moscow, Gosgeoltekhizdat, 1959.

Kreiter, V. M. Exploration and Prospecting for Minerals, Moscow, Gosgeolizdat, 1940.

Kuroda, P. K., and Sandell, E. B. "Geochemistry of Molybdenum." Geochim. et Cosmochim. Acta, 6, 1954.

Kuznetsov, V. A. "New Data on the Geological Structure of Tuva." Izvest. Akad. Nauk SSSR, Ser. Geol., No. 5, 1946.

Lakin, H. W., Stevens, R. E., and Almond, H. Y. "Field Method for the Determination of Zinc in Soils." Econ. Geol., 44(4), 1949.

Larsen, E. S., and Phair, G. "The Distribution of Uranium and Thorium in Igneous Rocks." Nuclear Geology, New York-London, 1955.

Lebedeva, Z. A. "Principal Characteristics of the Geology of Tuva." Trudy — Mongol'skoy Komissii Akad. Nauk SSSR, No. 26, 1938.

Levanidov, L. Ya., and Khilyukova, M. I. "The Problem of the Migration of Manganese in the Weathered Crust and in the Biosphere in the Southern Urals." Metodicheskii sbornik Chelyabinskogo gosudarstvennogo pedagogicheskogo instituta, Chelyabinsk, 1953.

Liebig, Justus von. Chemistry as Applied to Agriculture and Plant Physiology, Moscow-Leningrad, Sel'khozgiz, 1936.

Linstow, O. V. "Bodenanzeigende Pflanzen." Abhandl. preuss. Geol. Landesanst., N. F., 114, 1929.

Lomonosov, M. V. The Earth's Layers and Other Works on Geology (anniversary edition), Moscow-Leningrad, Gosgeolizdat, 1949.

Lovering, T. S., Huff, L. S., and Almond, H. "The Dispersion of Copper Around the San Manuel Copper Deposit near Pinal, Arizona." Geochemical Methods for the Exploration of Ore Deposits, Moscow, IL, 1954.

Lucas, R. E. "Chemical and Physical Behaviour of Copper in Organic Soils." Soil Sci. 66(2), 1948.

Lukashev, K. I. Principles of Lithology and the Geochemistry of the Weathered Crust, Minsk, Izd-vo Akad. Nauk BSSR, 1958.

Lundberg, H. "New Techniques in Geoexploration." Mining and Metallurgy, 22(413), 1941.

Madanov, P. V. "Biological Accumulation of Manganese in the Soils of the Volga-Kama Wooded Steppe and Its Accessibility to Agricultural Plants." Uchenye Zapiski Kazan. Gosudarst. Univ., Vol. 113, Book 7, Pochvovedenie, Kazan', 1953.

Magak'yan, A. K. Vegetation of the Armenian SSR, Moscow-Leningrad, Izd-vo Akad. Nauk SSSR, 1941.

Magak'yan, I. G. Copper-Molybdenum Provinces of the Armenian SSR, Yerevan, Izd-vo Akad. Nauk Arm. SSR, 1950.

Magak'yan, I. G. "Genetic Types of Foreign Uranium Deposits." Zapiski Vsesoyuz. Mineral. Obshchestva, Ser. 2, 84, No. 3, 1955.

Makarova, A. I. "Biogeochemical Investigations on Polymetallic Deposits." Geokhimiya, No. 7, 1960.

Malyanov, A. P. "Physical Properties of the Soils and the Root Systems of Plants in Bashkiria in the Southwestern Foothills of the Urals." Uchene Zapiski Moskov. Gosudarst. Univ., No. 12, Pochvovedenie, 1937.

Malyuga, D. P. "The Geochemistry of Dispersed Nickel." Trudy — Biogeokhim. Lab. Akad. Nauk SSSR, 5, 1939.

Malyuga, D. P. "The Problem of the Content of Cobalt, Nickel, and Copper in Soils." Doklady Akad. Nauk SSSR, 43(5), 1944.

Malyuga, D. P. "Soils and Plants as Indicators in Exploration for Metals." Priroda, No. 6, 1947a.

Malyuga, D. P. "The Relationships between the Elements of the Iron Family in Igneous Rocks." Doklady Akad. Nauk SSSR, 58(9), 1947b.

Malyuga, D. P. "The Problem of the Correlation of Permian Multicolored Minerals on the Basis of their Content of Cobalt, Copper, Nickel, and Other Elements of the Iron Group." Doklady Akad. Nauk SSSR, 58(8), 1947c.

Malyuga, D. P. "Investigation of Aerosols Collected in the Snow on the Zailiyskogo Ala-Tau." Meteoritika, No. 4, 1948.

Malyuga, D. P. "The Problem of the Content of Cobalt, Nickel, Copper, and Other Elements of the Iron Family in the Sediments of the Black Sea." Doklady Akad. Nauk SSSR, 67(6), 1949.

Malyuga, D. P. "Toward a Knowledge of the Nature of Tektites." Meteoritika, No. 6, 1949b.

Malyuga, D. P. "Biogeochemical Provinces in the Southern Urals." Doklady Akad. Nauk SSSR, 70(2), 1950.

Malyuga, D. P. "Experience in the Use of the Soil-Floristic Method of Exploration in the Trans-Ural Steppe Province." Doklady Akad. Nauk SSSR, 76(2), 1951.

Malyuga, D. P. "Dissemination of Cobalt in the Earth's Crust." Microelements in the Life of Plants and Animals, Moscow, Izd-vo Akad. Nauk SSSR, 1952.

Malyuga, D. P. "Experience with the Use of the Biogeochemical Method for Exploration of Ore Deposits in the Southern Urals." Trudy — Biogeokhim. Lab., Akad. Nauk SSSR, Vol. X, Moscow, 1954.

Malyuga, D. P. "A New Device for Obtaining Samples from the Soil Layer and the Residual Material." Razvedka i Okhrana Nedr, No. 5, 1955.

Malyuga, D. P. "Polarigraphic Determination of Heavy Metals in Rocks." Methods for Study of Sedimentary Rocks, Vol. 2, Moscow, Gosgeolizdat, 1957.

Malyuga, D. P. "Experience in Applying Biogeochemical Exploration in the Search for Mo in Armenia." Geokhimiya, No. 3, 1958.

Malyuga, D. P., and Makarova, A. I. "The Content of Microelements in Certain Soils Developed on Ore-Bearing Rocks." Pochvovedenie, No. 1, 1956.

Malyuga, D. P., Malashkina, N. S., and Makarova, A. I., "Biogeochemical Investigations at Kadzharan, Armenian SSR." Geokhimiya, No. 5, 1959.

Malyuga, D. P., Nadiradze, V. R., Chargeishvili, Ya. M., and Makarova, A. I. "Biogeochemical Method of Exploration in the High-Mountain Part of Western Georgia." Geokhimiya, No. 4, 1960.

Malyuga, D. P., and Petrunina, N. S. "Biogeochemical Investigations in the Tuvinskaya Autonomous Oblast." Geokhimiya, No. 3, 1961.

Manskaya, S. M., Drozdova, T. V., and Emel'yanova, M. P. "The Fixing of Uranium by Humic Acids and Melanoidines." Geokhimiya, No. 4, 1956.

Manskaya, S. M., Drozdova, T. V., and Emel'yanova, M. P. "The Fixing of Copper by Different Forms of Natural Organic Compounds." Pochvovedenie, No. 6, 1958.

Manskaya, S. M., Drozdova, T. V., and Emel'yanova, M. P. "The Distribution of Copper in the Peat and Peaty Soils of the Belorussian SSR." Geokhimiya, No. 6, 1960.

Marbut, K. F. "A Scheme for Soil Classification." Proc. First Intern. Congr. Soil Sci., 4, 1928.

Marmo, V. "Biogeochemical Investigations in Finland." Econ. Geol., 48:211, 1953.

McHargue, J. S. "The Occurrence of Copper, Manganese, Zinc, Nickel, and Cobalt in Soil, Plants, and Animals and their Possible Function as Vital Factors." J. Agric. Res., Vol. 30, 1925.

McKelvey, V. E., and Nelson, J. M. "Characteristics of Marine Uranium-Bearing Sedimentary Rocks." Econ. Geol., 45(1), 1950.

McLanghling, R. J. W. "Geochemical Changes Due to Weathering under Varying Climatic Conditions." Geochim. et Cosmochim. Acta, Vol. 8, 1955.

Mendeleev, D. I. Principles of Chemistry, Vol. 2, Moscow-Leningrad, Goskhimtekhizdat, 1932.

Miller, S. D. "Methods and Results of Metallometric Work in Kazakhstan." Geochemical Exploration for Ore Deposits, Moscow, Gosgeoltekhizdat, 1957.

Millikan, C. R. "Effects on Flax of a Toxic Concentration of B, Fe, Mo, Al, Cu, Zn, Mn, Co, or Ni in the Nutrient Solutions." Proc. Roy. Soc. Victoria, 61:25, 1949.

Minguzzi, C., and Vergano, O. "Nickel Content of the Ash of Alyssum Bartolonii." Atti soc. toscana sci. nat., Ser. A, 55, 1948.

Mitchell, R. L. "Cobalt and Nickel in Soils and Plants." Soil Sci., 60(1), 1945.

Mitchell, R. L. "Spectrochemical Methods in Soil Investigations." Soil Sci., No. 1, 1957.

Mitskevich, B. F. "Tin Migration in the Hypergene Zone." Doklady Akad. Nauk Ukr. SSR, No. 2, 1958.

Mkrtchyan, S. S. New Data on the Geochemical Structure of the Southern Part of the Armenian SSR, Yerevan, Izd-vo Arm. SSR, 1948.

Mohr, E. J., and Van Baren, F. A. Tropical Soils, Amsterdam, 1954.

Moiseenko, U. I. "Experience with the Use of a Biogeochemical Survey in Exploration for Uranium Deposits in Swampy Areas." Geokhimiya, No. 2, 1959.

Morris, H. T., and Lovering, T. S. "Hypergene and Hydrothermal Dispersion of Heavy Metals in Wall Rocks Near Ore Bodies in the Vicinity of Tantac, Utah." Geochemical Methods for the Exploration of Ore Deposits, Moscow, IL, 1954.

Mukanov, K. M. "Experience in the Study of Fields of Mineralization and Primary Dispersion Haloes of Ore Bodies. The Example of One of the Polymetallic Deposits of Kazakhstan." Geochemical Exploration of Ore Deposits in the USSR, Moscow, Gosgeoltekhizdat, 1957.

Nemchinov, V. I., Okoneshnikova, A. D., and others. Results of the Work of the Altai Geophysical Expedition During 1960, Book 3. Results of Biogeochemical Investigations in the Southwestern Altai (Published by the Altai Geophysical Expedition), Ust'-Kamenogorsk, 1960.

Nemec, B. "Gold in Zea Mays." Ber. deut. botan. Ges., No. 53, 1935.

Nemec, B., Babichka, J., and Obnorsky, A. "Über das Vorkommen von Gold in den Schachtelhalmen. Bull." Inst. Sci., Boheme, Nos. 1-7, 13, 1936.

Nesvetailova, N. G. "Geobotanical Investigations in the Exploration of Ore Deposits." Trudy – Vsesoyuz. Aerogeologicheskogo tresta, No. 1, Moscow, Gosgeoltekhizdat, 1955.

Nevol, J. "Flora der Serpentinberg in Steiermark." Acta Soc. Sci., Nat. Moravicae, Vol. 3, 1926.

Nischihara, G. S. "The Rate of Reduction of Acidity of Descending Waters by Certain Ore and Gangue Minerals and Its Bearing Upon Secondary Sulphide Enrichment." Econ. Geol., 9:743, 1914.

Nockolds, S. R., and Mitchell, R. L. "Geochemistry of Certain Caledonian Intrusive Rocks. Investigation of the Relationship between Primary and Dispersed Elements of Igneous Rocks and Their Minerals." Rare Elements in Igneous Rocks and Minerals (collection of articles), Moscow, IL, 1952.

Noddack, W. I. Das Rhenium, Freiburg, 1933.

Noddack, W. I. "Die Häufigkeit der Schwermetalle in Wassertieren." Arkiv. Zool., 4, 1939.

Ogil'vi, A. N. Concise Preliminary Report on the Radioactive Waters at Pyatigorsk, Izd-vo Geol. kom., Leningrad, 1929.

Pack, M. R., Toth, S. J., and Bear, F. E. "Copper Status of New Jersey Soils." Soil Sci., 75(6), 1953.

Painter, L. I., Toth, S. J., and Bear, F. E. "Nickel Status of New Jersey Soils." Soil Sci., 76(6), 1953.

Palmqvist, S., and Brundin, N. Svenska prospekterings Aktiebologet., 1939, P. M. angaende var geokemiska prospekterings method., Lund., 1939.

Parfenova, E. I. "Investigation of the Minerals of Podzol Soils in Relation to Their Genesis." Weathered Crust, No. 2, Moscow, Izd-vo Akad. Nauk SSSR, 1956.

Parfent'eva, N. S. Possibility of Using Vegetation in the Exploration for Lead Deposits in Calcareous Rocks of the Central Karatau Range (author's abstract), Moscow State University, 1955.

Pavlinov, V. N. "The Structure of Certain Laccoliths in the Vicinity of the Caucasus Mineral Waters." Byull. Moskov. Obshchestva Ispytatelei Prirody. Novaya Ser., 51, Otdel. Geol., Vol. 21(2), 1946.

Pavlov, N. V., and Livshits, S. Yu. "Outline of the Floristic Elements of the Syr-Dar'ya Karatau." Sovet. Botan., No. 1, 1934.

Peech, M. "Availability of Ions in Light Sandy Soils as Affected by Soil Reaction." Soil Sci., Vol. 51, 1941.

Peive, Ya. V. "Methods of Investigation in Agricultural Chemistry for Application to Soil Differentiation Fertilization." Izvest. Akad. Nauk, Latv. SSR, 1955.

Peive, Ya. V., and Aizupiete, I. P. "The Cobalt Content of Soil in the Latvian SSR." Izvest. Akad. Nauk, Latv. SSR, No. 3(22), 1949.

Peive, Ya. V., and Ivanova, N. N. "The Zinc Content in the Soils of the Latvian SSR." Microelements in Agriculture and Medicine, Riga, Izd-vo Akad. Nauk Latv. SSR, 1956.

Perel'man, A. I. "Typical Chemical Elements in the Environment." Priroda, No. 4, 1952.

Perel'man, A. I. Outlines of the Geochemistry of the Landscape, Moscow, Geografgiz, 1955.

Perel'man, A. I. "The ability of Chemical Elements to Migrate in the Weathered Crust." Weathered Crust No. 2, Moscow, Izd-vo Akad. Nauk SSSR, 1956.

Perel'man, A. I., and Saukov, A. A. "Geochemical Principles in the Exploration for Ore Deposits." Geochemical Exploration for Ore Deposits, Moscow, Gosgeoltekhizdat, 1957.

Perel'man, A. I., and Sharkov, Yu. V. "Experience in Defining Provinces and Regions of Provinces with Different Conditions for Geochemical Exploration in the USSR." Geochemical Principles for Exploration for Ore Deposits, Moscow, Gosgeoltekhizdat, 1957.

Perrson, N. New Bryol. Lich., 17, 1948.

Peterburgskii, A. V. "Contact Exchange and Its Role in the Assimilation of Calcium and Magnesium from the Solid Phase." Izvest. Akad. Nauk SSSR, Ser. Biolo., No. 4, 1944.

Peterburgskii, A. V. Exchange Absorption in Soils and the Assimilation of Nutrients by Plants, Moscow, Vysshaya shkola, 1959.

Petrov, B. F. Characteristics of the Soil Cover of the Tuvinskaya Autonomous Region, Izd-vo Akad. Nauk SSSR, 1952.

Petterson, H., and Rotschi, H. "The Nickel Content of Deep-Sea Deposits." Geochim. et Cosmochim. Acta, No. 2, 1951.

Polikarpochkin, V. V. "Primary Dispersion Haloes and their Significance in Exploration Work." Geochemical Exploration for Ore Deposits, Moscow, Gosgeoltekhizdat, 1957.

Polynov, B. B. Weathered Crust Part 1, Moscow, Izd-vo Akad. Nauk SSSR, 1934.

Polynov, B. B. "Geochemical Environments." Problems in Mineralogy, Geochemistry, and Petrography, Moscow, Izd-vo Akad. Nauk SSSR, 1946.

Polynov, B. B. "Principal Ideas in the Study of the Genesis of Eluvial Soils in Light of Current Knowledge." Commemorative Collection of Articles of the Akad. Nauk SSSR, Dedicated to the 30th Anniversary of the Great October Socialist Revolution, Vol. 2, Moscow, Izd-vo Akad. Nauk SSSR, 1947.

Popov, M. V. "The Vegetation of the Sary-Tau Mountains." Trudy — Tomsk. Gosudarst. Univ., No. 4, 1922.

Prasolov, L. I. Soils of the USSR as the Basis of Planning in Agriculture for the Second Five-Year Plan, 1932.

Pryanishnikov, D. N. Selected Writings, Vols. 1 and 2, Gos. izd-vo s.-kh. literatury, Moscow, 1952.

Pustovalov, L. V. Petrography of Sedimentary Rocks, Moscow, GNTI, 1940.

Raikov, I. A. "Materials on the Geobotanical Characteristics of the Pamirs." Izvest. TORGO, 17, 1924.

Rankama, K. "The Use of Traces of Elements in the Solution of Certain Problems in Applied Geology." Geochemical Methods for Exploration of Ore Deposits, Moscow, IL, 1954.

Ratevenko, I. N. Root Systems of Trees and Shrubby Species, Moscow-Leningrad, Goslesbumizdat, 1952.

Ratner, E. I. "The Accessibility of Exchange Cations to Plants in Relation to Problems in Chemical Improvement of Soils." Izvest. Akad. Nauk SSSR, Ser. Biolo., Nos. 5, 6; 1938.

Ratner, E. I. "The Interrelationship of the Absorption of Water and Mineral Matter by a Plant and the Role of Internal Factors." Doklady Akad. Nauk SSSR, 45(4), 1944.

Ratner, E. I. Mineral Nutrition of Plants and the Absorption Capacity of Soils, Moscow-Leningrad. Izd-vo Akad. Nauk SSSR, 1950.

Ratsbaum, E. A. "A Field Spectral Laboratory for Auxiliary Exploration Parties." Razvedka Nedr., No. 1, 1939.

Riddell, J. E. "Anomalous Copper and Zinc Values in Trees in Holland Township Gaspé - North County." Quebec Dept. Mines Prelim. Rept., No. 269, 1952.

Ringwood, A. E. "The Principles Governing Trace Element Distribution During Magmatic Crystallization." Geochim. et Cosmochim. Acta. Vol. 7, 1955.

Robinson, W. O. "Minor Elements in Plants and Some Accumulator Plants." Soil Sci., 60:15, 1945.

Robinson, W. O. "The Occurrence of Rare Earths in Plants and Soils." 56(1-6), 1949.

Robinson, W. O., Edington, G., and Byers, H. G. "Chemical Studies of Infertile Soils Derived from Rocks High in Magnesium and Generally High in Chromium and Nickel." Technical Bull. No. 471, U. S. Dept. of Agric.,1945.

Robinson, W. O., Lakin, H. W., and Reichen, L. E. "The Zinc Content of Plants on the Friedensville Zinc Slime Ponds in Relation to Biogeochemical Prospecting." Econ. Geol., 42(6):572, 1947.

Rodionov, V. V., and Sulin, A. F. Calculation of the Reserves of the Oktyabr'skoye Nickel Deposit, Vol. 1. Published by the Kimpersayskaya Geological Exploration Party. Batamshinsk, 1957.

Roklin, M. I. "Experience in the Use of a Stannometric Survey in the Permafrost Areas of the Arctic." Problemy Arktiki, No. 4, 1938.

Ronov, A. B., Malyuga, D. P., and Makarova, A. I. "Distribution of Small Quantities of Nickel, Cobalt, and Copper in the Clays of the Russian Platform." Doklady Akad. Nauk SSSR, 105(1), 1955.

Rosenqvist, A. M., and Vogt, T. V. Det Kong. Norske Videns. Selskab Forhandliger, 15(22), 1942.

Rubtsov, N. I. Vegetation of the Dzhungarskii Ala-Tau, Alma-Ata. Izd-vo Akad. Nauk Kaz. SSR, 1941.

Sabashvili, M. N. Soils of Georgia, Tbilisi, Izd-vo Gruz. SSR, 1948.

Sabinin, D. A. Physiological Principles of Plant Nutrition, Moscow, Izd-vo Akad. Nauk SSSR, 1955.

Safronov, N. I. "The Problem of the Dispersion Haloes of Mineral Deposits and Their Use in Exploration and Prospecting." Problemy Sovet. Geol., 6(4), 1936.

Salazkin, A. S. "Outline of the Vegetation of the Umba Riber Basin." Trudy — Inst. Biol. Akad. Nauk SSSR, Ser. 3, No. 3, 1936.

Samoilov, Ya. V. Bioliths, Leningrad, Nauchno-tekhnicheskoye izd-vo, 1929.

Saukov, A. A. "Geochemistry of Mercury." Trudy — Inst. Geol. Nauk, Akad. Nauk SSSR, No. 78. Mineralo-Geokhim-icheskaya Ser. (No. 17), 1946.

Saukov, A. A. Geochemistry, Moscow, Gosgeolizdat, 1950.

Schenk, P. W.,"Zur Einordnung der Lantaniden und Transurane in das Periodische System der Element." Angew Chem., Vol. 63, 1951.

Seaborg, G. T. Nucleonics, Vol. 5, 1949.

Sedletskii, I. D. Colloidal-Dispersive Mineralogy, Moscow, Izd-vo Akad. Nauk SSSR, 1945.

Selinov, I. P. Atomic Nuclei and Nuclear Transformations, Vol. 1, Moscow-Leningrad, Gos. izd-vo tekhn-teoret. literatury, 1951.

Selivanov, L. S. "Geochemistry and Biogeochemistry of Dispersed Bromine." Trudy — Biogeokhim. Lab. Akad. Nauk SSSR, 8, 1946.

Sendel, E. B. Colorimetric Determination of Traces of Metals, Moscow-Leningrad, Izd-vo khim. literatury, 1949.

Sendel, E. B., and Gol'dich, S. S. Rare Metals of Certain American Igneous Rocks (collection of articles), Moscow, IL, 1952.

Senftle, F. E., and Keevil, N. B. "Thorium-Uranium Ratios in the Theory of Genesis of Lead Ores." Trans. Am. Geophys. Union, Vol. 28, 1947.

Sergeev, E. A. "The Use of Drop Analysis in Exploration for Minerals." Razvedka Nedr., No. 12, 1936.

Sergeev, E. A. "The Physicochemical Method in the Exploration for Ore Deposits (Data from the All-Union Scientific Research Institute of Geological Exploration)." Geofizika, Nos. 9; 10, 1941.

Sergeev, E. A. "Investigation of Waters as a Means for Exploration of Polymetallic Deposits." Razvedka Nedr., 12, 1946.

Sergeev, E. A., and Solovov, A. P. "The Ionic Method in Geophysical Exploration (Data from the Central Scientific Research Institute of Geological Exploration)." Geofizika, No. 3, 1937.

Shcherbakov, D. I. Methods for Exploration and Preliminary Evaluation of Deposits of Rare Elements, Moscow, Gosgeolizdat, 1947.

Shcherbina, V. V. Geochemistry, Moscow-Leningrad, Izd-vo Akad. Nauk SSSR, 1939.

Shcherbina, V. V. Geochemistry of the Rare Earths, No. 1, Moscow-Leningrad, Gosgeolizdat, 1946.

Shcherbina, V. V. "Concentration and Dispersal of Chemical Elements in the Earth's Crust as a Result of Redox Processes." Doklady Akad. Nauk SSSR, 67(3), 1949.

Shcherbina, V. V., and Ignatova, L. N. "New Data on the Geochemistry of Copper in the Zone of Hypergenesis." Zapiski Vsesoyuz. Mineral. Obshchestva, Ser. 2, Part 84, No. 3, 1955.

Shibol'd, É. "Structure of Silicates." Principal Ideas in Geochemistry, No. 3, Leningrad, Khimteoretizdat, 1937.

Shkol'nik, M. Ya. Importance of Microelements in the Life of Plants and in Agriculture, Moscow, Izd-vo Akad. Nauk SSSR, 1950.

Shreter, A. I. Composition and Analysis of Flora in Central Tuva (author's abstract of dissertation), Moscow, MGU, 1954.

Shvyryaeva, A. M. "The Possibility of Applying the Biogeochemical Method in the Exploration of Boron Raw Materials." Geochemical Methods for Exploration of Ore Deposits in the USSR, Moscow, Gosgeoltekhizdat, 1957.

Singewald, J. T. "The Chrome Industry in Maryland." Md. Geol. Survey Repts., 12:158, 1928.

Sinyakova, S. I. "The Distribution of Lead in Soils." Doklady Akad. Nauk SSSR, 48(9), 1945.

Smirnov, S. S. Zone of Oxidation of Sulfide Deposits, 3rd Ed., Izd-vo Akad. Nauk SSSR, 1951.

Smirnov, V. I. Geochemical Methods for the Exploration of Ore Deposits (Forword to the Book), Moscow, IL, 1954.

Smirnov, V. I. "Problems Involved in the Exploration of Ore Deposits Which do not Outcrop at the Earth's Surface." Sovets. Geol., No. 49, 1955.

Smurov, A. A. "Chemical Characteristics of the Ground Water of the Tyulenevskoye and Krestovskoye Nickel Silicate Ore Deposits." Zapiski Vesesoyuz. Mineral. Obshchestva, Part 69, No. 1, 1940.

Sobolev, V. S. Introduction to the Mineralogy of Silicates, L'vov, Izd-vo L'vovskogo Univ., 1949.

Sobolevskaya, K. A. Vegetation of Tuva, Poligrafizdat, Novosibirsk, 1950.

Sokolov, A. V. Distribution of Nutrients in the Soil and Plant Harvests, Moscow, Izd-vo Akad. Nauk SSSR, 1947.

Sokolov, G. A. Chromites of the Urals, their Composition, Crystallization Conditions, and Patterns of Distribution, Moscow, Izd-vo Akad. Nauk SSSR, 1948.

Solovov, A. P. "Theory and Practice of Metallometric Surveys." Geochemical Exploration of Ore Deposits, Moscow, Gosgeoltekhizdat, 1957.

Solovov, A. P. Principles of the Theory and Practice of Metallometric Surveys, Alma-Ata, Izd-vo Akad. Nauk Kaz. SSR, 1959.

Sprygin, I. I. "Rock Outcrops of the Tatarskii Stage of the Permian System in the Trans-Volga Area as One of the Centers of Speciation in the Chalcophylic Plant Group." Sovets. Botan., No. 4, 1934.

Starik, I. E. "Forms of Occurrence and Conditions for the Primary Migration of Radioelements in Nature." Uspekhi Khim., 12(4), 1943a.

Starik, I. E. "Radiological Study of the Caucasus Mineral Waters." Izvest. Akad. Nauk SSSR, Ser. khim., No. 6, 1943b.

Starynkevich-Borneman, I. D., Borovik, S. A., and Borovskii, I. B. "Rare Earths in Plants and Soils." Doklady Akad. Nauk SSSR, 30(3), 1941.

Stiles, W. Microelements in the Lives of Plants and Animals, Moscow, IL, 1950.

Storozheva, M. M. "Teratological Phenomena in the Anemone (Pulsatilla patens (L.) Mill.) in a Nickel Ore Field." Trudy — Biogeokhim. Lab. Akad. Nauk SSSR, 10, 1954.

Strakhov, N. M. Principles of the Theory of Lithogenesis, Vols. 1; 2, Moscow, Izd-vo Akad. Nauk SSSR, 1960.

Studenikova, Z. V., Glinkina, M. I., and Pavlenko, L. I. "The Problem of the Distribution of Molybdenum in Intrusive Rocks." Geokhimiya, No. 2, 1957.

Tanfil'ev, G. I. "The Problem of the Dying Out of Trapa natans." Trudy —St. Petersburg, Obshchestva Estestvoispyt., 17, 1886.

Tenner, D. D. "Geological Outline of the Neighborhood of the Khagareysko Deposit." Materialy po geologii Vostochnoy Sibiri, No. 5, Novosibirsk, Kraygiz, 1932.

Teodorovich, V. I. "The Central Tuvian Anticline." Doklady Akad. Nauk SSSR, 68(3), 1949.

Terekhova, R. V. Geochemical Exploration of Ore Deposits in the USSR (address to the First All-Union Conference on Geochemical Methods of Exploration for Ore Deposits), Moscow, Gosgeoltekhizdat, 1957.

Thiessen, S. "Geochemical and Phytobiological Relationships in the Light of Applied Geophysics." Geochemical Methods for the Exploration of Ore Deposits, Moscow, IL, 1954.

Tikhomirov, N. I., and Miller, S. D. "The Physicochemical Method for the Exploration for Molybdenum in the Semidesert Climate of the Area North of Lake Balkash." Razvedka Nedr., No. 2, 1946.

Tkachenko, M. E., Asoskov, A. I., and Sinev, V. N. General Forestry, Leningrad, Goslestekhizdat, 1939.

Tkalich, S. M. Experience in the Investigation of Plants as Indicators in Geological Exploration and Prospecting. Vestnik Dal'nevostoch. Filiala Akad. Nauk SSSR, No. 32(5), 1938.

Tkalich, S. M. "Botanical Methods in Geological Investigations." Botan. Zhurn., Moscow, Izd-vo Akad. Nauk SSSR, Vol. 37, 1952.

Tkalich, S. M. "The Iron Content of Plants as an Indicator in Geological Exploration Work." Priroda, No. 1, 1953.

Tkalich, S. M. "The Biogeochemical Method of Exploration of Ore Deposits." Materials of the Conference of Geologists of Eastern Siberia and the Far East on the Methods Used in Geological Survey and Exploration Work, Chita, 1956.

Tkalich, S. M. Practical Manual on the Biogeochemical Method of Exploration of Ore Deposits, Moscow, Gosgeol- tekhizdat, 1959.

Tolmachev, Yu. M. "Adsorption of Uranyl Salts by Solid Adsorbents." Vestnik Akad. Nauk SSSR, 1, 1943.

Tomkeiff, S. I. "The Geochemistry of Uranium." Sci. Progr., 34(136), 1946.

Trelease, S. F., and Beath, O. A. "Selenium − Its Geological Occurrence and Its Biological Effects in Relation to Botany, Chemistry, Agriculture, Nutrition, and Medicine." New York, N. Y. (published by the authors − Box 42, Schermerhorn, Columbia Univ.) 1949.

Tret'yak, Z. A. Investigation of Certain Colored Complex Compounds of Uranium of Importance in Analytical Chemistry (author's abstract),Khar'kovskii Gosudarstvennii Univ. im. A. M. Gor'kogo, 1953.

Tsung–Shan, K. Sci. Sinica (Peking), 6:1105, 1957.

Tyulina, L. K. "Evolution of the Vegetation Cover of the Foothills of the Southern Urals." Trudy − Zlatoustovs. Obshch. Krayeveden. i Gosudarstven. il'menskogo Zapovednika, No. 1, 1928.

Tyurin, I. V. "Geochemical Regularities in Humus Formation." Trudy − Commemorative Session Dedicated to the Birthday of V. V. Dokuchayev, Moscow, Izd-vo Akad. Nauk SSSR, 1949.

Tyutina, N. A., Aleskovskii, V. B., and Vasil'ev, P. I. "Experience with Biogeochemical Sampling and a Method for Determining Niobium in Plants." Geokhimiya, No. 6, 1959.

Unger, G. Über Einfluss des Bodens auf die Verteilung der Gewächse, Vienna, 1836.

Vernadskii, V. I. "Titanium in Soils." Pochvovedenie, No. 3, 1910.

Vernadskii, V. I. "Notes on the Study of Living Matter from the Geochemical Point of View." Append. to the Proceed. of the 8th Conf. of the Sov. Acad. of Sci. − Phys. − Math. Sec.; 11 May 1921.

Vernadskii, V. I. Chemical Composition of Living Matter in Relation to the Chemistry of the Earth's Crust, Izd-vo "Bremya," 1922.

Vernadskii, V. I. The Biosphere, Prague, 1926.

Vernadskii, V. I. "The Biochemical Study of the Phenomena of Life." Doklady Akad. Nauk SSSR, No. 6, 1931.

Vernadskii, V. I. Problems in Biogeochemistry, I. − The Importance of Biogeochemistry for an Understanding of the Biosphere. 2nd Ed., Leningrad, Izd-vo Akad. Nauk SSSR, 1934a.

Vernadskii, V. I. Geochemistry, Moscow-Leningrad, Gorgeonefteizdat, 1934b.

Vernadskii, V. I. "The Geochemistry of Manganese in Relation to Mineral Science." Trudy − Conf. on the Origin of Manganous and Ferric Ores, Moscow-Leningrad, Izd-vo Akad. Nauk SSSR, 1937.

Viktorov, S. V. "Biological Indicators in Geology." Uspekhi Sovremennoi Biol., 23(2), 1947.

Viktorov, S. V. The Use of the Geobotanical Method in Geological and Hydrogeological Research, Moscow, Izd-vo Akad. Nauk SSSR, 1955.

Viktorov, S. V. "Vegetation as an Indicator of the Lithological and Soil-Geochemical Conditions in Deserts." Problems in Indication Geobotany, Moscow, Izd-vo MOIP, 1960.

Viktorov, S. V., et al. Geobotanical Methods in Geological Research, Moscow, Gosgeolizdat, 1955.

Vil'yams, V. R. Soil Science. Collected Writings in 2 Volumes, Vol. 1, Moscow, Izd-vo s.-kh. literatury, 1949.

Vinogradov, A. P. "Copper Content of Various Soils." Doklady Akad. Nauk SSSR, 27(9), 1940.

Vinogradov, A. P. "The Chlorine-Bromine Coefficient of Ground Water." Doklady Akad. Nauk SSSR, 44(2), 1944a.

Vinogradov, A. P. "The Geochemistry of Dispersed Elements in Sea Water." Uspekhi Khim., 13: 1; 3, 1944b.

Vinogradov, A. P. "A Chemical Understanding of the Biosphere." Pochvovedenie, No. 7, 1945.

Vinogradov, A. P. Biogeochemical Provinces. Trudy − Session of the Soil Inst. Dedicated to the Centennial of the Birth of V. V. Dokuchayeva, Moscow-Leningrad, Izd-vo Akad. Nauk SSSR, 1949.

Vinogradov, A. P. Geochemistry of Rare and Dispersed Chemical Elements in Soils, Moscow, Izd-vo Akad. Nauk SSSR, 1950.

Vinogradov, A. P. "Principal Patterns in the Distribution of Microelements between Plants and the Environment." Microelements in the Life of Plants and Animals, Moscow, Izd-vo Akad. Nauk SSSR, 1952.

Vinogradov, A. P. "The Exploration for Ore Deposits Using Plants and Soils." Trudy – Biogeokhim. Lab. Akad. Nauk SSSR, Vol. 10, 1954.

Vinogradov, A. P. Patterns in the Distribution of Chemical Elements in the Earth's Crust, Izd-vo MGU, 1955.

Vinogradov, A. P. "Patterns in the Distribution of Chemical Elements in the Earth's Crust." Geokhimiya, No. 1, 1956.

Vinogradov, A. P. "The Genesis of Biogeochemical Provinces." Trudy – Biogeokhim. Lab. Akad. Nauk SSSR, Vol. 11, 1960.

Vinogradov, A. P., and Borovik-Romanova, T. F. "The Alkalis Li, Na, K, Rb (and Cs) in the Soils of the USSR." Sbornik Pochven. Inst. im. V. V. Dokuchayeva, No. 15, 1949.

Vinogradov, A. P., and Malyuga, D. P. "Biogeochemical Methods for the Exploration for Ore Deposits." Geochemical Exploration of Ore Deposits in the USSR, Moscow, Gosgeoltekhizdat, 1957.

Vinogradov, A. P., and Malyuga, D. P. "The Biogeochemical Method of Exploration of Ore." 20th Int'l. Geol. Cong. in Mexico, Mexico, 1958.

Vinogradov, A. P., and Vinogradova, Kh. G. "Molybdenum in the Soils of the USSR." Doklady Akad. Nauk SSSR, Nov. ser., 62(5), 1948.

Vinogradova, Kh. G. "Molybdenum Content in Plants of the Family Leguminosae." Doklady Akad. Nauk SSSR, 40(1), 1943.

Vinogradova, Kh. G. "Molybdenum in Plants in Relation to Their Systematic Position." Trudy – Biogeokhim. Lab. Akad. Nauk SSSR, Vol. 10, 1954.

Vlasyuk, P. A. "The Content of Mobile Forms of the Microelements Zinc, Boron, Cobalt, and Copper in the Soils of the Ukrainian SSR." Microelements in Agriculture and Medicine, Riga, Izd-vo Akad. Nauk Latv. SSR, 1956.

Vogt, T. "Nickel in Igneous Rocks." Econ. Geol., Vol. 28, 1923.

Vogt, T. Skr. Norske Vid. Acad. Oslo. Math.-Naturw. Klasse, No. 7, 1931.

Vogt, T. "Kjemisk og 'botanisk malmleting ved Røoras' I." Det Kong. Norske Videns Selskab Forhandlinger, 12(23), 1939.

Vogt, T. "Geokjemisk og Geobotanisk malmleting, II." Det Kong. Norske Videns. Selskab Forhandlinger, Vol. 15, 1942.

Vogt, T. "Geochemical and Geobotanical Ore Prospecting – Some Notes on the Vegetation of the Ore Deposits of Røros." Det. Kong. Norske Videns. Selskab Forhandlinger, 15(6):21, 1942a.

Vogt, T. "Geokjemisk og Geobotanisk malmleting, IV." Det. Kong. Norske Videns. Selskab Forhandlinger, 15(7), 1942b.

Vogt, T. "Spor elementor i myrmalm og sjomalm, VII." Det. Kong. Norske Videns. Selskab Forhandlinger, 15(24), 1942d.

Vogt, T. "Geokjemisk og Geobotanisk malmleting, VIII, Bestemmelse av kobber i planter fra Rørosfeltet ved kvantitativ røntgenanalyse." Det. Kong. Norske Videns. Selskab Forhandlinger, 16(14), 1943.

Vogt, T., and Berg, H. "Bestemmelse av Kobber i jordprover, X." Det. Kong. Norske Videns. Selskab Forhandlinger, 19(21), 1946.

Vogt, T., and Berg, H. "Sink og Pb i jordprøver. Geokjemisk og Geobotanisl malmleting, XI." Det. Kong. Norske Videns. Selskab Forhandlinger, 20(26), 1947.

Vogt, T., and Berg, H. "Bestemmelse av jern og mangan i jordprover, XII." Det. Kong. Norske. Videns. Selskab Forhandlinger, 20(27), 1947.

Vogt, T., Bradlie, O., and Berg, H. "Geokjemisk og Geobotanisk malmleting, IX. Bestemmelse Cu, Zn, Pb, Mn, og Fe i planter fra Rørosfeltet." Det. Kong.Norske Videns. Selskab Forhandlinger, 16(15), 1943a.

Vogt, T., and Rosenqvist, A. M. "Bestemmelse ov Kobber in Vannprover fra Rørosfeltet, VI." Det. Kong. Norske Videns. Selskab Forhandlinger, 15(23), 1942c.

Voinar, A. O., The Biological Role of Microelements in the Organism of Animals and Man, Moscow, Izd-vo "Vysshaya Shkola," 1953.

Vostokova, E. A. "The Botanical Method of Exploration of Uranium-Bearing Ores." Razvedka i Okhrana Nedr., No. 7, 1957.

Vysotskii, N. K. "Certain Geobotanical Observations in the Northern Urals." Pochvovedenie, 6(2), 1904.

Wallace, T. "Trace Elements in Plant Physiology." Int'l. Union of Biol. Sci. Colloq., Ser. B, (1):5 (Chronica Botanica, Waltham, Mass, 1951).

Warren, H. V., and Delavault, R. E. "Biogeochemical Investigations in British Columbia." Geophysics, Vol. 13, 1948.

Warren, H. V., and Delavault, R. E. "Further Studies in Biogeochemistry." Bull. Geol. Soc. Am., 60:531, 1949.

Warren, H. V., and Delavault, R. E. "Gold and Silver Content of Some Trees and Horsetails in British Columbia." Bull. Geol. Soc. Am., 61:123, 1950.

Warren, H. V., and Delavault, R. E. "Variations in the Nickel Content of Some Canadian Trees." Trans. Roy. Soc. Can., Sec. IV, 48:71, 1954.

Warren, H. V., Delavault, R. E., and Irish, R. I. "Biogeochemical Researches on Copper in British Columbia." Trans. Roy. Soc. Can., Sec. III, Vol. 43, 1949.

Warren, H. V., Delavault, R. E., and Irish, R. I. "Preliminary Investigation of the Biogeochemistry of Iron and Manganese." Geochemical Methods for the Exploration of Ore Deposits, Moscow, IL, 1954.

Warren, H. V., and Howaston, C. H. "Biogeochemical Prospecting for Copper and Zinc." Bull. Geol. Soc. Am., 58(9):803, 1947.

White, W. H. "Plant Anomalies Related to Some British Columbia Ore Deposits." Can. Mining and Met. Bull., 43(459), 1950.

Worthington, J. E. "Biogeochemical Prospecting of the Shawangunk Mine." Econ. Geol., 50(4), 1955.

Yanishevskii, E. M. "Behavior of Molybdenum in the Zone of Oxidation of Ore Deposits." Trudy — Moscow Geol. Inst., Vol. 1, Moscow-Leningrad, Izd-vo NKTP, 1936.

Yarilova, E. A. "The Crystallization of Phytolitharia in Soils." Doklady Akad. Nauk SSSR, 83(6), 1952.

Yarilova, E. A. "Mineralogical Investigation of Subalpine Chernozem Andesite-Basalt." Weathered Crust, No. 2, Moscow, Izd-vo Akad. Nauk SSSR, 1956.

Yuneev, M. V. "Possibilities of Exploratory Geophysics in Exploration of Manganese Deposits in the Southern Urals." (Materials from the All-Union Scientific Research Institute of Geological Exploration.) Geofizika, Sbornik 12, 1948.

Zaichikova, L. B. "The Use of Thiourea in Colorimetric Determinations of Molybdenum." Zavod. Lab., 15, 1949.